QUANTIFICATION

A HISTORY OF THE MEANING OF
MEASUREMENT IN THE NATURAL
AND SOCIAL SCIENCES

Conference on the History of Quantification in the Sciences, New York, 1959

QUANTIFICATION

A HISTORY OF THE MEANING OF
MEASUREMENT IN THE NATURAL
AND SOCIAL SCIENCES

Edited by Harry Woolf

THE **BOBBS-MERRILL** COMPANY, INC.
A SUBSIDIARY OF HOWARD W. SAMS & CO., INC.
Publishers • INDIANAPOLIS • NEW YORK

CONTENTS

QUANTIFICATION

A HISTORY OF THE MEANING OF
MEASUREMENT IN THE NATURAL
AND SOCIAL SCIENCES

The Conference on the History of Quantification in the Sciences

Measurement has long been considered a hallmark of science properly practiced, and once a new discipline has developed a mathematical discourse, it has almost immediately laid claim, at least in the language of its most enthusiastic disciples, to the significant status—science! In the larger task of understanding the world, quantification or measurement may not only give precision to the perpetual dialogue between nature and the scholar, but it may also enable such a conversation to include an ever-growing portion of the manifold and the complex through the employment of increasingly higher levels of abstraction. Thus, in an age concerned not only with the fine analysis of nature, but also with the characteristics of its own methods and tools, the meaning of measurement in all science becomes of fundamental concern to theory and practice alike.

Towards this end then, an understanding of the measurer and the measured, the papers in this volume are directed. They are the result of an extraordinary conference held in the offices of the Social Science Research Council on 20-21 November, 1959, a conference whose origin goes back to 1955 and the founding of the Joint Social Science Research Council-National Research Council Committee on the History of Science. Taking precedent from the panel on the history of science established under Dr. Harry Alpert at the National Science Foundation, and with the cooperation of Dr. Detlev Bronk, then president of the National Academy of Science, the Joint Committee was created and first met in December 1955. The members of the original committee were I. B. Cohen, G. W. Corner (who later resigned to be replaced by R. B. Lindsay), H. Guerlac, M. H. Ingraham, R. K. Merton, H. L. Shapiro, G. R. Willey and R. H. Shryock as chairman.

In its meetings since 1955, the Joint Committee has been concerned with various aspects of the history and sociology of science, including the status of the field itself. In the spring of 1956 ideas were developed within the Committee for two conferences, which have since taken place: the first was devoted to the problems of interpretation in the history of science, and the second, at Dr. Shryock's suggestion, dealt with a composite analysis of the introduction and development of quantitative techniques in the natural and social sciences—the theme of the papers in this volume. The first conference took place at the University of Wisconsin on 1-10 September 1957. Under Professor Marshall Clagett's superb management, an excellent program developed, ranging in interest from the formation of the idea of the conservation of energy to problems in teaching the history of science. The papers and formal comments of this Wisconsin conference were assembled afterwards as *Critical Problems in the History of Science,* edited by Marshall Clagett and published by the University of Wisconsin Press, 1959.

Between 1956 and 1958, plans for the second conference to emerge from the deliberations of the Joint Committee matured, and Dr. Pendleton Herring, of the Social Science Research Council, requested and received the necessary support for this special meeting from the National Science Foundation. When it took place, the Conference on the History of Quantification in the Sciences was attended by some thirty scholars representing eleven academic disciplines: the history of science, physics, chemistry, biology, botany, mathematics, psychology, sociology, economics, political science and anthropology. The geographical and institutional distribution of the group was as varied as the professional interests of its members, for in addition to Professors Cohen, Guerlac, Lindsay, Merton and Shryock of the Joint Committee, the following took part: Harry Alpert, University of Oregon; Bernard Barber, Barnard College; Edwin G. Boring, Harvard University; Marshall Clagett, University of Wisconsin; A. C. Crombie, Oxford University (in residence at Princeton University at the time); Philip Frank, Harvard University; R. W. Gerard, University of Michigan; David R. Goddard, University of Pennsylvania; Mark Graubard, University of Minnesota; Earl J. Hamilton, University of Chicago; Pendleton Herring, Social Science Research Council; Alexandre Koyré, Institute for Advanced Study, Princeton; Simon Kuznets, The Johns Hopkins University; Thomas S. Kuhn, University of California, Berkeley; Paul F. Lazarsfeld, Columbia University; Daniel Lerner, Massachusetts Institute of Technology; Solomon Pines, Hebrew University, Jerusalem; Derek J. Price, Yale University; Albert C. Spaulding, National Science Foundation; Joseph J. Spengler, Duke University; M. H. Trytten, National Research Council; Charles F. Voegelin, Indiana University; S. S. Wilks, Princeton University; Harry Woolf, University of Washington.

The papers for each session were distributed to the participants in advance of the conference, and each of the four sessions was limited to a discussion of two papers. Instead of a chorus of separate and independent voices, the members of the conference discovered that not only had they much to say to one another, but upon occasion they could sing in close harmony indeed. Collaboration came naturally as the participants dealt with the problem of emerging quantification in different disciplines at different times, and almost from the very beginning the conference became a true symposium in the classic mold. The bracketed texts which appear in some of the articles and the appendices attached to others represent changes and additions made by the authors in response to the discussion of their papers at the conference.

Thus, these papers are presented to the reader with the hope that the intellectual gain registered by all who took part in the Conference on the History of Quantification in the Sciences may go beyond the offices of the Social Science Research Council where it took place. That it is possible is due to the generous cooperation of the authors involved, the patience and wise counsel of Dr. Herring and Dr. Shryock and the funds of the National Science Foundation. In the face of extraordinary conditions, the able assistance of Mrs. Carol B. Hewitt and Miss Dorothy Stratton helped to make the publication of these papers possible. For so much freely given, the editor of *Isis* can only express his warmest thanks.

Madras, India
18 April 1961

Harry Woolf, Editor of *Isis*

Some Aspects of Quantification in Science

By S. S. Wilks*

IT is a difficult assignment for a person who is neither a philosopher nor a historian of science to fill the place of Professor Ernest Nagel in initiating discussion at this conference on quantification in the sciences. Professor Nagel, if he could have been here, would have performed these duties as a philosopher with broad experience and knowledge about the nature and history of quantification in the sciences. I can only approach the task as a mathematical statistician who has given some thought to the nature of quantification in science without much knowledge, however, of the history of quantification in the various sciences.

The subject of quantification in science is an enormous one with many aspects. The foundation of quantification is measurement, and any discussion of the nature of quantification must necessarily begin with a discussion of the nature of measurement. In this paper I shall not try to do more than to direct your attention to some of the basic concepts and requirements involved in measurement and quantification as we see them today, without attempting to trace the origin and development of these concepts historically. Having had an opportunity to read all of the manuscripts prepared for the Conference, I have observed that most of these concepts occur at least implicitly in concrete settings at various points in the manuscripts, and are thereby placed somewhat in historical perspective by the various speakers at this Conference.

The first requirement about measurement which should be mentioned is that making a measurement must be an *operationally definable process*. That is, a measurement process must be defined by specifying a set of realizable experimental conditions and a sequence of operations to be made under these conditions which will yield the measurement. The basic reason for such a requirement is to make the measurement process as objective as possible so that different competent scientists operating the process can obtain comparable results.

Making a measurement is an extremely widely applicable concept. At the lower end of the scale of complexity, counting and recording the number of rows of grains in an ear of corn or even counting and recording the number of heads one obtains if a single coin is tossed once are acts of making measurements. The existence of an ear of corn or a coin and an observer with an ability to count up to twenty and record his results are sufficient to make such a measurement.

At the upper end of the scale are highly complicated measurement processes

* Princeton University.

5

like determining the velocity of light or picking weak signals out of radio astronomy recordings loaded with background noise. While there are many measurement operations in the physical sciences which are complex from the point of view of instrumentation, and specification of measurement conditions, there are measurement operations in other fields of inquiry, particularly the social sciences, which are at least as complex in other ways. A good example is the procedure used by the Bureau of the Census[1] in estimating the number of employed and unemployed workers in the United States during a given week. In making such a measurement, great care is required in the selection, by certain randomization procedures, of a national sample of households to be contacted, in standardizing and controlling the interviewing procedures to be used by a nation-wide field staff, and in coding and analyzing the results. Stephan and McCarthy[2] have given a full discussion of measurement processes of this type.

It should be pointed out that operationally definable processes do not necessarily have to terminate in measurement-taking. For example, the manufacture of an article under mass-production conditions is an operationally definable process. Repeating such a process, however, would normally yield articles comparable with respect to the outcomes of any measurement process which might be made on them.

The second basic requirement of a measurement process is that of *reproducibility* of the outcome. Once a measurement process has been defined as objectively as possible, repeating the process should yield measurements in "reasonable agreement" with each other. That is, two competent scientists performing the measurement process independently, should obtain determinations in "reasonable agreement" with each other. The more objectively and accurately the measurement process is defined, the closer, in general, is the agreement to be expected. This property of reproducibility of a measurement process is sometimes called the *reliability* or the *precision* of the process. There are many conditions, of course, in which it is impossible to repeat a measurement process in a strict sense. For example, if conditions change markedly in time, repeatability may involve repetitions of the measurement process as nearly simultaneously as possible. Or if the object being measured is destroyed in the process of making the measurement, as often occurs in making life tests and other critical tests on mass-produced articles, repetition would involve applying the measurement process to a second article from the mass-produced lot.

The requirement of reproducibility of a measurement process is not always properly appreciated even in the older branches of science, not to mention the newer ones. There is often great temptation to *assume* that the measurement process is so carefully and objectively defined and controlled that determinations which would result from two independent runs of the measurement process will inevitably be in "reasonable agreement," and hence that there is

[1] United States Bureau of the Census (1954), *The Measurement of Employment and Unemployment by the Bureau of the Census in its Current Population Survey*, Report of Special Advisory Committee on Employment Statistics.

[2] Frederick F. Stephan and Philip J. Mc-Carthy, *Sampling Opinions* (New York: John Wiley and Sons, 1958).

no need of repeating the measurement process. This is one of the most hazardous assumptions which can be made in any field of science. An excellent discussion of many of the factors which can upset such an assumption in scientific research has been given by Wilson.[3]

When results of scientific research have practical application and when the measurement procedures pass over into the hands of practitioners, the concept of reproducibility is frequently completely abandoned, unless it is incorporated into procedural doctrine. For example, it has been found by Chiang, Hodges and Yerushalmy[4] that diagnoses of tuberculosis based on chest x-ray negatives have low reliability in medical practice. The unreliability apparently stems from the subjectivity with which the clinician interprets what he sees on the negative. If the chest x-ray negatives carry sufficient information for correct diagnosis of tuberculosis, the unreliability is due to failure to define sufficiently objectively what the clinician must do to elicit this information. If, as is more likely the case, they carry only partial information for correct diagnosis, then there is a definite limit to the reliability which can be achieved.

The third requirement of basic importance for a measurement process is that of the *validity* or the *accuracy* of the process: that is, the extent to which the process yields "true" measurements of the object being measured. The notion of reproducibility or reliability or precision is not to be confused with that of validity or accuracy of a measurement process. A satisfactory measurement process requires high reliability and high validity. There can be situations in which the measurement process has high reliability but low validity. For example, if the sight on a good rifle is not properly aligned, a good rifleman with a steady hand would be expected to achieve high reliability but low validity with his marksmanship. That is, he could place successive shots close together but *not* around the bull's eye. To achieve high reliability and also high validity he would have to place the shots close together *and* around the bull's eye, a result to be expected from an expert rifleman and a good rifle with its sights properly aligned.

In the example of chest x-ray diagnoses for tuberculosis, high consistency between the conclusions of two clinicians working independently on a large number of x-ray negatives would not imply validity of their diagnoses. But high validity would imply that both clinicians working independently would agree on their diagnosis from nearly all films, and furthermore nearly all films diagnosed as positive would be from persons infected with tuberculosis while nearly all films diagnosed as negative would be from persons not infected.

The problem of achieving validity by a measurement process is usually much more difficult than that of achieving reliability. For reliability merely requires reproducibility of two or more repetitions of the measurement process, while validity requires that the numerical value produced by the measurement process be approximately the same as the true value of the quantity being measured as determined by some independent and valid procedure. In many

[3] E. Bright Wilson, Jr., *An Introduction to Scientific Research* (New York: McGraw-Hill Book Company, 1952).

[4] C. L. Chiang, J. L. Hodges, Jr. and J.

Yerushalmy, "Statistical Problems in Medical Diagnosis," Vol. IV, *Third Berkeley Symposium* (Berkeley: University of California Press, 1956).

situations such an independent procedure does not exist, and hence the problem of establishing validity in the true sense of the word cannot be solved. In such situations the case for validity is made to rest on the logic and experimental rigor of the measurement process together with cross checks of the measurement results with independently acquired facts. For example, Michelson's[5] procedure for measuring the velocity of light yielded quite highly reproducible results from trial to trial, but the validity of his estimate of the velocity of light is allowed to rest on the fact that the use of his estimate in describing physical phenomena involving the velocity of light does not lead to significant contradictions or inconsistencies. To take an example from the social sciences, we may ask whether the current Bureau of the Census procedure for measuring (estimating) the number of employed and unemployed persons in the United States from 35,000 households each month is valid, that is whether the values obtained are "reasonably close" to the true values of the number of unemployed in these months. The problem of validity here is extremely difficult. The case for validity is made partly on the logic of the design of the sampling system and the control exercised in the execution of the design and analysis of the results, and partly on the precision with which various statistical quantities known from previous censuses and surveys can be estimated from the sample results.

It should be pointed out that there are situations in which the purpose of a measurement process is to provide a sort of index for which the concept of validity has meaning only in some general and usually unmeasurable sense. But in such a situation the importance of the requirement of reliability is in no way diminished. An examination in a given subject taken by a group of individuals is an example of such a process. The purpose of the examination is to provide scores or indices on the individuals indicative in some general sense of how much they know about the subject. The notion of a "true" score for an individual is useful for conceptual purposes, but it is unmeasurable. Even so, the examination can and should possess as much reliability as possible, that is, if a second similar examination in the subject is given to the group of individuals the ranking of their scores on the second examination should be in "reasonable agreement" with the ranking of their scores on the first examination. For a thorough discussion of reliability of an examination, the reader is referred to Gulliksen[6] who also discusses the problem of evaluating the validity of an examination. Procedures for determining values of cost of living indices, economic indicators, and measures of the effectiveness of competing weapon systems are further examples of such a measurement process.

There is a class of highly practical measurement processes in which validity is crucial and verifiable, which we may call calibration processes. In a calibration process a scale of values of an auxiliary but easy-to-measure variable y is constructed so that the values of y corresponding to various specified values of the basic but difficult-to-measure variable x are determined experimentally.

[5] A. A. Michelson, E. G. Pease, and F. Pearson, "Measurement of the velocity of light in a partial vacuum," *Astrophys. J.*, 1935, *82*: 26-61.

[6] Harold Gulliksen, *Theory of Mental Tests* (New York: John Wiley and Sons, 1950).

These pairs of corresponding values of x and y are then used to construct by interpolation a scale of y values corresponding to all x values in the range of interest. Then to each value of y selected by an indicator would correspond a value of x. Most instrumentation dials are applications of the calibration process. An automobile speedometer is a typical example. Values of y in miles per hour are printed at appropriate points along the y scale. A pointer activated by the speed of the automobile would indicate a value of y in miles per hour. Validity of the speedometer thus requires that the speed of the automobile as indicated by the pointer on the y scale must agree "within practical limits" with the true speed x of the automobile as determined by any valid method independent of the automobile's own speedometer.

Let us now turn to some quantification concepts concerning aggregates or systems of measurements. It must be emphasized first of all that the quality of an aggregate or system of measurements depends on the quality of individual measurements which, in turn, depend on the degree to which the underlying measurement process satisfies the three fundamental requirements already discussed, namely that the process be operationally definable, that it yield reliable measurements, and that it yield valid measurements.

Perhaps the simplest kind of an aggregate of measurements is one generated by applying a measurement process to each member of a *sample* of objects drawn from a *population* of such objects. The main purpose of such an aggregate of measurements is to learn something about the variation of the measurements from object to object in the sample and to estimate the mean, or some other function, of the measurements one would obtain if all objects in the population were subjected to the given measurement process. Measurements on samples to make estimates of population characteristics are widely used in science and technology. For example, samples of articles from mass-produced lots are widely used for estimating quality characteristics of the entire lots. Samples of households are used for estimating characteristics of the population of households in a city, county, state or the entire nation.

In order for a sample to provide a scientific basis for estimating the mean or other parameters of the population of interest to the investigator, special attention must be given to the process of drawing the sample from the population. Procedures for drawing such samples are based on *randomization principles*, which have been highly developed and widely used in many branches of science. The reader will find a thorough discussion of these principles in Cox.[7]

Principles of sampling are also used in comparative experiments. In the simplest kind of a comparative experiment, two random samples are drawn from a given population of objects. The objects in one sample are held as controls and the objects in the other are subjected to the treatment under study. The given measurement process is then applied to all objects in both samples. The mean or some other quantity is computed from each sample, and a significance test based on probability theory is used to determine whether the measurements in the two samples are behaving like measurements in two random samples from identical populations. If the hypothesis of identical

[7] D. R. Cox, *The Planning of Experiments* (New York: John Wiley and Sons, 1958).

populations is strongly contradicted by the significance test as applied to the measurements, it is concluded that the treatment has a definite effect which can then be estimated from the measurements.

Such a comparative experimental procedure is used widely in many branches of science and technology, but hardly at all in others. One still finds hazardous conclusions in scientific papers typified as follows: that a certain treatment produced an effect based on an experimental set-up involving a small control group and a small experimental group, when as a matter of fact, differences between the means of the two groups at least equal in magnitude to the observed difference could have occurred with relatively high probability under the assumption that the treatment had no effect whatever.

A comment should be made here about the importance of using the principle of randomization in drawing the two samples involved in a comparative experiment. If the two samples are selected from the population by any other principle than randomization, significance testing based on probability theory becomes inapplicable, and the possibility of other factors than the treatment under study cannot be ruled out as the cause of observed differences between the two samples. The current controversy over whether heavy cigarette smoking causes lung cancer hinges on this point. In the usual statistical studies of this problem, incidence of lung cancer in a large sample of heavy smokers is compared with that in a large sample of non-smokers, and is found to be larger. But since the two samples of persons are self-selected and not selected at the outset by principles of randomization, the possibility cannot be eliminated that persons who elect to smoke heavily may be constitutionally more susceptible to cancer (and other diseases) than those who do not smoke. As a matter of fact, it has been pointed out by Berkson[8] and others that heavy cigarette smokers have not only a greater incidence of lung cancer than non-smokers, but also a greater incidence of circulatory and other kinds of disorders.

The quantification of inference procedures from random samples to populations has been developed for a very wide range of experimental situations. Experimental designs have been developed for studying effects of several factors or treatments simultaneously. Highly specialized analysis of variance procedures have been devised for decomposing total variability of measurements in a sample into components and identifying causes of various components of this variability, thus making it possible to reduce variability by eliminating some of the causes. Modern industrial quality control methods originated by Shewhart[9] and further developed by others are founded largely on procedures of this type.

I would now like to turn to other systems of measurements. It will be recalled that the first basic requirement for a measurement process involves the specification of a set of conditions under which the measurement process is to be operated. Very often the specification of a set of conditions amounts to holding important *independent variables* fixed at certain values and then op-

[8] Joseph Berkson, "Smoking and Lung Cancer: Some Observations on Two Recent Reports," *J. Amer. Statist. Ass.*, 1958, *53:* 28-37.

[9] Walter A. Shewhart, *Economic Control of Quality of Manufactured Product* (New York: Van Nostrand, 1931).

erating the measurement process. If a measurement is made one or more times for each of a number of combinations of values of these independent variables, then, by suitable interpolatory smoothing, one may find the quantity being measured as a function of these variables. Boyle's law relating pressure and volume of a gas at a fixed temperature is an example of such a system of measurements. Thus, at a fixed temperature if the volume v of gas is measured for each of a set of fixed values of pressure p, we obtain a set of points in the pv plane which is closely fitted by a curve having an equation of form $v = c/p$ where c is a constant depending on temperature, thus giving v as a function of p. If we have several independent variables, which for simplicity we keep to two, namely x_1, x_2, and obtain measurements on a quantity q for various combinations of values of the variables x_1, x_2, we obtain points in the 3-dimensional space of q, x_1, x_2. If a smooth function of form $f(x_1, x_2)$ is fitted to these points by some statistical technique such as least squares, we obtain a smooth *regression surface* for q on x_1, x_2 having an equation $q = f(x_1, x_2)$ which "fits" the *observed* points, that is the points obtained by measurement. If the observed points fall "reasonably close" to this fitted regression surface, we then have a model useful for estimating the value of q for any point (x_1, x_2) in the domain covered by the experiment. If q_1, q_2, ..., q_n are the observed values of q corresponding respectively to n combinations of values of (x_1, x_2), say (x_{11}, x_{21}), (x_{12}, x_{22}), ..., (x_{1n}, x_{2n}), then $q_1 - f(x_{11}, x_{21})$, $q_2 - f(x_{12}, x_{22})$, ..., $q_n - f(x_{1n}, x_{2n})$ are the "errors" of the observed points with respect to the regression surface. The larger these errors in magnitude, the lower the quality of this regression surface for estimating q for given values of (x_1, x_2).

Regression functions of the type discussed above which may involve several independent variables x_1, x_2, ..., x_k are used for estimating the value of q for given values of x_1, x_2, ..., x_k in many branches of science and technology. In the particular case where the regression function is satisfactorily approximated by a linear form such as $\beta_0 + \beta_1 x_1 + ..., + \beta_k x_k$, the problem of fitting it to the observed points involves the solution of a system of linear equations in the unknown β's. The standard procedure for determining the β's is by the method of least squares which yields a matrix for the set of equations whose elements are readily computable from the observations. As a matter of fact, the solution of sets of linear equations of this kind in many variables is now a routine matter for high speed digital computors.

It should be noted from the preceding discussion that regression functions are essentially mathematical models for estimating values of the quantity q for specified values of the independent variables, x_1, x_2, ..., x_k for which no observed value of q was obtained. While this type of mathematical model, that is the function $f(x_1, x_2, ..., x_k)$ chosen to be fitted to the observed points, is rather empirical, it is often remarkably realistic in terms of making useful estimates or predictions of measurement outcomes for all combinations of values of the independent variables in the domain of study.

Finally, I would like to comment on what we may regard as perhaps the highest form of quantification in science. This consists of the mathematical models which describe the essential features of the quantitative relationships inherent in vast systems of measurements. A model of this type not only provides a relatively simple and elegant scheme for describing a system of measurements which have already been made but also serves as a dependable instrument for predicting the outcome of further measurements which would belong to the system if they were made. Examples of such models are Kepler's laws of planetary motion, Newton's more general laws of motion, the focal laws of optics, differential equations of fluid mechanics, Mendelian laws of genetics, laws of probability for independent events, the Weber-Fechner law in psychophysics, and so on.

A great deal of effort is expended in devising and testing mathematical models based on specified assumptions in an attempt to describe systems of measurements. Frequently, models are devised which describe "reasonably well" existing sets of measurements but which do not stand the test of validity in satisfactorily predicting the outcome of further measurements. Many branches of science and technology abound in mathematical model-building activity done purely on the basis of assumptions, and often with little, if any, experimental knowledge to go on. Such model-building usually occurs as a "theoretical analysis" done in connection with the study of alternative designs of devices and systems as a guide to the selection of a design from the alternatives in advance of the construction of the device or system. For example, development of the "Mousetrap" device early in World War II for throwing barrages of small contact depth charges forward in attacking a submarine was preceded by a great deal of probability analysis to compare its expected effectiveness with that of conventional "ash can" depth charge attack procedures. Mathematical model-building as an effort to provide a description of a system of measurements or observations to be expected if they were made, but which is never actually followed up and tested against experimental results, must be regarded as a mathematical exercise rather than as scientific quantification.

Quantification in Medieval Physics

By A. C. Crombie*

A WORTH-WHILE discussion of quantification in medieval physics requires particular care in deciding what is to be talked about. The whole question is obviously much less clear and much more equivocal in this period than it became later. So it is important to begin with some distinctions. I shall distinguish first between quantified procedures and quantified concepts, and I shall take a quantified procedure in science to be one that aims at measurement, that is, any procedure that assigns numbers in a scale. To be complete such a procedure must comprise both mathematical techniques for operating the scale theoretically and measuring techniques for using it to explore the world. Technology need contain little more than procedures of these kinds, which provide for the measurements and calculations with which it is concerned. But most sciences aim beyond these at providing explanations by means of a system of theory. So a quantified science, as distinct from quantified technology, comprises not only quantified procedures but also quantified explanatory concepts, each applicable to the other within a theoretical system. The development of a science then takes place through a dialogue between its theories and its procedures, the former offering an exploration of the expected world through predictions and explanations made by means of the technical procedures, and the latter confronting these theoretical expectations with the test of quantified data.

A dialogue of this kind requires that both sides should speak the same language. We are so familiar with the close and precise adaptation of conceptual and procedural language to each other in modern physics that it may come as a surprise to find authentic scientific systems in which this is not the case. Yet we do not have to look very far to find examples. In the contemporary social sciences and in psychology, they are notorious. We do not have to go many decades back in the history of modern genetics to find a very incomplete and interrupted dialogue between theories and procedures. Somewhat earlier, in the eighteenth century, we find the same situation in chemistry. The main interest of medieval physics in this context seems to me to be that it provides the earliest example in the development of modern science in which we can study the state of affairs when the dialogue between concepts and procedures was incomplete or absent. Then we can study the difference it made when clear and exact communication was opened, as it was in the seventeenth century. I shall assume that it is my brief to discuss medieval physics as a case history of a general problem. At the same time, I shall as-

* Princeton University; Oxford University.

sume that this case history has a special historical interest because of its bearing on the particular question of the origins of modern scientific thinking.[1]

I propose to pursue the inquiry through two general questions. First, what internal intellectual needs and external practical and professional pressures were felt, leading to the quantification of theoretical concepts and theoretical procedures? Secondly, what internal intellectual needs and external practical and professional pressures were felt, leading to the collecting of quantitative factual data and to confront theoretical analysis with exact and repeatable measurements?

All the information about medieval physics that has been brought to light recently shows that a far greater need was felt that concepts and theoretical and mathematical procedures should be quantified than that actual measurements should be made. The choice between different possible theoretical formulations was often decided on purely theoretical grounds within a theoretical system. When we look at how the scientific and philosophical problems concerned developed historically, this distribution of interest seems natural enough. Yet it appears as something of a paradox. We seem to be dealing with philosophical decisions that did not immediately yield much in the way of quantified physics that was empirically true, yet with decisions that may seem to have been necessary for the later development of such a physics. The paradox appears when we ask ourselves, on the one hand, what the medieval physicists themselves thought they were doing, and on the other, what we ourselves may judge their contribution to have been to the later development of quantified science. So we must consider this further question: to what extent did medieval natural philosophical ideas, in advance of factual knowledge and often also of much deep understanding of the scientific use to which they could be put, suggest physical problems and methods of conceptualizing physics in what turned out to be a fruitful direction? This question must be faced by any historian of a tradition of developing truth such as Western science. I do not think that

---

[1] I have based my discussion in this paper on information taken from the following sources, which should be consulted for further details and bibliography: Guy Beaujouan and Emmanuel Poulle, "Les origines de la navigation astronomique aux XIVe et XVe siècles" in *Le Navire et l'économie maritime du XVe au XVIIIe siècle: travaux du colloque tenu le 17 mai 1956 à l'Académie de Marine* présentés par Michel Mollat avec la collaboration d'Olivier de Prat, Paris, 1957; D. A. Callus (ed.), *Robert Grosseteste, Scholar and Bishop* (Oxford, 1955), chapter by A. C. Crombie; Marshall Clagett, *The Science of Mechanics in the Middle Ages* (Madison, Wisc., 1959); Marshall Clagett (ed.), *Critical Problems in the History of Science* (Madison, Wisc., 1959), paper by A. C. Crombie and commentary by I. E. Drabkin and Ernest Nagel; A. C. Crombie, *Robert Grosseteste and the Origins of Experimental Science 1100-1700* (Oxford, 1953), and *Medieval and Early Modern Science* (New York, 1959) (2 vols. Doubleday Anchor Books); E. J. Dijksterhuis, *Die Mechanisering van het Wereldbeeld* (Amsterdam, 1950) (German translation, 1955); Pierre Duhem, *Le Systeme du monde* (Paris, 1913-16) I-V, (1954-58) VI-VIII; C. W. Jones (ed.), *Bedae Opera de Temporibus* (Cambridge, Mass., 1943); Anneliese Maier, *Die Vorläufer Galileis im 14, Jahrhundert* (Rome, 1959), *Zwei Grundprobleme der Scholastischen Naturphilosophie*, 2nd ed. (Rome, 1951), *An der Grenze von Scholastik und Naturwissenschaften*, 2nd ed. (Rome, 1952), *Zwischen Philosophie und Mechanik* (Rome, 1958); E. A. Moody and Marshall Clagett, *The Medieval Science of Weights* (Madison, Wisc., 1952); Charles Singer *et al.* (eds.), *A History of Technology* (Oxford, 1957), III—chapters by Sir Harold Spencer Jones, H. Alan Lloyd, Derek J. Price, Charles Singer, Cyril Stanley Smith and R. J. Forbes, and E. G. R. Taylor; René Taton (ed.), *Histoire générale des sciences* (Paris, 1957), I.

we should be bothered by the suggestion of teleology this question carries. It can be dealt with by trying first to determine what problems the natural philosophers of the past were aiming to solve in their own period and what their intentions and preoccupations were, and by trying then to see what difference their work made in the short and in the long run. It will cause no surprise that ideas and habits of thought may come to have applications undreamed of at an earlier stage of their history—so much so that an idea may generate a completely different one with a change of context.

Some intellectual need to produce some kind of quantified conceptualization of physics can be seen as early as the twelfth century, for example, in the Chartres school. The sources of this are a form of neoplatonic philosophy derived from St. Augustine and from Plato's *Timaeus,* and such scriptual texts as that from the *Wisdom of Solomon* stating that God had "ordered all things in measure and number and weight." Vague as it is, this notion suggested kinds of explanation to look for. For example, Thierry of Chartres, in attempting to give a rational analysis of the formation of the world at the creation, replaced Plato's demiurge with the Christian God. He said that God had created space or chaos and then had ordered it so as to form the universe in accordance with the mathematical ideas in His mind. So Thierry concluded that in order to understand the story of *Genesis* rationally, it was necessary to master the mathematics of the *quadrivium,* for mathematics was the key to all rational explanation of the physical world. We might perhaps call Thierry's programme "proto-quantitative." It included such elements as attempting to account for differences between qualities as observed, in terms of geometrical differences between Plato's geometrical particles. It is hopeful and for us suggestive. But it involves no numbers or measurements. It is hardly what we regard as science.

The first more seriously scientific moves towards the quantification of concepts and procedures in medieval physics were made in the course of a controversy that arose in the thirteenth century over the Aristotelian categories of "quantity" and "quality." In effect the origin of the controversy was a critique of Aristotle's qualitative physics from two other points of view also derived from Greek sources. These were first, the Pythagorean or Platonic physical concept that qualitative differences might be reducible to differences in geometrical structure, number and movement, that is to differences in quantities; and secondly, certain mathematical concepts and procedures.

The characteristics of Aristotle's conception of physics that strike us now as most alien to the thought of modern quantified physics are not only that it was explicitly qualitative, but also that it looked for its explanations in terms of a direct classification of immediate experience. Thus Aristotle's distinctions between motion up, down, and in a circle, and between natural and violent motion, were based on a direct classification of what bodies are actually seen to do. The cosmological system in which such motions were supposed to find their explanation was built up simply as a classification of these and similar directly observed distinctions. The "natures" that were supposed to be the explanatory sources of the behavior of different things were characterized simply by a direct description of what things actually did. Thus they gave no further information beyond that already obtained from direct observation. Their characterization included both quantitative and qualitative attributes. But these were irreducibly different. Certainly Aristotle's physics made use of some quantitative relationships, such as when he said that a body would move twice the distance in a given time when acted on by twice the power. But it did not aim except incidentally at measurement, calculation, and quantitative prediction. It aimed at *episteme, scientia,* true and certain rational knowledge. Aristotle held that he had found such knowledge when he had discovered the "nature" through direct observation.

The medieval critique of this conception of the aims of physics as a science certainly fell a good way short of the position Galileo was to take up. Galileo did his best to drop all the questions to which Aristotelian physics was the answer and to ask new kinds of questions. But the new elements by means of which both the medievals and Galileo introduced a new conception of physics were analogous. On the other hand, in certain fields medieval "Platonists" looked, like Galileo, for explanations not in immediate experience but in theoretical concepts at a remove from it and capable of quantification. On the other hand, both reduced the sharp distinction made by Plato and Aristotle between *episteme* and *techne, ars,* the manipulative skills, including mathematics.

This last distinction seems to me to supply one of the various keys that historians can offer to an understanding of what happened in the Scientific Revolution. Thus in Greek scientific thought Ptolemy's mathematical astronomy, which could predict the celestial motions but could not explain them, was supposed to be a distinct field of inquiry from Aristotle's physics, which was held to explain these motions. The technical mathematical devices of astronomy were *techne.* So it was possible to hold that alternative technical devices, for example, in the middle ages those of Eudoxus and Ptolemy and in the sixteenth and early seventeenth centuries those of Ptolemy, Copernicus, and Tycho Brahe, could be combined with the same system of physics, the same *episteme.* The dynamical analysis of terrestrial and celestial motion finally brought out into the open by Kepler, Galileo, and eventually Newton showed that this was a very superficial view of the matter. It showed that in so far as the "physics" of motion was left untouched by calculation and measurement, it could be disregarded. It was irrelevant. And it showed that in so far as "physics" was exposed to calculation and measurement it was subject to the same quantitative tests as the mathematical devices used in making predictions. The essence of the seventeenth-century revolution in physics can thus be seen, from this point of view, as the using of *techne,* "art," in fact the "new experimental-mathematical philosophy," to yield a true science of nature. This was not the certain rational knowledge of Plato's and Aristotle's *episteme,* but as Pascal, Huygens, and Newton pointed out it was the nearest to the physical truth that we could get.

In medieval physics the distinction between the science of "natures" and the art of applying mathematics to physical problems was certainly not abolished or reorganized as it became in the seventeenth century. But mathematical art, the so-called *scientia media,* was introduced into the science of nature far beyond Aristotle. So at the same time there were at least some quantified physical concepts, and others that were not yet quantified but were capable of being so. The weakest of the elements that have become essential to physics since the seventeenth century was measurement. I shall now consider some examples of these elements in the quantification of medieval physics.

An example of the "proto-quantification" of physical concepts, aiming to show how to express qualitative differences in terms of differences in quantities, but without yet assigning any quantities, is provided by thirteenth-century optics. Much of this is better described as a speculative program than as theory. The deductive machinery for making calculations from theory to data is largely missing. But medieval natural philosophers were certainly aware that such machinery should be supplied in a scientific system, and in optics they made some attempt to supply it. In some problems they reached a state of primitive quantification by assigning numbers.

Consider first the conception of optics as a physical science developed in the thirteenth century by Robert Grosseteste and Roger Bacon. Grosseteste conceived the "nature" that was the cause of given events as something, not open to direct inspection, in which the event was prefigured. The ultimate physical "nature" or substance in which all physical events were prefigured he held to be light (*lux*). This had the fundamental property of self-propagation which he characterized geometrically from two points of view: (1) *super lineas et angulos*, that is along straight lines that may change direction by reflection and refraction; and (2) *super figuras*, that is in a sphere from a centre or in a cone. Thus characterized, Grosseteste described how this light, from an originally created point, generated the dimensions of space and the spheres of the universe, and operated as the efficient cause in all motion. So for Grosseteste optics became the fundamental physical science, and in order to make it work as an explanatory system he said that it was essential to operate it by means of mathematics. "Hence," he wrote, "these rules and principles and fundamentals having been given by the power of geometry, the careful observer of natural things can give the causes of all natural effects by this method. And it will be impossible otherwise, as is already clear in respect of the universal, since every natural action is varied in strength and weakness through variation of lines, angles and figures. But in respect of the particular this is even clearer, first in natural action upon matter and later upon the senses."[2]

With Grosseteste, the Aristotelian "nature" or "form" thus became mathematically characterized. Roger Bacon, continuing Grosseteste's description of this program, wrote: "All categories (*praedicamenta*) depend on a knowledge of quantity, concerning which mathematics treats, and therefore the whole power of logic depends on mathematics."[3] He then used language indicating a further shift towards a quantified physics looking for its explanations not in definitions of essences or "natures" but in mathematically expressed laws. Bacon is the first writer I know to have used the term "law of nature" (*lex*

---

[2] "De Natura Locorum," in *Die Philosophischen Werke des Robert Grosseteste*, ed. L. Baur (*Beiträge zur Geschichte der Philosophie des Mittelalters*, IX, Münster, 1912), pp. 59-60.

[3] *Opus Maius*, ed. J. H. Bridges (Oxford, 1897), I, 103.

naturae) in the scientific sense familiar since the seventeenth century. Thus he wrote: "That the laws of reflection and refraction are common to all natural actions I have shown in the treatise on geometry,"[4] and he claimed to have demonstrated "by the law of refraction" how the image was formed in the eye.

As a piece of speculation this mathematicizing program has a number of features suggestive and interesting for us because we know what happened in the long run. In his account of *multiplicatio specierum,* Grosseteste distinguished between the physical activity by which visible light, heat, sound, and other forms of efficient causality were propagated through the medium, and the sensations they produced when they acted on the appropriate sense organs of a sentient being. This is not of course an original distinction; it was made by the Greek atomists. But in the thirteenth century it made a significant departure from Aristotle by conceiving the world of physical science as something removed from direct observation and something capable of mathematical characterization. Grosseteste himself attempted to formulate a geometrical, almost mechanical conception of the rectilinear propagation of light and of sound as a succession of "pulses" or "waves" transmitted from part to part. He tried to use this to account for reflection and refraction, and he offered a quantitative law or "rule" for determining the angle of refraction.[5] Roger Bacon, and later Witelo and Theodoric of Freiberg, made a similar distinction between directly perceived visible qualities and light as a geometrically conceived physical activity producing these qualities. They proposed that different visible qualities were effects produced by quantitative differences in the physical activity of light. Thus Witelo and Theodoric of Freiberg developed along these lines a suggestion made by Averroes giving a quasi-quantitative account of Aristotle's explanation of colour as a mixture of light and darkness. They observed experimentally that the colours of the spectrum were in an order of increasing amounts of refraction from red to blue. They attributed this to a progressive weakening of white light by refraction, so that progressively larger amounts of darkness became mixed with it. Similarly Grosseteste correlated intensity of illumination and of heat with the angle at which the rays were received and with their concentration. In the fourteenth century another Oxford natural philosopher, John of Dumbleton, speculated with the formulation of a quantitative law relating intensity of illumination to distance from the luminous source.

We might consider these speculations as part of the pre-history of a quantified conceptualization of the science of optics. If now we ask for their cash value in quantified procedures and firm scientific knowledge, we get another side to the story. In the whole conceptual development of optics following Grosseteste, there was almost no attempt at precise mathematical definition, at expressing the amounts of change quantitatively in numbers, or at measurement. One reason for this was certainly that these speculations carried the subject far beyond not only the facts but also the available mathematical

---

[4] *Un fragment inédit de l'Opus Tertium,* ed. P. Duhem (Quaracchi, 1909), p. 90; cf. p. 78.
[5] Cf. C. M. Turbayne, "Grosseteste and an ancient optical principle," *Isis,* 1959, *50:* 467-472.

techniques and concepts, which did not go farther than those of elementary geometrical optics. But if we descend from high speculation closer to the world of fact and of *techne,* we still find a gap between promise and fulfillment. We find ourselves in a scientific milieu in which certainly some natural philosophers had a more or less clear idea of how to proceed in science and in which some discoveries were made. For example, Roger Bacon's analysis and classification of the refractive properties of different curved interfaces, and his use of a geometrical model of the eye to analyze how the different refracting media focused the image, are highly intelligent examples of proto-quantitative scientific procedures. But in the milieu of medieval academic science neither intellectual need nor social pressure for consistent quantitative accuracy seems to have been felt strongly enough to produce reliably consistent results. In the academic science of the universities the chances of data being challenged by repetition must have been small. It was only where investigations had some definite practical value, such as astronomical observations had for the calendar, astrology and navigation, and chemical assaying had for commercial metallurgy, that there was a strong enough demand to ensure exact and repeatable measurements.

Some further examples from optics will illustrate this unreliability in measurement characteristic of medieval academic science in practice, however much quantitative procedures may have been advocated in principle. One of the most impressive pieces of quantitative academic science in the thirteenth century is Witelo's account of the measurement of the values of the angles of refraction of light passing between air, water and glass, with angles of incidence increasing by 10 degrees to a maximum of 80 degrees. Witelo described in detail the construction and use of an apparatus for making these measurements, set out the results in tables showing concomitant variations between angles of incidence and amounts of refraction, generalized these in a set of rules assigning greater or lesser amounts of refraction but not numbers, and offered a physical explanation in terms of the densities of the refracting media. But did Witelo ever actually make these measurements? Two facts raise doubts. First, the values in the tables showing refraction from air into water and into glass, and from water into glass, which are fairly accurate, are identical with those in Ptolemy's tables for similar experiments. Secondly, Witelo's tables show very inaccurate or impossible reciprocal values.[6] (Ptolemy did not include these.) It seems that Witelo derived these values from a misapplication of the law that the paths of the rays are the same whether we are considering the light passing, for example, from air into water or from water into air. He did not know that at the higher angles of incidence, all the light striking the under surface of the water will be reflected and none will be refracted into the air. If Witelo had actually made these experiments, he would have discovered this phenomenon, but it was not discovered until the fourteenth century.

Another revealing example is provided by the studies of the rainbow.[7] According to the conception of scientific methodology developed in the thirteenth

[6] Crombie, *Robert Grosseteste,* pp. 223-225.
[7] *Ibid.,* pp. 64-66, 124-127, 155-162, 196-200, 226-277, 290-292.

and fourteenth centuries, the explanation of an event was to be sought through an analysis of the conditions necessary and sufficient to produce it. The conditions producing a rainbow were stated in the form that if there be postulated a certain refracting medium, namely rain drops, at a position at which the incident sunlight makes an angle of 42 degrees with the line connecting the rain drops and an observer, then the observer will see a rainbow. Roger Bacon states that he measured with an astrolabe this angle subtended by the radius of the rainbow. Later investigators, especially Witelo and Theodoric of Freiberg, proceeded most intelligently to try to find out what happened to the light when it struck the rain drops. They set up geometrical models, rejected models that did not yield the observed results, and Theodoric finally carried out a successful analysis showing, by means of spherical flasks of water used as model raindrops, how the sunlight, by refraction and internal reflection, produced the order and shape of the colours seen in both the primary and the secondary bows. He stated correctly that the angle between these two bows is 11 degrees. But he also stated that he had measured with an astrolabe the angle subtended by the radius of the primary bow and had found it to be 22 degrees. It is obvious that he could not have obtained by measurement this value for an angle that is approximately 42 degrees. Theodoric's work is characteristic of a large part of medieval optics and medieval physics as a whole. He had an intelligent analytical procedure. Neither his procedure nor his conceptualization of the problem were explicitly quantified, but both were a preliminary to the quantification that Descartes, for example, was to give to the problem of the rainbow by assigning numbers by means of the newly discovered law of refraction. But Theodoric was unreliable in his measurements.

It is obvious that when they were dealing with problems in academic science, the kinds of problems that might be discussed in commentaries on texts of Aristotle and other authors used in the arts faculties of universities, medieval natural philosophers suffered not simply from a lack of quantified procedures for dealing with their speculation, but also from a lack of firm intention to apply such procedures in experimental measurement. The dialogue in their own minds between concepts and procedures for measurement had not become properly established. The fact is that however much some of them may have discussed the methodology of experimental quantitative science and advocated putting it into practice, nearly all medieval natural philosophers were primarily theoreticians. They made consistent *measurements* only when some *practical* need demanded it. But they found the development of a dialogue between concepts and quantified *theoretical* procedures something that followed naturally from their academic problems. To this aspect of medieval physics, to the development of quantified theoretical and mathematical procedures and related concepts without measurement, I must now turn.

This theoretical quantification of academic medieval physics was developed out of an attempt to provide the same procedures for representing changes of any kind, quantitative or qualitative. Behind this was the conception that all real differences could be reduced to differences in the category of quantity, for example, that a change in the intensity of a quality such as heat could be expressed as a magnitude in the same way as could a change in a quantity such as length. The question was opened in a theological context by Peter Lombard's assertion that the virtue of charity could increase and decrease in an individual and be more or less intense at different times. How was this to be understood? Two schools of thought developed and their divergent principles were taken over into physics.

The conservative school supported Aristotle's principle that since quality and quantity belonged to absolutely different categories, the one could not be reduced to the other. Examples of changes in quantity were changes in length or number, which were brought about by the addition or subtraction of either continuous or discontinuous homogeneous parts. That was all the change involved. But a change in a quality such as heat was quite different. Heat might exist in different degrees of intensity, but a change in intensity was not brought about, for example, by adding one homogeneous part of heat to another. The heats of two bodies brought into contact did not make a greater heat, as the lengths of two bodies made a greater length. So Aristotle and his supporters considered that each degree of intensity of heat was a different quality, and that a change in the intensity was brought about by loss of one quality of heat and the acquisition of another. The same went for every change in quality.

The radical school aiming at quantifying physics had to make several moves in order to deal with these opposing arguments and achieve their goal. Some philosophers distinguished between a body and its qualities and said that, for example, if the heat or the weight of one body were abstracted from it and then added to another, the latter would become hotter and heavier in amounts capable of expression in numerical degrees. Following this line of thought, definitions and distinctions of quantities were sharpened. For example, in the fourteenth century the expression "specific weight" was used to distinguish density, or intensity of weight proportional to volume, from gross weight. Another problem that arose concerned the characterization of scales. Greek writers conceived of qualities as existing in pairs of opposites: hot-cold, wet-dry, heavy-light, bright-dark, and so on. Thus Galen had suggested representing both heat and cold in numerical degrees. This conception of pairs of opposites was a major obstacle to the quantification of physics until the general introduction of linear scales from the seventeenth century. For example, when Buridan, in developing the dynamical concept of *impetus,* proposed as a measure of "quantity of motion" the product of "speed" multiplied by "quantity of matter," this applied only to "heavy" and not to "light" bodies.

In the end, whatever view they took of the real nature of qualities and of qualitative change, natural philosophers and mathematicians made two important contributions to the quantification of physics in the fourteenth century. They created concepts for quantifying space, time, speed, and other magnitudes. And they devised procedures for *representing* any kind of change numerically and for manipulating the quantities concerned. The best illustration of this is found in kinematics and dynamics.

The theoretical quantification of the science of local motion began with a critique of those parts of Aristotle's treatment of the subject that had themselves some implied quantification. The technical procedures were derived in the first place from the theory of proportions expounded by Euclid and Archimedes. Consider first the stages in the critique of the Aristotelian relationship making speed (v) directly proportional to the motive power (p) and inversely proportional to the resistance (r) of the medium: $v \propto p/r$. The first thing that had to be done was to put the relationship into this form, which was impossible for the Greeks because they did not consider speed (v) to be a magnitude. According to the Greek conception, a magnitude could result only from a "true" proportion, that is from a ratio of two "like" quantities such as two distances (s) or two times (t).[8] So Aristotle could express the relationship only by considering it in separate stages. Thus

$$\frac{s_1}{s_2} = \frac{t_1}{t_2}, \quad \text{i.e. speed is uniform, when } p_1 = p_2 \text{ and } r_1 = r_2;$$

$$\frac{s_1}{s_2} = \frac{p_1}{p_2} \quad \text{when } t_1 = t_2 \text{ and } r_1 = r_2;$$

$$\frac{s_1}{s_2} = \frac{r_2}{r_1} \quad \text{when } t_1 = t_2 \text{ and } p_1 = p_2.$$

A metric definition of speed as a magnitude determined by the ratio between two "unlike" quantities, distance and time, i.e. $v = s/t$, was foreshadowed in the thirteenth century by Gerard of Brussels but made explicit only in the fourteenth century by Thomas Bradwardine and other mathematicians at Oxford.

Bradwardine was now in a position to propose an alternative to the Aristotelian expression $v \propto p/r$, which could not apply to cases where $p = r$ and $v = 0$. After considering some other proposals, he came to the conclusion that the relationship was one which we would now call exponential and which we can express as $v = \log (p/r)$. Since $\log 1/1 = 0$, the condition is satisfied that when $p = r$, $v = 0$, and the relationship gives a continual gradual change in v as p/r approaches 1. It is clear that Bradwardine was concerned with obtaining a relationship consistent within his theoretical system that would also describe actual motions. He also made the important and influential move of shifting the ground of the discussion from the causal "why" to the mathematical "how," that is, from the physical causes of movement to the spatio-temporal effects of movement. But he does not seem to have thought of making experimental measurements to decide whether his expression did in fact describe actual motions.

Following Bradwardine, the theoretical quantification of the science of motion was carried several stages further at Oxford and Paris, but all without experimental measurement. Bradwardine's analysis had related velocity to instantaneous changes. At Merton College, William Heytesbury, Richard Swineshead, and John of Dumbleton went on to develop a concept of instantaneous velocity and with it an analysis of various kinds of acceleration, which Heytesbury defined as "the velocity of a velocity." (I use "velocity" in this context nonvectorially as synonymous with "speed.") This analysis grew out

---

[8] See Clagett, *The Science of Mechanics in the Middle Ages*, pp. 165ff.

of the problem of representing the amounts and rates of change of any quality or quantity, which was known as "the intension and remission of forms," or "the latitude of forms." A "form" in this context was any variable quality or quantity. The "intensity" or "latitude" of a form, for example velocity, was the numerical value that was assigned to it, and thus it was possible to speak of the rate at which the intensity of the variable form, velocity, changed in relation to an invariable form known as the "extension" or "longitude," such as distance or time. Velocity was said to be "uniform" when equal distances were covered in equal successive intervals of time, and "difform" when unequal distances were covered as in accelerated or retarded motion. Further distinctions were made between "uniformly difform" motion, that is uniform acceleration or retardation, "difformly difform" motion, and so on. A very important definition was that of uniformly accelerated movement as one in which equal increments of velocity were acquired in equal intervals of time.

The problem of the relationship between the categories of quality and quantity that is behind this analysis is reflected in the distinction of the intensity of a velocity as its "quality," in contrast to the distance covered which was its "quantity." In cases of acceleration, the quality of velocity was said to vary from instant to instant. Thus instantaneous velocity was the intensity or quality of a velocity at an instant. It was measured numerically by the distance that *would* be covered by a point if it were allowed to move for a given time at the velocity it had at that instant. In Paris Nicole Oresme applied a graphical method to this analysis, using two-dimensional figures to represent changes of variable forms in relation to invariable ones. Thus he represented the "extension" of time by a horizontal straight line and the intensity of velocity at each instant by a perpendicular raised at a corresponding point on the horizontal. The height of the perpendicular represented the intensity or "quality" of the velocity, whereas the area of the whole figure, which is dimensionally equivalent to the distance covered in the movement, was its "quantity" or "total" velocity.[9]

Out of this theoretical quantification and analysis of motion came a number of interesting and valuable procedures and theorems. The most significant procedures occur in the associated development of the concept of functional dependence. The best known theorem is the so-called Mean Speed Rule of Merton College. This makes an approach that has become characteristic of modern kinematics, seeing as the basic objective of analysis the representation of nonuniform velocities by uniform velocities. The Merton theorem states that a uniform acceleration produces the same "quantity of motion," as measured by distance travelled in a given time, as a uniform velocity equal to the instantaneous velocity at the middle instant of the time of the acceleration. This theorem has application to the motion of freely falling bodies, which in the fourteenth century was discussed as a case of uniform acceleration. Yet none of these academic mathematical philosophers cleared up the question whether the velocity of falling bodies increased in proportion to distance fallen or to the time. That had to wait until the sixteenth century. And none of them checked the mathematical analysis against measurements made with fall-

[9] Cf. Clagett, *op. cit.,* pp. xxv-xxvi.

ing bodies. The analysis of the problem within the framework of the Greek theory of proportions made measurement largely inapplicable. That had to wait until Galileo's experiments with a ball rolling down an inclined plane. The reason for these omissions is undoubtedly that these mathematical philosophers were primarily theoreticians, interested in philosophical method and mathematics. They felt no compelling intellectual need or social pressure to take a particular interest in falling bodies or any other particular phenomena in nature.

By far the most sophisticated and exact part of physical science in the thirteenth and fourteenth centuries was based on concepts quantified in this way for theoretical and mathematical manipulation, without thought of actual experimental measurements. As a general phenomenon arising in the arts faculty, this kind of approach to physical problems represented a union of the philosophical approach of Aristotle with the mathematical approach of Archimedes. Another example is the work in statics, where, for example, in the treatises associated with the name of Jordanus Nemorarius, trajectories and levers were analyzed into the effective quantities involved—vertical rectilinear displacement, horizontal distance from the fulcrum, "gravity according to position," and so on. This analysis made implicit use of the important new principle of virtual displacements. A further example is Jean Buridan's move towards the quantification of dynamics through the concept of impetus. This was put forward as a solution of the problem, arising within Aristotelian physics, of providing a cause for the continual motion of projectiles and for the accelerated motion of falling bodies. But by giving a quantitative measure of impetus as the quantity of matter in the moving body multiplied by its velocity, Buridan provided a measure of the *effect* of motion clearly analogous to the definition of quantity of motion or momentum used in seventeenth century mechanics. Similarly his account of the production of acceleration in falling bodies by the continuous action of a *constant* gravity has analogies with Newton's definition of force. Theoretical quantification was thus taking physics out of the irreducible Aristotelian categories. Metaphysical or "physical" restrictions, for example to considering velocity a magnitude or to comparing linear and circular motion, began to be put on one side.[10] In a quantified physics, mathematics treats all quantities as belonging to the same category.

The notion of proportions used in medieval science does not lead to the measurement; hence measurements were not appropriate to the inquiry being undertaken. Nevertheless the investigation of proportions in the fourteenth century did lead to the formulation of important mathematical and logical definitions and theorems that were *later* taken over into seventeenth-century mathematical physics—for example, velocity, acceleration, instantaneous velocity, the Mertonian Mean Speed Rule. Thus, although the scholastics did not have precisely the same aims and intentions as seventeenth-century physicists, they did produce results which became part of the main history of physics—especially in kinematics. But we must not forget that medieval writers on "latitude of forms" applied their quantitative methods not only to physical

10 Cf. Clagett, *op. cit.,* p. 181.

problems such as motion, but also to degrees of divine grace, sin and other qualities. The fact that they considered such a wide range of questions by means of their method marks an important difference between their focus of attention and that of seventeenth-century physicists.) The same is true of medieval work in the field of optics. A writer might consider within the same general framework the propagation not only of the light but also of influences from the stars and even of divine grace. Yet at the same time valuable work was done in optics strictly speaking, for example on refraction and the rainbow and on the analysis of the eye as an optical instrument by imposing a geometrical model on anatomy. Some of the numerical figures given can have been obtained only by actual measurement, for example 42 degrees for the radius of the rainbow. Yet we may doubt whether many of the figures given as if they were the results of measurements were really obtained in actual experiments. Until *after* Galileo such figures were in fact usually derived from mathematical theory.

Yet although the main development of quantification in academic medieval physics was in theory divorced from actual experiment, it would be mistaken to suppose that these philosophers were totally uninterested in the application of their theoretical analysis to the observable world and in checking it by reference to observations. Buridan, for example, continually invoked common-sense observations to illustrate his conclusions. At the same time there is evidence of a general move in practical life to quantify space, time, weight, and other aspects of the world as experienced and used. For example, by the time Henri de Vick's mechanical clock, divided into 24 equal hours, had been set up on the Palais Royale in Paris in 1370, the time of practical life was on the way to becoming abstract mathematical time of units on a scale that belongs to the world of science. King Charles V ordered all churches in Paris to ring the hours and quarters according to the time by de Vick's clock. The division of hours into 60 minutes and of minutes into 60 seconds also came into general use in the fourteenth century. Space also became abstractly quantified. In painting, the symbolic arrangements and size of subjects according to their importance in the theological hierarchy began to give way in the fourteenth century to the division of the canvas into an abstract checkerboard according to the rules of perspective. And besides maps arranging the world symbolically round a heavenly Jerusalem, there appeared maps by cartographers in which a terrestrial traveler or mariner could find his position on an abstract system of co-ordinates of latitude and longitude. Similarly in commerce and fiscal administration, exchanges and obligations were estimated in abstract units of money and bills of exchange and regulated by standardized units of weight and measure. In theoretical academic science the relating of quantified theory to measurement could remain a matter of private, internal interest. But in practical life exact and repeatable measurements are of the essence and are consequently subject to external demand. My final set of examples will show that when a similar external demand was made from science, it likewise produced exact measurements. But since the demand was primarily practical and utilitarian in its bearing, its effect upon scientific theory was far less intimate than that of contemporary theoretical discussions.

The hypothesis that in the medieval period it was normally external practical demand rather than an internal feeling of intellectual need that led to the development and use of procedures and instruments for obtaining accurate and consistent measurements, and that such measurements were lacking when such a demand was absent, whatever the field, can be tested by means of some quantities that appear in more than one context. Consider the treatment of three such quantities, time, space and weight, in academic natural philosophy and the practical crafts.

Time was the principal practical concern of astronomy, a science belonging to the academic *quadrivium*. Until the seventeenth century, astronomy was far ahead of all other theoretical sciences in the extent to which it was accurately and systematically quantified with actual measurements. For the medieval astronomers, Ptolemy's writings provided an example not only of quantified mathematical theory and procedures but also of systematic numerical observational data. The reason for the early development of astronomy in these respects was certainly that from remote antiquity the various regular movements of heavenly bodies had provided the standard measures and divisions of time regulating practical affairs, and also that since the main divisions into the solar year and day and the lunar month are all incommensurable, their relation to each other in the mathematical calendars and systems available required periodic checking by fresh measurements.

There were two main practical problems in the middle ages: to get an accurate perpetual calendar, relating especially the lunar year used in calculating the date of Easter to the solar year; and to devise means for telling the time of day at different times of year and different latitudes by observing the elevation of the sun or some other heavenly body. From the time Bede wrote on the subject early in the eighth century, these problems taught medieval scholars to think in numbers and to measure, calculate, and check against further measurements. They created a demand for mathematical knowledge and skill and for measuring instruments. Thus Bede gave a table for use with a sundial showing the length of a 6-ft. gnomon at noon, 9 a.m., and 3 p.m. at intervals of about a fortnight throughout the year, at a latitude of 55°, corresponding to that of his monastery at Jarrow.[11] From the period when the full influence of Greek and Arabic astronomy was felt in the thirteenth century, a variety of instruments for making astronomical measurements and telling the time were manufactured and put into use in the West. The most important were the astrolabe, the quadrant, and the sundial, which were improved in various ways for greater accuracy and range. At the same time improvements were made in mathematical techniques for making numerical calculations. The "Arabic" numerals and positional arithmetic introduced in the thirteenth century came into wide use first in calendars and astronomical tables and then in commercial transactions. In both fields it had an obvious practical advantage over the Roman system. The development of modern trigonometry dates from mathematical work done in Oxford and France in the fourteenth century in connection with astronomy.

The practical demand for an accurate knowledge of time put a premium on

[11] See D. J. Price, in *History of Technology*, III, 595.

the precision of instruments and calculations. For observations made with the naked eye, the limit of accuracy is about 5 minutes of arc for angle-measurements, 20 seconds of time estimated by the earth's daily rotation, and 2½ degrees of terrestrial longitude estimated by means of eclipses and other methods involving lunar positions.[12] Ptolemy's mathematical astronomical theory had in most particulars reached this degree of accuracy. But an angle of 5 minutes subtends a distance of only 1 millimetre on a divided circle of 1½ metres in diameter. So to attain the precision required by the interaction of theory and measurement, instrument makers had to develop a very refined skill. Precision was achieved by the accuracy and closeness of the divisions, by making instruments large, and by paying attention to jointing and stability. There were considerable difficulties. For example, there was no method of geometrical construction for angles less than 15 degrees; below that divisions were made by eye. Yet with an ordinary thirteenth-century astrolabe the time could be told to within 2-5 minutes. The precision attained was well sufficient to enable astronomers to recognize by the end of the thirteenth century that Ptolemy's mathematical astronomy was much more accurate than Aristotle's. For example, in 1290 Guillaume of St. Cloud determined the latitude of Paris correctly as 48° 50′ and the obliquity of the ecliptic as 23° 34′, which compares well with the modern value of 23° 32′ for the obliquity at that date.

Thus the practical demands made on them forced astronomers to achieve an accuracy that enabled them to make a choice between theories on grounds of measurement. Compared with the systematic and regular method of observing introduced in the sixteenth century by Tycho Brahe, using instruments of measured degree of error, the irregular observations made by the medieval astronomers still allowed many discrepancies between theory and fact to pass undetected. But they made measurements to a degree undreamed-of in fields of contemporary academic physics that had no immediate practical applications. Demands made by such applications could lead the same scholar or group of scholars, for example, those beginning with Grosseteste who for over a century were concerned with the reform of the Julian calendar, to recognize the decisive importance of numerical measurements in a practical problem while showing no such awareness in their work in purely academic physics.

The same contrast appears in a comparison of academic treatment of space and distance, for example in discussions of motion, with the treatment given in contemporary methods of surveying, navigation, cartography, and later of gunnery. Here again practical demands forced an attention to numerical measurement and calculation and led to the development of instruments and mathematical techniques. Surveying methods were being taught in the *quadrivium* by the twelfth century, and in the whole practical quantification of space scholarly mathematics played an essential part in supplying mathematical procedures to the empirical methods of mariners, instrument makers, and other craftsmen. One example will suffice. In the sixteenth century the compass-charts or *portolani* used in navigating gave two essential pieces of information: the route to follow and the angle it must make with the North-South axis as given by a magnetized needle; and the distance to run in the direction

---

[12] *Ibid.*, pp. 583-584.

thus determined. Ideally the navigator went on a line at a constant angle from the line of the magnetized needle until he reached his destination. If this was impossible or if he went off course for a time, rudimentary trigonometrical tables, called *martelogio*, showed how to return to his original route. These seem to have been the product of scholarly mathematics. An early indication of them is given by Raymond Lulle in his *Ars Magna* (1305-1308), where he wrote: "When a ship runs eight miles towards the south-east, these eight miles are equivalent to only six miles towards the east."[13] In modern terminology, $8 \cos 45° = 5.6466$. This provided for numerical measurements and calculations such as were not found in contemporary academic discussions of motion.

The quantification of weight by measurement likewise occurred only when there was a practical demand, but here this was felt almost entirely in the field of the practical crafts and not in academic science. For example, practical metallurgists wanted to be able to produce alloys of desired and repeatable properties, coins of known and honest value, and so on. The earliest physical property of metals to be quantitatively measured was density. A table dating from the eleventh or twelfth century gives a list of weights relative to wax to show the founder how much metal to melt.[14] But it was in assaying that quantitative methods based on measuring weight with a balance were most extensively developed. Ores were assayed for economic value and coins or jewelry to determine their quality and to detect fraud. The product was put through various processes, and weighing was carried out at appropriate stages with balances of various degrees of sensitivity. The most sensitive showed about 0.1 milligram.[15] There were beam-lifting devices to protect the knife-edge from shock, and in the course of time these became more accurate with further refinements, just as was happening with other scientific instruments. In quantitative factual knowledge, practical chemistry was far ahead of theory in the middle ages and remained so until the eighteenth century. The assayer excelled the alchemist in all but the desire for a systematized philosophy. But a dialogue between them and between the two sides of chemistry they represented was virtually impossible. The assayer concentrated his attention on changes in weight, the alchemist on changes in color and appearance. The former had no theory and the latter a theory based on the wrong concepts. The predicament of medieval chemistry is the most extreme case of the whole medieval scientific predicament of intellectual aspiration failing to get into communication with practical demand and so with quantified fact.

No claim could be made that this analysis is anything more than a preliminary exploration that may raise some questions for discussion and suggest some comparisons with problems of quantification in other periods and branches of science. But this I take to be the purpose of the papers prepared for this symposium. To give openings for discussion I will conclude by set-

---

[13] See Beaujouan and Poulle, *op. cit.*, pp. 106-107.
[14] See C. S. Smith and R. J. Forbes, in *History of Technology*, III, 59.
[15] *Ibid.*, p. 60.

ting out the main answers, suggested by my analysis, to the questions asked at the beginning.

1. The primary internal, intellectual need felt by medieval natural philosophers was for rational, theoretical clarification and understanding rather than for knowledge acquired through observation. This need arose in a desire to understand rationally and clarify (a) the features of cosmogony and cosmology accepted as having been revealed, and (b) the system of natural philosophy presented in the Latin translations of Aristotle and the other Greek and the Arabic philosophers and mathematicians.

2. Consequently, medieval natural philosophers discussed quantification and other problems of scientific method primarily as theoretical problems without systematic reference to actual scientific measurement. They directed their intellectual effort towards quantifying theoretical concepts and procedures, especially in response to problems arising within Aristotelian philosophy and out of its relationship with concepts and procedures presented by Greek mathematics. As a result, they made some useful progress with theoretical problems. But, although they made some measurements, their intellectual interests did not by themselves provide an intellectual need strong enough to ensure that measurements in academic science were in fact accurate and that decisions between different theoretical principles or concepts were always made on grounds of actual measurements.

3. This theoretical emphasis in intellectual interests was supported and maintained by the aims, content, and methods of the education provided by the medieval universities, where the basis of both the arts course and of the higher courses in theology, law, and medicine was the making of a critical study and commentary on theoretical problems raised by standard texts.

4. Departure from this purely theoretical emphasis occurred only when there was a strong external, practical demand for exact measurements. When this was present, theoretical concepts and procedures became quantified in such a way that measurement was applicable, accurate measurements were made and used to test and decide between different theories, and instruments were developed to get increasing precision. The effect of such external, practical pressure appears in both theoretical science and the practical crafts, and in the work of both scholars and craftsmen, but because of its strongly practical, utilitarian character it did not have a profound influence on the accepted theoretical concepts of physics. Medieval academic science and medieval technology were in fact two almost completely independent monologues.

5. Thus there was in medieval physics a very incomplete dialogue between theoretical concepts and procedures on the one hand, and practical quantifying procedures in contact with the data of observation on the other. As a result, medieval physics never escaped from its Aristotelian framework. Interesting quantified procedures and conclusions were formulated within these general limits, and some of these were taken over into seventeenth-century physics, but the framework of physics as a whole was never completely rethought and reconstructed by the medieval philosophers.

6. The establishment of a complete dialogue between quantified theory and quantified theoretical and experimental procedures, between *episteme* and *techne,* is one of the principal changes that occurred in the seventeenth century. Systematic measurement became the procedure both for collecting exact data and for testing theories or challenging whole systems of theory. As this complete dialogue developed it was both felt as an internal, intellectual need and also demanded by external, practical pressure. Thus it became an intellectual and practical requirement for the new scientific profession that grew up with aims that had important differences from those of the medieval scholars. Intellectual, professional, and practical pressures all now demanded a quantified study of nature and not simply of theory.

7. This case history of medieval physics seems to suggest certain analogies in other fields and periods in the history of science, which seems to be an especially suitable subject for the comparative method of analysis.

The Function of Measurement in Modern Physical Science

By Thomas S. Kuhn[*]

AT the University of Chicago, the façade of the Social Science Research Building bears Lord Kelvin's famous dictum: "If you cannot measure, your knowledge is meager and unsatisfactory."[1] Would that statement be there if it had been written, not by a physicist, but by a sociologist, political scientist, or economist? Or again, would terms like "meter reading" and "yardstick" recur so frequently in contemporary discussions of epistemology and scientific method were it not for the prestige of modern physical science and the fact that measurement so obviously bulks large in its research? Suspecting that the answer to both these questions is no, I find my assigned role in this conference particularly challenging. Because physical science is so often seen as *the* paradigm of sound knowledge and because quantitative techniques seem to provide an essential clue to its success, the question how measurement has actually functioned for the past three centuries in physical science arouses more than its natural and intrinsic interest. Let me therefore make my general position clear at the start. Both as an ex-physicist and as an historian of physical science I feel sure that, for at least a century and a half, quantitative methods have indeed been central to the development of the fields I study. On the other hand, I feel equally convinced that our most prevalent notions both about the function of measurement and about the source of its special efficacy are derived largely from myth.

Partly because of this conviction and partly for more autobiographical reasons,[2] I shall employ in this paper an approach rather different from that of most other contributors to this conference. Until almost its close my essay will include no narrative of the increasing deployment of quantitative techniques in physical science since the close of the Middle Ages. Instead, the two

* University of California, Berkeley

[1] For the façade see, *Eleven Twenty-Six: A Decade of Social Science Research,* ed. Louis Wirth (Chicago, 1940), p. 169. The sentiment there inscribed recurs in Kelvin's writings, but I have found no formulation closer to the Chicago quotation than the following: "When you cannot express it in numbers, your knowledge is of a meagre and unsatisfactory kind." See Sir William Thomson, "Electrical Units of Measurement," *Popular Lectures and Addresses,* 3 vols. (London, 1889-91), I, 73.

[2] The central sections of this paper, which was added to the present program at a late date, are abstracted from my essay, "The Role of Measurement in the Development of Natural Science," a multilithed revision of a talk first given to the Social Sciences Colloquium of the University of California, Berkeley. That version will be published in a volume of papers on "Quantification in the Social Sciences" that grows out of the Berkeley colloquium. In deriving the present paper from it, I have prepared a new introduction and last section, and have somewhat condensed the material that intervenes.

central questions of this paper—how has measurement actually functioned in physical science, and what has been the source of its special efficacy—will be approached directly. For this purpose, and for it alone, history will truly be "philosophy teaching by example."

Before permitting history to function even as a source of examples, we must, however, grasp the full significance of allowing it any function at all. To that end my paper opens with a critical discussion of what I take to be the most prevalent image of scientific measurement, an image that gains much of its plausibility and force from the manner in which computation and measurement enter into a profoundly unhistorical source, the science text. That discussion, confined to Section I below, will suggest that there is a textbook image or myth of science and that it may be systematically misleading. Measurement's actual function—either in the search for new theories or in the confirmation of those already at hand—must be sought in the journal literature, which displays not finished and accepted theories, but theories in the process of development. After that point in the discussion, history will necessarily become our guide, and Sections II and III will attempt to present a more valid image of measurement's most usual functions drawn from that source. Section IV employs the resulting description to ask why measurement should have proved so extraordinarily effective in physical research. Only after that, in the concluding section, shall I attempt a synoptic view of the route by which measurement has come increasingly to dominate physical science during the past three hundred years.

[One more caveat proves necessary before beginning. A few participants in this conference seem occasionally to mean by measurement any unambiguous scientific experiment or observation. Thus, Professor Boring supposes that Descartes was measuring when he demonstrated the inverted retinal image at the back of the eye-ball; presumably he would say the same about Franklin's demonstration of the opposite polarity of the two coatings on a Leyden jar. Now I have no doubt that experiments like these are among the most significant and fundamental that the physical sciences have known, but I see no virtue in describing their results as measurements. In any case, that terminology would obscure what are perhaps the most important points to be made in this paper. I shall therefore suppose that a measurement (or a fully quantified theory) always produces actual numbers. Experiments like Descartes' or Franklin's, above, will be classified as qualitative or as nonnumerical, without, I hope, at all implying that they are therefore less important. Only with that distinction between qualitative and quantitative available can I hope to show that large amounts of qualitative work have usually been prerequisite to fruitful quantification in the physical sciences. And only if that point can be made shall we be in a position even to ask about the effects of introducing quantitative methods into sciences that had previously proceeded without major assistance from them.]

I. TEXTBOOK MEASUREMENT

To a very much greater extent than we ordinarily realize, our image of physical science and of measurement is conditioned by science texts. In part that influence is direct: textbooks are the sole source of most people's firsthand acquaintance with the physical sciences. Their indirect influence is, however, undoubtedly larger and more pervasive. Textbooks or their equivalent are the unique repository of the finished achievements of modern physical scientists. It is with the analysis and propagation of these achievements that most writings on the philosophy of science and most interpretations of science for the nonscientist are concerned. As many autobiographies attest, even the research scientist does not always free himself from the textbook image gained during his first exposures to science.[3]

I shall shortly indicate why the textbook mode of presentation must inevitably be misleading, but let us first examine that presentation itself. Since most participants in this conference have already been exposed to at least one textbook of physical science, I restrict attention to the schematic tripartite summary in the following figure. It displays, in the upper left, a series of

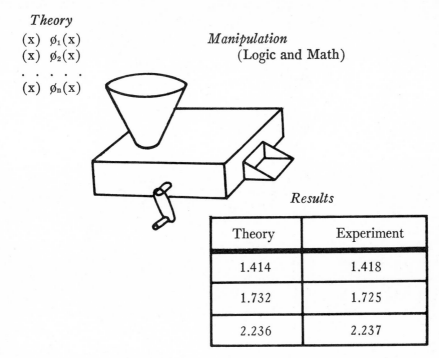

Theory

$(x) \ \phi_1(x)$
$(x) \ \phi_2(x)$
. . . . . .
$(x) \ \phi_n(x)$

Manipulation
(Logic and Math)

Results

Theory	Experiment
1.414	1.418
1.732	1.725
2.236	2.237

theoretical and "lawlike" statements, $(x) \ \phi_i(x)$, which together constitute the theory of the science being described.[4] The center of the diagram represents the logical and mathematical equipment employed in manipulating the theory. "Lawlike" statements from the upper left are to be imagined fed into the

[3] This phenomenon is examined in more detail in my monograph, *The Structure of Scientific Revolutions*, to appear when completed as Vol. II, No. 2, in the *International Encyclopedia of Unified Science*. Many other aspects of the textbook image of science, its sources and its strengths, are also examined in that place.

[4] Obviously not all the statements required to constitute most theories are of this particular logical form, but the complexities have no relevance to the points made here. R. B. Braithwaite, *Scientific Explanation* (Cambridge, England, 1953) includes a useful, though very general, description of the logical structure of scientific theories.

hopper at the top of the machine together with certain "initial conditions" specifying the situation to which the theory is being applied. The crank is then turned; logical and mathematical operations are internally performed; and numerical predictions for the application at hand emerge in the chute at the front of the machine. These predictions are entered in the left-hand column of the table that appears in the lower right of the figure. The right-hand column contains the numerical results of actual measurements, placed there so that they may be compared with the predictions derived from the theory. Most texts of physics, chemistry, astronomy, etc. contain many data of this sort, though they are not always presented in tabular form. Some of you will, for example, be more familiar with equivalent graphical presentations.

The table at the lower right is of particular concern, for it is there that the results of measurement appear explicitly. What may we take to be the significance of such a table and of the numbers it contains? I suppose that there are two usual answers: the first, immediate and almost universal; the other, perhaps more important, but very rarely explicit.

Most obviously the results in the table seem to function as a test of theory. If corresponding numbers in the two columns agree, the theory is acceptable; if they do not, the theory must be modified or rejected. This is the function of measurement as confirmation, here seen emerging, as it does for most readers, from the textbook formulation of a finished scientific theory. For the time being I shall assume that some such function is also regularly exemplified in normal scientific practice and can be isolated in writings whose purpose is not exclusively pedagogic. At this point we need only notice that on the question of practice, textbooks provide no evidence whatsoever. No textbook ever included a table that either intended or managed to infirm the theory the text was written to describe. Readers of current science texts accept the theories there expounded on the authority of the author and the scientific community, not because of any tables that these texts contain. If the tables are read at all, as they often are, they are read for another reason.

I shall inquire for this other reason in a moment but must first remark on the second putative function of measurement, that of exploration. Numerical data like those collected in the right-hand column of our table can, it is often supposed, be useful in suggesting new scientific theories or laws. Some people seem to take for granted that numerical data are more likely to be productive of new generalizations than any other sort. It is that special productivity, rather than measurement's function in confirmation, that probably accounts for Kelvin's dictum's being inscribed on the façade at the University of Chicago.[5]

It is by no means obvious that our ideas about this function of numbers are related to the textbook schema outlined in the diagram above, yet I see no other way to account for the special efficacy often attributed to the results of measurement. We are, I suspect, here confronted with a vestige of an admittedly outworn belief that laws and theories can be arrived at by some

[5] Professor Frank Knight, for example, suggests that to social scientists the "practical meaning [of Kelvin's statement] tends to be: 'If you cannot measure, measure anyhow.'" *Eleven Twenty-Six,* p. 169.

process like "running the machine backwards." Given the numerical data in the "Experiment" column of the table, logico-mathematical manipulation (aided, all would now insist, by "intuition") can proceed to the statement of the laws that underlie the numbers. If any process even remotely like this is involved in discovery—if, that is, laws and theories are forged directly from data by the mind—then the superiority of numerical to qualitative data is immediately apparent. The results of measurement are neutral and precise; they cannot mislead. Even more important, numbers are subject to mathematical manipulation; more than any other form of data, they can be assimilated to the semimechanical textbook schema.

I have already implied my skepticism about these two prevalent descriptions of the function of measurement. In Sections II and III each of these functions will be further compared with ordinary scientific practice. But it will help first critically to pursue our examination of textbook tables. By doing so I would hope to suggest that our stereotypes about measurement do not even quite fit the textbook schema from which they seem to derive. Though the numerical tables in a textbook do not there function either for exploration or confirmation, they are there for a reason. That reason we may perhaps discover by asking what the author of a text can mean when he says that the numbers in the "Theory" and "Experiment" column of a table "agree."

At best the criterion must be in agreement within the limits of accuracy of the measuring instruments employed. Since computation from theory can usually be pushed to any desired number of decimal places, exact or numerical agreement is impossible in principle. But anyone who has examined the tables in which the results of theory and experiment are compared must recognize that agreement of this more modest sort is rather rare. Almost always the application of a physical theory involves some approximation (in fact, the plane is *not* "frictionless," the vacuum is *not* "perfect," the atoms are *not* "unaffected" by collisions), and the theory is not therefore expected to yield quite precise results. Or the construction of the instrument may involve approximations (e.g., the "linearity" of vacuum tube characteristics) that cast doubt upon the significance of the last decimal place that can be unambiguously read from their dial. Or it may simply be recognized that, for reasons not clearly understood, the theory whose results have been tabulated or the instrument used in measurement provides only estimates. For one of these reasons or another, physical scientists rarely expect agreement quite within instrumental limits. In fact, they often distrust it when they see it. At least on a student lab report overly close agreement is usually taken as presumptive evidence of data manipulation. That no experiment gives quite the expected numerical result is sometimes called "The Fifth Law of Thermodynamics."[6] The fact that, unlike some other scientific laws, it has acknowledged exceptions does not diminish its utility as a guiding principle.

It follows that what scientists seek in numerical tables is not usually "agree-

[6] The first three Laws of Thermodynamics are well known outside the trade. The "Fourth Law" states that no piece of experimental apparatus works the first time it is set up. We shall examine evidence for the Fifth Law below.

ment" at all, but what they often call "reasonable agreement." Furthermore, if we now ask for a criterion of "reasonable agreement," we are literally forced to look in the tables themselves. Scientific practice exhibits no consistently applied or consistently applicable external criterion. "Reasonable agreement" varies from one part of science to another, and within any part of science it varies with time. What to Ptolemy and his immediate successors was reasonable agreement between astronomical theory and observation was to Copernicus incisive evidence that the Ptolemaic system must be wrong.[7] Between the times of Cavendish (1731-1810) and Ramsay (1852-1916), a similar change in accepted chemical criteria for "reasonable agreement" led to the study of the noble gases.[8] These divergences are typical and they are matched by those between contemporary branches of the scientific community. In parts of spectroscopy "reasonable agreement" means agreement in the first six or eight left-hand digits in the numbers of a table of wave lengths. In the theory of solids, by contrast, two-place agreement is often considered very good indeed. Yet there are parts of astronomy in which any search for even so limited an agreement must seem utopian. In the theoretical study of stellar magnitudes agreement to a multiplicative factor of ten is often taken to be "reasonable."

Notice that we have now inadvertently answered the question from which we began. We have, that is, said what "agreement" between theory and experiment must mean if that criterion is to be drawn from the tables of a science text. But in doing so we have gone full circle. I began by asking, at least by implication, what characteristic the numbers of the table must exhibit if they are to be said to "agree." I now conclude that the only possible criterion is the mere fact that they appear, together with the theory from which they are derived, in a professionally accepted text. When they appear in a text, tables of numbers drawn from theory and experiments cannot demonstrate anything but "reasonable agreement." And even that they demonstrate only by tautology, since they alone provide the definition of "reasonable agreement" that has been accepted by the profession. That, I think, is why the tables are there: they define "reasonable agreement." By studying them, the reader learns what can be expected of the theory. An acquaintance with the tables is part of an acquaintance with the theory itself. Without the tables, the theory would be essentially incomplete. With respect to measurement, it would be not so much untested as untestable. Which brings us very close to the conclusion that, once it has been embodied in a text—which for present purposes means, once it has been adopted by the profession—no theory is recognized to be testable by any quantitative tests that it has not already passed.[9]

[7] T. S. Kuhn, *The Copernican Revolution* (Cambridge, Mass., 1957), pp. 72-76, 135-143.

[8] William Ramsay, *The Gases of the Atmosphere: the History of Their Discovery* (London, 1896), Chapters 4 and 5.

[9] To pursue this point would carry us far beyond the subject of this paper, but it should be pursued because, if I am right, it relates to the important contemporary controversy over the distinction between analytic and synthetic truth. To the extent that a scientific theory must be accompanied by a statement of the evidence for it in order to have empirical meaning, the full theory (which includes the evidence) must be analytically true. For a statement of the philosophical problem of analyticity see W. V. Quine, "Two Dogmas of Empiricism" and other essays in *From a Logi-*

Perhaps these conclusions are not surprising. Certainly they should not be. Textbooks are, after all, written some time after the discoveries and confirmation procedures whose *outcomes* they record. Furthermore, they are written for purposes of pedagogy. The objective of a textbook is to provide the reader, in the most economical and easily assimilable form, with a statement of what the contemporary scientific community believes it knows and of the principal uses to which that knowledge can be put. Information about the ways in which that knowledge was acquired (discovery) and in which it was enforced on the profession (confirmation) would at best be excess baggage. Though including that information would almost certainly increase the "humanistic" values of the text and might conceivably breed more flexible and creative scientists, it would inevitably detract from the ease of learning the contemporary scientific language. To date only the last objective has been taken seriously by most writers of textbooks in the natural sciences. As a result, though texts may be the right place for philosophers to discover the logical structure of finished scientific theories, they are more likely to mislead than to help the unwary individual who asks about productive methods. One might equally appropriately go to a college language text for an authoritative characterization of the corresponding literature. Language texts, like science texts, teach how to *read* literature, not how to create or evaluate it. What signposts they supply to these latter points are most likely to point in the wrong direction.[10]

II. MOTIVES FOR NORMAL MEASUREMENT

These considerations dictate our next step. We must ask how measurement comes to be juxtaposed with laws and theories in science texts. Furthermore, we must go for an answer to the journal literature, the medium through which natural scientists report their own original work and in which they evaluate that done by others.[11] Recourse to this body of literature immediately casts doubt upon one implication of the standard textbook schema. Only a miniscule fraction of even the best and most creative measurements undertaken by

---

cal Point of View (Cambridge, Mass., 1953). For a stimulating, but loose, discussion of the occasionally analytic status of scientific laws, see N. R. Hanson, *Patterns of Discovery* (Cambridge, England, 1958), pp. 93-118. A new discussion of the philosophical problem, including copious references to the controversial literature, is Alan Pasch, *Experience and the Analytic: A Reconsideration of Empiricism* (Chicago, 1958).

[10] The monograph cited in note 3 will argue that the misdirection supplied by science texts is both systematic and functional. It is by no means clear that a more accurate image of the scientific processes would enhance the research efficiency of physical scientists.

[11] It is, of course, somewhat anachronistic to apply the terms "journal literature" and "textbooks" in the whole of the period I have been asked to discuss. But I am concerned to emphasize a pattern of professional communication whose origins at least can be found in the seventeenth century and which has increased in rigor ever since. There was a time (different in different sciences) when the pattern of communication in a science was much the same as that still visible in the humanities and many of the social sciences, but in all the physical sciences this pattern is at least a century gone, and in many of them it disappeared even earlier than that. Now all publication of research results occurs in journals read only by the profession. Books are exclusively textbooks, compendia, popularizations, or philosophical reflections, and writing them is a somewhat suspect, because nonprofessional, activity. Needless to say this sharp and rigid separation between articles and books, research and nonresearch writings, greatly increases the strength of what I have called the textbook image.

natural scientists are motivated by a desire to discover new quantitative regularities or to confirm old ones. Almost as small a fraction turn out to have
had either of these effects. There are a few that did so, and I shall have
something to say about them in Sections III and IV. But it will help first to
discover just why these exploratory and confirmatory measurements are so
rare. In this section and most of the next, I therefore restrict myself to measurement's most usual function in the normal practice of science.[12]

Probably the rarest and most profound sort of genius in physical science is
that displayed by men who, like Newton, Lavoisier, or Einstein, enunciate a
whole new theory that brings potential order to a vast number of natural
phenomena. Yet radical reformulations of this sort are extremely rare, largely
because the state of science very seldom provides occasion for them. Moreover, they are not the only truly essential and creative events in the development of scientific knowledge. The new order provided by a revolutionary new
theory in the natural sciences is always overwhelmingly a *potential* order.
Much work and skill, together with occasional genius, are required to make
it *actual*. And actual it must be made, for only through the process of actu-
alization can occasions for new theoretical reformulations be discovered. The
bulk of scientific practice is thus a complex and consuming mopping-up operation that consolidates the ground made available by the most recent theoretical breakthrough and that provides essential preparation for the break-
through to follow. In such mopping-up operations, measurement has its
overwhelmingly most common scientific function.

Just how important and difficult these consolidating operations can be is
indicated by the present state of Einstein's general theory of relativity. The
equations embodying that theory have proved so difficult to apply that (ex-
cluding the limiting case in which the equations reduce to those of special
relativity) they have so far yielded only three predictions that can be compared with observation.[13] Men of undoubted genius have totally failed to
develop others, and the problem remains worth their attention. Until it is
solved, Einstein's general theory remains a largely fruitless, because unexploit-
able, achievement.[14]

Undoubtedly the general theory of relativity is an extreme case, but the
situation it illustrates is typical. Consider, for a somewhat more extended
example, the problem that engaged much of the best eighteenth-century scien-

---

[12] Here and elsewhere in this paper I ignore
the very large amount of measurement done
simply to gather factual information. I think
of such measurements as specific gravities,
wave lengths, spring constants, boiling points,
etc., undertaken in order to determine parameters that must be inserted into scientific theories but whose numerical outcome those theories do not (or did not in the relevant period)
predict. This sort of measurement is not without interest, but I think it widely understood.
In any case, considering it would too greatly
extend the limits of this paper.

[13] These are: the deflection of light in the
sun's gravitational field, the precession of the
perihelion of Mercury, and the red shift of
light from distant stars. Only the first two
are actually quantitative predictions in the
present state of the theory.

[14] The difficulties in producing concrete applications of the general theory of relativity
need not prevent scientists from attempting to
exploit the scientific viewpoint embodied in
that theory. But, perhaps unfortunately, it
seems to be doing so. Unlike the special theory, general relativity is today very little studied by students of physics. Within fifty years
we may conceivably have totally lost sight of
this aspect of Einstein's contribution.

tific thought, that of deriving testable numerical predictions from Newton's three Laws of motion and from his principle of universal gravitation. When Newton's theory was first enunciated late in the seventeenth century, only his Third Law (equality of action and reaction) could be directly investigated by experiment, and the relevant experiments applied only to very special cases.[15] The first direct and unequivocal demonstrations of the Second Law awaited the development of the Atwood machine, a subtly conceived piece of laboratory apparatus that was not invented until almost a century after the appearance of the *Principia*.[16] Direct quantitative investigations of gravitational attraction proved even more difficult and were not presented in the scientific literature until 1798.[17] Newton's First Law cannot, to this day, be directly compared with the results of laboratory measurement, though developments in rocketry make it likely that we have not much longer to wait.

It is, of course, direct demonstrations, like those of Atwood, that figure most largely in natural science texts and in elementary laboratory exercises. Because simple and unequivocal, they have the greatest pedagogic value. That they were not and could scarcely have been available for more than a century after the publication of Newton's work makes no pedagogic difference. At most it only leads us to mistake the nature of scientific achievement.[18] But if Newton's contemporaries and successors had been forced to wait that long for quantitative evidence, apparatus capable of providing it would never have been designed. Fortunately there was another route, and much eigthteenth-century scientific talent followed it. Complex mathematical manipulations, exploiting all the laws together, permitted a few other sorts of prediction capable of being compared with quantitative observation, particularly with laboratory observations of pendula and with astronomical observations of the motions of the moon and planets. But these predictions presented another and equally severe problem, that of essential approximations.[19] The suspen-

[15] The most relevant and widely employed experiments were performed with pendula. Determination of the recoil when two pendulum bobs collided seems to have been the main conceptual and experimental tool used in the seventeenth century to determine what dynamical "action" and "reaction" were. See A. Wolf, *A History of Science, Technology, and Philosophy in the 16th & 17th Centuries,* new ed. prepared by D. McKie (London, 1950), pp. 155, 231-235; and R. Dugas, *La mécanique au xviiᵉ siècle* (Neuchatel, 1954), pp. 283-298; and *Sir Isaac Newton's Mathematical Principles of Natural Philosophy and his System of the World,* ed. F. Cajori (Berkeley, 1934), pp. 21-28. Wolf (p. 155) describes the Third Law as "the only *physical* law of the three."

[16] See the excellent description of this apparatus and the discussion of Atwood's reasons for building it in Hanson, *Patterns of Discovery,* pp. 100-102 and notes to these pages.

[17] A. Wolf, *A History of Science, Technology, and Philosophy in the Eighteenth Century,* 2nd ed. revised by D. McKie (London, 1952), pp. 111-113. There are some precursors

of Cavendish's measurements of 1798, but it is only after Cavendish that measurement begins to yield consistent results.

[18] Modern laboratory apparatus designed to help students study Galileo's law of free fall provides a classic, though perhaps quite necessary, example of the way pedagogy misdirects the historical imagination about the relation between creative science and measurement. None of the apparatus now used could possibly have been built in the seventeenth century. One of the best and most widely disseminated pieces of equipment, for example, allows a heavy bob to fall between a pair of parallel vertical rails. These rails are electrically charged every 1/100th of a second, and the spark that then passes through the bob from rail to rail records the bob's position on a chemically treated tape. Other pieces of apparatus involve electric timers, etc. For the historical difficulties of making measurements relevant to this law, see below.

[19] All the applications of Newton's Laws involve approximations of some sort, but in the following examples the approximations

sions of laboratory pendula are neither weightless nor perfectly elastic; air resistance damps the motion of the bob; besides, the bob itself is of finite size, and there is the question of which point of the bob should be used in computing the pendulum's length. If these three aspects of the experimental situation are neglected, only the roughest sort of quantitative agreement between theory and observation can be expected. But determining how to reduce them (only the last is fully eliminable) and what allowance to make for the residue are themselves problems of the utmost difficulty. Since Newton's day much brilliant research has been devoted to their challenge.[20]

The problems encountered when applying Newton's Laws to astronomical prediction are even more revealing. Since each of the bodies in the solar system attracts and is attracted by every other, precise prediction of celestial phenomena demanded, in Newton's day, the application of his Laws to the simultaneous motions and interactions of eight celestial bodies. (These were the sun, moon, and six known planets. I ignore the other planetary satellites.) The result is a mathematical problem that has never been solved exactly. To get equations that could be solved, Newton was forced to the simplifying assumption that each of the planets was attracted only by the sun, and the moon only by the earth. With this assumption, he was able to derive Kepler's famous Laws, a wonderfully convincing argument for his theory. But deviation of planets from the motions predicted by Kepler's Laws is quite apparent to simple quantitative telescopic observation. To discover how to treat these deviations by Newtonian theory, it was necessary to devise mathematical estimates of the "perturbations" produced in a basically Keplerian orbit by the interplanetary forces neglected in the initial derivation of Kepler's Laws. Newton's mathematical genius was displayed at its best when he produced a first crude estimate for the perturbation of the moon's motion caused by the sun. Improving his answer and developing similar approximate answers for the planets exercised the greatest mathematical minds of the eighteenth and early nineteenth centuries, including those of Euler, Lagrange, Laplace, and Gauss.[21] Only as a result of their work was it possible to recognize the anomaly in Mercury's motion that was ultimately to be explained by Einstein's general theory. That anomaly had previously been hidden within the limits of "reasonable agreement."

As far as it goes, the situation illustrated by quantitative application of Newton's Laws is, I think perfectly typical. Similar examples could be produced from the history of the corpuscular, the wave, or the quantum mechanical theory of light, from the history of electromagnetic theory, quantitative chemical analysis, or any other of the numerous natural scientific theories with quantitative implications. In each of these cases, it proved immensely difficult to find many problems that permitted quantitative comparison of theory and observation. Even when such problems were found, the highest scientific talents were often required to invent apparatus, reduce perturbing effects, and

have a quantitative importance that they do not possess in those that precede.

[20] Wolf, *Eighteenth Century*, pp. 75-81, provides a good preliminary description of this work.

[21] *Ibid.*, pp. 96-101. William Whewell, *History of the Inductive Sciences*, rev. ed., 3 vols. (London, 1847), II, 213-271.

estimate the allowance to be made for those that remained. This is the sort of work that most physical scientists do most of the time *insofar as their work is quantitative*. Its objective is, on the one hand, to improve the measure of "reasonable agreement" characteristic of the theory in a given application and, on the other, to open up new areas of application and establish new measures of "reasonable agreement" applicable to them. For anyone who finds mathematical or manipulative puzzles challenging, this can be fascinating and intensely rewarding work. And there is always the remote possibility that it will pay an additional dividend: something may go wrong.

Yet unless something does go wrong—a situation to be explored in Section IV—these finer and finer investigations of the quantitative match between theory and observation cannot be described as attempts at discovery or at confirmation. The man who is successful proves his talents, but he does so by getting a result that the entire scientific community had anticipated someone would someday achieve. His success lies only in the explicit demonstration of a *previously implicit* agreement between theory and the world. No novelty in nature has been revealed. Nor can the scientist who is successful in this sort of work quite be said to have "confirmed" the theory that guided his research. For if success in his venture "confirms" the theory, then failure ought certainly "infirm" it, and nothing of the sort is true in this case. Failure to solve one of these puzzles counts only against the scientist; he has put in a great deal of time on a project whose outcome is not worth publication; the conclusion to be drawn, if any, is only that his talents were not adequate to it. If measurement ever leads to discovery or to confirmation, it does not do so in the most usual of all its applications.

III. THE EFFECTS OF NORMAL MEASUREMENT

There is a second significant aspect of the normal problem of measurement in natural science. So far we have considered why scientists usually measure; now we must consider the results that they get when they do so. Immediately another stereotype enforced by textbooks is called in question. In textbooks the numbers that result from measurement usually appear as the archetypes of the "irreducible and stubborn facts" to which the scientist must, by struggle, make his theories conform. But in scientific practice, as seen through the journal literature, the scientist often seems rather to be struggling with facts, trying to force them into conformity with a theory he does not doubt. Quantitative facts cease to seem simply "the given." They must be fought for and with, and in this fight the theory with which they are to be compared proves the most potent weapon. Often scientists cannot get numbers that compare well with theory until they know what numbers they should be making nature yield.

Part of this problem is simply the difficulty in finding techniques and instruments that permit the comparison of theory with quantitative measurements. We have already seen that it took almost a century to invent a machine that could give a straightforward quantitative demonstration of Newton's Second Law. But the machine that Charles Atwood described in 1784 was not the first instrument to yield quantitative information relevant to that Law.

Attempts in this direction had been made ever since Galileo's description of his classic inclined plane experiment in 1638.[22] Galileo's brilliant intuition had seen in this laboratory device a way of investigating how a body moves when acted upon only by its own weight. After the experiment he announced that measurement of the distance covered in a measured time by a sphere rolling down the plane confirmed his prior thesis that the motion was uniformly accelerated. As reinterpreted by Newton, this result exemplified the Second Law for the special case of a uniform force. But Galileo did not report the numbers he had gotten, and a group of the best scientists in France announced their total failure to get comparable results. In print they wondered whether Galileo could himself have tried the experiment.[23]

In fact, it is almost certain that Galileo did perform the experiment. If he did, he must surely have gotten quantitative results that seemed to him in *adequate* agreement with the law ($s = \frac{1}{2} at^2$) that he had shown to be a consequence of uniform acceleration. But anyone who has noted the stop-watches or electric timers, and the long planes or heavy flywheels needed to perform this experiment in modern elementary laboratories may legitimately suspect that Galileo's results were not in *unequivocal* agreement with his law. Quite possibly the French group looking even at the same data would have wondered how they could seem to exemplify uniform acceleration. This is, of course, largely speculation. But the speculative element casts no doubt upon my present point: whatever its source, disagreement between Galileo and those who tried to repeat his experiment was entirely natural. If Galileo's generalization had not sent men to the very border of existing instrumentation, an area in which experimental scatter and disagreement about interpretation were inevitable, then no genius would have been required to make it. His example typifies one important aspect of theoretical genius in the natural sciences—it is a genius that leaps ahead of the facts, leaving the rather different talent of the experimentalist and instrumentalist to catch up. In this case catching up took a long time. The Atwood Machine was designed because, in the middle of the eighteenth century, some of the best Continental scientists still wondered whether acceleration provided the proper measure of force. Though their doubts derived from more than measurement, measurement was still sufficiently equivocal to fit a variety of different quantitative conclusions.[24]

The preceding example illustrates the difficulties and displays the role of theory in reducing scatter in the results of measurement. There is, however, more to the problem. When measurement is insecure, one of the tests for reliability of existing instruments and manipulative techniques must inevitably be their ability to give results that compare favorably with existing theory. In some parts of natural science, the adequacy of experimental technique can be judged only in this way. When that occurs, one may not even speak of "insecure" instrumentation or technique, implying that these could be improved without recourse to an external theoretical standard.

[22] For a modern English version of the original see Galileo Galilei, *Dialogues Concerning Two New Sciences,* trans. Henry Crew and A. De Salvio (Evanston and Chicago, 1946), pp. 171-172.

[23] This whole story and more is brilliantly set forth in A. Koyré, "An Experiment in Measurement," *Proc. Amer. Phil. Soc.,* 1953, 97: 222-237.

[24] Hanson, *Patterns of Discovery,* p. 101.

For example, when John Dalton first conceived of using chemical measurements to elaborate an atomic theory that he had initially drawn from meteorological and physical observations, he began by searching the existing chemical literature for relevant data. Soon he realized that significant illumination could be obtained from those groups of reactions in which a single pair of elements, e.g., nitrogen and oxygen, entered into more than one chemical combination. If his atomic theory were right, the constituent molecules of these compounds should differ only in the ratio of the number of whole atoms of each element that they contained. The three oxides of nitrogen might, for example, have molecules N_2O, NO, and NO_2, or they might have some other similarly simple arrangement.[25] But whatever the particular arrangements, if the weight of nitrogen were the same in the samples of the three oxides, then the weights of oxygen in the three samples should be related to each other by simple whole-number proportions. Generalization of this principle to all groups of compounds formed from the same group of elements produced Dalton's Law of Multiple Proportions.

Needless to say, Dalton's search of the literature yielded some data that, in his view, sufficiently supported the Law. But—and this is the point of the illustration—much of the then extant data did not support Dalton's Law at all. For example, the measurements of the French chemist Proust on the two oxides of copper yielded, for a given weight of copper, a weight ratio for oxygen of 1.47:1. On Dalton's theory the ratio ought to have been 2:1, and Proust is just the chemist who might have been expected to confirm the prediction. He was, in the first place, a fine experimentalist. Besides, he was then engaged in a major controversy involving the oxides of copper, a controversy in which he upheld a view very close to Dalton's. But, at the beginning of the nineteenth century, chemists did not know how to perform quantitative analyses that displayed multiple proportions. By 1850 they had learned, but only by letting Dalton's theory lead them. Knowing what results they should expect from chemical analyses, chemists were able to devise techniques that got them. As a result chemistry texts can now state that quantitative analysis confirms Dalton's atomism and forget that, historically, the relevant analytic techniques are based upon the very theory they are said to confirm. Before Dalton's theory was announced, measurement did not give the same results. There are self-fulfilling prophecies in the physical as well as in the social sciences.

That example seems to me quite typical of the way measurement responds to theory in many parts of the natural sciences. I am less sure that my next, and far stranger, example is equally typical, but colleagues in nuclear physics assure me that they repeatedly encounter similar irreversible shifts in the results of measurement.

[25] This is not, of course, Dalton's original notation. In fact, I am somewhat modernizing and simplifying this whole account. It can be reconstructed more fully from: A. N. Meldrum, "The Development of the Atomic Theory: (1) Berthollet's Doctrine of Variable Proportions," *Manch. Mem.*, 1910, *54:* 1-16; and "(6) The Reception accorded to the Theory advocated by Dalton," *ibid.*, 1911, *55:* 1-10; L. K. Nash, *The Atomic Molecular Theory,* Harvard Case Histories in Experimental Science, Case 4 (Cambridge, Mass., 1950); and "The Origins of Dalton's Chemical Atomic Theory," *Isis*, 1956, *47:* 110-116. See also the useful discussions of atomic weight scattered through J. R. Partington, *A Short History of Chemistry*, 2nd ed. (London, 1951).

Very early in the nineteenth century, P. S. de Laplace, perhaps the greatest and certainly the most famous physicist of his day, suggested that the recently observed heating of a gas when rapidly compressed might explain one of the outstanding numerical discrepancies of theoretical physics. This was the disagreement, approximately 20 per cent, between the predicted and measured values of the speed of sound in air—a discrepancy that had attracted the attention of all Europe's best mathematical physicists since Newton had first pointed it out. When Laplace's suggestion was made, it defied numerical confirmation (note the recurrence of this typical difficulty), because it demanded refined measurements of the thermal properties of gases, measurements that were beyond the capacity of apparatus designed for measurements on solids and liquids. But the French Academy offered a prize for such measurements, and in 1819 the prize was won by two brilliant young experimentalists, Delaroche and Berard, men whose names are still cited in contemporary scientific literature. Laplace immediately made use of these measurements in an indirect theoretical computation of the speed of sound in air, and the discrepancy between theory and measurement dropped from 20 per cent to 2.5 per cent, a recognized triumph in view of the state of measurement.[26]

But today no one can explain how this triumph can have occurred. Laplace's interpretation of Delaroche and Berard's figures made use of the caloric theory in a region where our own science is quite certain that that theory differs from directly relevant quantitative experiment by about 40 per cent. There is, however, also a 12 per cent discrepancy between the measurements of Delaroche and Berard and the results of equivalent experiments today. We are no longer able to get their quantitative result. Yet, in Laplace's perfectly straightforward and essential computation from the theory, these two discrepancies, experimental and theoretical, cancelled to give close final agreement between the predicted and measured speed of sound. We may not, I feel sure, dismiss this as the result of mere sloppiness. Both the theoretician and the experimentalists involved were men of the very highest caliber. Rather we must here see evidence of the way in which theory and experiment may guide each other in the exploration of areas new to both.

These examples may enforce the point drawn initially from the examples in the last section. Exploring the agreement between theory and experiment into new areas or to new limits of precision is a difficult, unremitting, and, for many, exciting job. Though its object is neither discovery nor confirmation, its appeal is quite sufficient to consume almost the entire time and attention of those physical scientists who do quantitative work. It demands the very best of their imagination, intuition, and vigilance. In addition—when combined with those of the last section—these examples may show something more. They may, that is, indicate why new laws of nature are so very seldom discovered simply by inspecting the results of measurements made without advance knowledge of those laws. Because most scientific laws have so few quantitative points of contact with nature, because investigations of those contact points usually demand such laborious instrumentation and approximation, and because nature itself needs to be forced to yield the appropriate results, the route from theory

---

[26] T. S. Kuhn, "The Caloric Theory of Adiabatic Compression," *Isis*, 1958, *49:* 132-140.

or law to measurement can almost never be travelled backwards. Numbers gathered without some knowledge of the regularity to be expected almost never speak for themselves. Almost certainly they remain just numbers.

This does not mean that no one has ever discovered a quantitative regularity merely by measuring. Boyle's Law relating gas pressure with gas volume, Hooke's Law relating spring distortion with applied force, and Joule's relationship between heat generated, electrical resistance, and electric current were all the direct results of measurement. There are other examples besides. But, partly just because they are so exceptional and partly because they never occur until the scientist measuring knows *everything but* the particular form of the quantitative result he will obtain, these exceptions show just how improbable quantitative discovery by quantitative measurement is. The cases of Galileo and Dalton—men who intuited a quantitative result as the simplest expression of a qualitative conclusion and then fought nature to confirm it—are very much the more typical scientific events. In fact, even Boyle did not find his Law until both he and two of his readers had suggested that precisely that law (the simplest quantitative form that yielded the observed qualitative regularity) ought to result if the numerical results were recorded.[27] Here, too, the quantitative implications of a qualitative theory led the way.

One more example may make clear at least some of the prerequisites for this exceptional sort of discovery. The experimental search for a law or laws describing the variation with distance of the forces between magnetized and between electrically charged bodies began in the seventeenth century and was actively pursued through the eighteenth. Yet only in the decades immediately preceding Coulomb's classic investigations of 1785 did measurement yield even an approximately unequivocal answer to these questions. What made the difference between success and failure seems to have been the belated assimilation of a lesson learned from a part of Newtonian theory. Simple force laws, like the inverse square law for gravitational attraction, can generally be expected only between mathematical points or bodies that approximate to them. The more complex laws of attraction between gross bodies can be derived from the simpler law governing the attraction of points by summing all the forces between all the pairs of points in the two bodies. But these laws will seldom take a simple mathematical form unless the distance between the two bodies is large compared with the dimensions of the attracting bodies themselves. Under these circumstances the bodies will behave as points, and experiment may reveal the resulting simple regularity.

Consider only the historically simpler case of electrical attractions and repulsions.[28] During the first half of the eighteenth century—when electrical forces were explained as the results of effluvia emitted by the entire charged body—almost every experimental investigation of the force law involved placing a charged body a measured distance below one pan of a balance and then

---

[27] Marie Boas, *Robert Boyle and Seventeenth-Century Chemistry* (Cambridge, England, 1958), p. 44.

[28] Much relevant material will be found in Duane Roller and Duane H. D. Roller, *The Development of the Concept of Electric Charge:* *Electricity from the Greeks to Coulomb,* Harvard Case Histories in Experimental Science, Case 8 (Cambridge, Mass., 1954), and in Wolf, *Eighteenth Century,* pp. 239-250, 268-271.

measuring the weight that had to be placed in the other pan to just overcome
the attraction. With this arrangement of apparatus, the attraction varies in
no simple way with distance. Furthermore, the complex way in which it does
vary depends critically upon the size and material of the attracted pan. Many
of the men who tried this technique therefore concluded by throwing up their
hands; others suggested a variety of laws including both the inverse square
and the inverse first power; measurement had proved totally equivocal. Yet
it did not have to be so. What was needed and what was gradually acquired
from more qualitative investigations during the middle decades of the century
was a more "Newtonian" approach to the analysis of electrical and magnetic
phenomena.[29] As this evolved, experimentalists increasingly sought not the
attraction between bodies but that between point poles and point charges. In
that form the experimental problem was rapidly and unequivocally resolved.

This illustration shows once again how large an amount of theory is needed
before the results of measurement can be expected to make sense. But, and
this is perhaps the main point, when that much theory is available, the law
is very likely to have been guessed without measurement. Coulomb's result,
in particular, seems to have surprised few scientists. Though his measurements were necessary to produce a firm consensus about electrical and magnetic attractions—they had to be done; science cannot survive on guesses—
many practitioners had already concluded that the law of attraction and repulsion must be inverse square. Some had done so by simple analagy to Newton's gravitational law; others by a more elaborate theoretical argument; still
others from equivocal data. Coulomb's Law was very much "in the air" before
its discoverer turned to the problem. If it had not been, Coulomb might not
have been able to make nature yield it.

[Repeated discussions of this Section indicate two respects in which my text
may be misleading. Some readers take my argument to mean that the committed scientist can make nature yield any measurements that he pleases. A
few of these readers, and some others as well, also think my paper asserts that
for the development of science, experiment is of decidedly secondary importance when compared with theory. Undoubtedly the fault is mine, but I intend
to be making neither of these points.

If what I have said is right, nature undoubtedly responds to the theoretical
predispositions with which she is approached by the measuring scientist. But
that is not to say either that nature will respond to any theory at all or that
she will ever respond very much. Reexamine, for a historically typical example, the relationship between the caloric and dynamical theory of heat. In their
abstract structures and in the conceptual entities they presuppose, these two
theories are quite different and, in fact, incompatible. But, during the years

---

[29] A fuller account would have to describe
both the earlier and the later approaches as
"Newtonian." The conception that electric
force results from effluvia is partly Cartesian
but in the eighteenth century its *locus-classicus*
was the aether theory developed in Newton's
Opticks. Coulomb's approach and that of several of his contemporaries depends far more
directly on the mathematical theory in Newton's *Principia*. For the differences between
these books, their influence in the eighteenth
century, and their impact on the development
of electrical theory, see I. B. Cohen, *Franklin
and Newton: An Inquiry into Speculative
Newtonian Experimental Science and Franklin's Work in Electricity as an Example Thereof* (Philadelphia, 1956).

when the two vied for the allegiance of the scientific community, the theoretical predictions that could be derived from them were very nearly the same (see the reference cited in note 26). If they had not been, the caloric theory would never have been a widely accepted tool of professional research nor would it have succeeded in disclosing the very problems that made transition to the dynamical theory possible. It follows that any measurement which, like that of Delaroche and Berard, "fit" one of these theories must have "very nearly fit" the other, and it is only within the experimental spread covered by the phrase "very nearly" that nature proved able to respond to the theoretical predisposition of the measurer.

That response could not have occurred with "any theory at all." There are logically possible theories of, say, heat that no sane scientist could ever have made nature fit, and there are problems, mostly philosophical, that make it worth inventing and examining theories of that sort. But those are not our problems, because those merely "conceivable" theories are not among the options open to the practicing scientist. His concern is with theories that seem to fit what is known about nature, and all these theories, however different their structure, will necessarily seem to yield very similar predictive results. If they can be distinguished at all by measurements, those measurements will usually strain the limits of existing experimental techniques. Furthermore, within the limits imposed by those techniques, the numerical differences at issue will very often prove to be quite small. Only under these conditions and within these limits can one expect nature to respond to preconception. On the other hand, these conditions and limits are just the ones typical in the historical situation.

If this much about my approach is clear, the second possible misunderstanding can be dealt with more easily. By insisting that a quite highly developed body of theory is ordinarily prerequisite to fruitful measurement in the physical sciences, I may seem to have implied that in these sciences theory must always lead experiment and that the latter has at best a decidedly secondary role. But that implication depends upon identifying "experiment" with "measurement," an identification I have already explicitly disavowed. It is only because significant quantitative comparison of theories with nature comes at such a late stage in the development of a science that theory has seemed to have so decisive a lead. If we had been discussing the *qualitative* experimentation that dominates the earlier developmental stages of a physical science and that continues to play a role later on, the balance would be quite different. Perhaps, even then, we would not wish to say that experiment is prior to theory (though experience surely is), but we would certainly find vastly more symmetry and continuity in the ongoing dialogue between the two. Only some of my conclusions about the role of measurement in physical science can be readily extrapolated to experimentation at large.]

IV. EXTRAORDINARY MEASUREMENT

To this point I have restricted attention to the role of measurement in the normal practice of natural science, the sort of practice in which all scientists are mostly, and most scientists are always, engaged. But natural science also displays abnormal situations—times when research projects go consistently astray and when no usual techniques seem quite to restore them—and it is through these rare situations that measurement shows its greatest strengths. In particular, it is through abnormal states of scientific research that measurement comes occasionally to play a major role in discovery and in confirmation.

Let me first try to clarify what I mean by an "abnormal situation" or by what I am elsewhere calling a "crisis state."[30] I have already indicated that it is a response by some part of the scientific community to its awareness of an anomaly in the ordinarily concordant relationship between theory and experiment. But it is not, let us be clear, a response called forth by any and every anomaly. As the preceding pages have shown, current scientific practice always embraces countless discrepancies between theory and experiment. During the course of his career, every natural scientist again and again notices *and passes by* qualitative and quantitative anomalies that just conceivably might, if pursued, have resulted in fundamental discovery. Isolated discrepancies with this potential occur so regularly that no scientist could bring his research problems to a conclusion if he paused for many of them. In any case, experience has repeatedly shown that, in overwhelming proportion, these discrepancies disappear upon closer scrutiny. They may prove to be instrumental effects, or they may result from previously unnoticed approximations in the theory, or they may, simply and mysteriously, cease to occur when the experiment is repeated under slightly different conditions. More often than not the efficient procedure is therefore to decide that the problem has "gone sour," that it presents hidden complexities, and that it is time to put it aside in favor of another. Fortunately or not, that is good scientific procedure.

But anomalies are not always dismissed, and of course they should not be. If the effect is particularly large when compared with well-established measures of "reasonable agreement" applicable to similar problems, or if it seems to resemble other difficulties encountered repeatedly before, or if, for personal reasons, it intrigues the experimenter, then a special research project is likely to be dedicated to it.[31] At that point the discrepancy will probably vanish through an adjustment of theory or apparatus; as we have seen, few anomalies resist persistent effort for long. But it may resist, and, if it does, we may have the beginning of a "crisis" or "abnormal situation" affecting those in whose usual area of research the continuing discrepancy lies. They, at least, having exhausted all the usual recourses of approximation and instrumentation, may be forced to recognize that something has gone wrong, and their behavior as scientists will change accordingly. At this point, to a vastly greater extent than at any other, the scientist will start to search at random, trying anything at all which he thinks may conceivably illuminate the nature of his difficulty. If that difficulty endures long enough, he and his colleagues may even begin to wonder whether their entire approach to the now problematic range of natural phenomena is not somehow askew.

---

[30] See note 3.

[31] A recent example of the factors determining pursuit of an anomaly has been investigated by Bernard Barber and Renée C. Fox, "The Case of the Floppy-Eared Rabbits: An Instance of Serendipity Gained and Serendipity Lost," *Amer. Soc. Rev.*, 1958, *64*: 128-136.

This is, of course, an immensely condensed and schematic description. Unfortunately, it will have to remain so, for the anatomy of the crisis state in natural science is beyond the scope of this paper. I shall remark only that these crises vary greatly in scope: they may emerge and be resolved within the work of an individual; more often they will involve most of those engaged in a particular scientific specialty; occasionally they will engross most of the members of an entire scientific profession. But, however widespread their impact, there are only a few ways in which they may be resolved. Sometimes, as has often happened in chemistry and astronomy, more refined experimental techniques or a finer scrutiny of the theoretical approximations will eliminate the discrepancy entirely. On other occasions, though I think not often, a discrepancy that has repeatedly defied analysis is simply left as a known anomaly, encysted within the body of more successful applications of the theory. Newton's theoretical value for the speed of sound and the observed precession of Mercury's perihelion provide obvious examples of effects which, though since explained, remained in the scientific literature as known anomalies for half a century or more. But there are still other modes of resolution, and it is they which give crises in science their fundamental importance. Often crises are resolved by the discovery of a new natural phenomenon; occasionally their resolution demands a fundamental revision of existing theory.

Obviously crisis is not a prerequisite for discovery in the natural sciences. We have already noticed that some discoveries, like that of Boyle's Law and of Coulomb's Law, emerge naturally as a quantitative specification of what is qualitatively already known. Many other discoveries, more often qualitative than quantitative, result from preliminary exploration with a new instrument, e.g., the telescope, battery, or cyclotron. In addition, there are the famous "accidental discoveries," Galvani and the twitching frog's legs, Roentgen and X-rays, Becquerel and the fogged photographic plates. The last two categories of discovery are not, however, always independent of crises. It is probably the ability to recognize a significant anomaly against the background of current theory that most distinguishes the successful victim of an "accident" from those of his contemporaries who passed the same phenomenon by. (Is this not part of the sense of Pasteur's famous phrase, "In the fields of observation, chance favors only the prepared mind"?)[32] In addition, the new instrumental techniques that multiply discoveries are often themselves by-products of crises. Volta's invention of the battery was, for example, the outcome of a long attempt to assimilate Galvani's observations of frogs' legs to existing electrical theory. And, over and above these somewhat questionable cases, there are a large number of discoveries that are quite clearly the outcome of prior crises. The discovery of the planet Neptune was the product of an effort to account for known anomalies in the orbit of Uranus.[33] The nature of both chlorine and carbon monoxide was discovered through attempts to reconcile Lavoisier's new chemistry with observation.[34] The so-called noble gases were the prod-

[32] From Pasteur's inaugural address at Lille in 1854 as quoted in René Vallery-Radot, *La Vie de Pasteur* (Paris, 1903), p. 88.

[33] Angus Armitage, *A Century of Astronomy* (London, 1950), pp. 111-115.

[34] For chlorine see Ernst von Meyer, *A History of Chemistry from the Earliest Times to the Present Day,* trans. G. M'Gowan (London, 1891), pp. 224-227. For carbon monoxide see J. R. Partington, *A Short History of*

ucts of a long series of investigations initiated by a small but persistent anomaly in the measured density of nitrogen.[35] The electron was posited to explain some anomalous properties of electrical conduction through gases, and its spin was suggested to account for other sorts of anomalies observed in atomic spectra.[36] The discovery of the neutrino presents still another example, and the list could be extended.[37]

I am not certain how large these discoveries-through-anomaly would rank in a statistical survey of discovery in the natural sciences.[38] They are, however, certainly important, and they require disproportionate emphasis in this paper. To the extent that measurement and quantitative technique play an especially significant role in scientific discovery, they do so precisely because, by displaying serious anomaly, they tell scientists when and where to look for a new qualitative phenomenon. To the nature of that phenomenon, they usually provide no clues. When measurement departs from theory, it is likely to yield mere numbers, and their very neutrality makes them particularly sterile as a source of remedial suggestions. But numbers register the departure from theory with an authority and finesse that no qualitative technique can duplicate, and that departure is often enough to start a search. Neptune might, like Uranus, have been discovered through an accidental observation; it had, in fact, been noticed by a few earlier observers who had taken it for a previously unobserved star. What was needed to draw attention to it and to make its discovery as nearly inevitable as historical events can be was its involvement, as a source of trouble, in existing quantitative observation and existing theory. It is hard to see how either electron-spin or the neutrino could have been discovered in any other way.

The case both for crises and for measurement becomes vastly stronger as soon as we turn from the discovery of new natural phenomena to the invention of fundamental new theories. Though the sources of individual theoretical inspiration may be inscrutable (certainly they must remain so for this paper), the conditions under which inspiration occurs is not. I know of no fundamental theoretical innovation in natural science whose enunciation has not been preceded by clear recognition, often common to most of the profession, that something was the matter with the theory then in vogue. The state

---

Chemistry, 2nd ed. (London, 1948), pp. 140-141; and J. R. Partington and D. McKie, "Historical Studies of the Phlogiston Theory: IV. Last Phases of the Theory," *Annals of Science*, 1939, 4: 365.

[35] See note 7.

[36] For useful surveys of the experiments which led to the discovery of the electron see T. W. Chalmers, *Historic Researches: Chapters in the History of Physical and Chemical Discovery* (London, 1949), pp. 187-217, and J. J. Thomson, *Recollections and Reflections* (New York, 1937), pp. 325-371. For electron-spin see F. K. Richtmeyer, E. H. Kennard, and T. Lauritsen, *Introduction to Modern Physics*, 5th ed. (New York, 1955), p. 212.

[37] Rogers D. Rusk, *Introduction to Atomic and Nuclear Physics* (New York, 1958), pp. 328-330. I know of no other elementary account recent enough to include a description of the physical detection of the neutrino.

[38] Because scientific attention is often concentrated upon problems that seem to display anomaly, the prevalence of discovery-through-anomaly may be one reason for the prevalence of simultaneous discovery in the sciences. For evidence that it is not the only one see T. S. Kuhn, "Conservation of Energy as an Example of Simultaneous Discovery," *Critical Problems in the History of Science*, ed. Marshall Clagett (Madison, 1959), pp. 321-356, but notice that much of what is there said about the emergence of "conversion processes" also describes the evolution of a crisis state.

of Ptolemaic astronomy was a scandal before Copernicus' announcement.[39] Both Galileo's and Newton's contributions to the study of motion were initially focused upon difficulties discovered in ancient and medieval theory.[40] Newton's new theory of light and color originated in the discovery that existing theory would not account for the length of the spectrum, and the wave theory that replaced Newton's was announced in the midst of growing concern about anomalies in the relation of diffraction and polarization to Newton's theory.[41] Lavoisier's new chemistry was born after the observation of anomalous weight relations in combustion; thermodynamics from the collision of two existing nineteenth-century physical theories; quantum mechanics from a variety of difficulties surrounding black-body radiation, specific heat, and the photoelectric effect.[42] Furthermore, though this is not the place to show it, each of these difficulties, except the optical one observed by Newton, had been a source of concern before (but usually not long before) the theory that resolved it was announced.

I suggest, therefore, that though a crisis or an "abnormal situation" is only

[39] Kuhn, *Copernican Revolution,* pp. 138-140, 270-271; A. R. Hall, *The Scientific Revolution, 1500-1800* (London, 1954), pp. 13-17. Note particularly the role of agitation for calendar reform in intensifying the crisis.

[40] Kuhn, *Copernican Revolution,* pp. 237-260, and items in bibliography on pp. 290-291.

[41] For Newton see T. S. Kuhn, "Newton's Optical Papers," in *Isaac Newton's Papers & Letters on Natural Philosophy,* ed. I. B. Cohen (Cambridge, Mass., 1958), pp. 27-45. For the wave theory see E. T. Whittaker, *History of the Theories of Aether and Electricity,* The Classical Theories, 2nd ed. (London, 1951), pp. 94-109, and Whewell, *Inductive Sciences,* II, 396-466. These references clearly delineate the crisis that characterized optics when Fresnel independently began to develop the wave theory after 1812. But they say too little about eighteenth-century developments to indicate a crisis prior to Young's earlier defense of the wave theory in and after 1801. In fact, it is not altogether clear that there was one, or at least that there was a new one. Newton's corpuscular theory of light had never been quite universally accepted, and Young's early opposition to it was based entirely upon anomalies that had been generally recognized and often exploited before. We may need to conclude that most of the eighteenth century was characterized by a low-level crisis in optics, for the dominant theory was never immune to fundamental criticism and attack.

That would be sufficient to make the point that is of concern here, but I suspect a careful study of the eighteenth-century optical literature will permit a still stronger conclusion. A cursory look at that body of literature suggests that the anomalies of Newtonian optics were far more apparent and pressing in the two decades before Young's work than they

had been before. During the 1780's the availability of achromatic lenses and prisms led to numerous proposals for an astronomical determination of the relative motion of the sun and stars. (The references in Whittaker, *op. cit.,* p. 109, lead directly to a far larger literature.) But these all depended upon light's moving more quickly in glass than in air and thus gave new relevance to an old controversy. L'Abbé Haüy demonstrated experimentally (*Mem. de l'Acad.* [1788], pp. 34-60) that Huyghen's wave-theoretical treatment of double refraction had yielded better results than Newton's corpuscular treatment. The resulting problem leads to the prize offered by the French Academy in 1808 and thus to Malus' discovery of polarization by reflection in the same year. Or again, the *Philosophical Transactions* for 1796, 1797, and 1798 contain a series of two articles by Brougham and a third by Prevost which show still other difficulties in Newton's theory. According to Prevost, in particular, the sorts of forces which must be exerted on light at an interface in order to explain reflection and refraction are not compatible with the sorts of forces needed to explain inflection (*Phil. Trans.,* 1798, 84: 325-328. Biographers of Young might pay more attention than they have to the two Brougham papers in the preceding volumes. These display an intellectual commitment that goes a long way to explain Brougham's subsequent vitriolic attack upon Young in the pages of the Edinburgh Review.)

[42] Richtmeyer *et al., Modern Physics,* pp. 89-94, 124-132, and 409-414. A more elementary account of the black-body problem and of the photoelectric effect is included in Gerald Holton, *Introduction to Concepts and Theories in Physical Science* (Cambridge, Mass., 1953), pp. 528-545.

one of the routes to *discovery* in the natural sciences, it is prerequisite to *fundamental inventions* of theory. Furthermore, I suspect that in the creation of the particularly deep crisis that usually precedes theoretical innovation, measurement makes one of its two most significant contributions to scientific advance. Most of the anomalies isolated in the preceding paragraph were quantitative or had a significant quantitative component, and, though the subject again carries us beyond the bounds of this essay, there is excellent reason why this should have been the case.

Unlike discoveries of new natural phenomena, innovations in scientific theory are not simply additions to the sum of what is already known. Almost always (always, in the mature sciences) the acceptance of a new theory demands the rejection of an older one. In the realm of theory, innovation is thus necessarily destructive as well as constructive. But, as the preceding pages have repeatedly indicated, theories are, even more than laboratory instruments, the essential tools of the scientist's trade. Without their constant assistance, even the observations and measurements made by the scientist would scarcely be scientific. A threat to theory is therefore a threat to the scientific life, and, though the scientific enterprise progresses through such threats, the individual scientist ignores them while he can. Particularly, he ignores them if his own prior practice has already committed him to the use of the threatened theory.[43] It follows that new theoretical suggestions, destructive of old practices, rarely if ever emerge in the absence of a crisis that can no longer be suppressed.

No crisis is, however, so hard to suppress as one that derives from a quantitative anomaly that has resisted all the usual efforts at reconciliation. Once the relevant measurements have been stabilized and the theoretical approximations fully investigated, a quantitative discrepancy proves persistently obtrusive to a degree that few qualitative anomalies can match. By their very nature, qualitative anomalies usually suggest *ad hoc* modifications of theory that will disguise them, and once these modifications have been suggested there is little way of telling whether they are "good enough." An established quantitative anomaly, in contrast, usually suggests nothing except trouble, but at its best it provides a razor-sharp instrument for judging the adequacy of proposed solutions. Kepler provides a brilliant case in point. After prolonged struggle to rid astronomy of pronounced quantitative anomalies in the motion of Mars, he invented a theory accurate to 8' of arc, a measure of agreement that would have astounded and delighted any astronomer who did not have access to the brilliant observations of Tycho Brahe. But from long experience Kepler knew Brahe's observations to be accurate to 4' of arc. To us, he said, Divine goodness has given a most diligent observer in Tycho Brahe, and it is therefore right that we should with a grateful mind make use of this gift to find the true celestial motions. Kepler next attempted computations with non-

---

[43] Evidence for this effect of prior experience with a theory is provided by the well-known, but inadequately investigated, youthfulness of famous innovators as well as by the way in which younger men tend to cluster to the newer theory. Planck's statement about the latter phenomenon needs no citation. An earlier and particularly moving version of the same sentiment is provided by Darwin in the last chapter of *The Origin of Species*. (See the 6th ed. [New York, 1889], II, 295-296.)

circular figures. The outcome of those trials was his first two Laws of planetary motion, the Laws that for the first time made the Copernican system work.[44]

Two brief examples should make clear the differential effectiveness of qualitative and quantitative anomalies. Newton was apparently led to his new theory of light and color by observing the surprising elongation of the solar spectrum. Opponents of his new theory quickly pointed out that the existence of elongation had been known before and that it could be treated by existing theory. Qualitatively they were quite right. But utilizing Snell's quantitative law of refraction (a law that had been available to scientists for less than three decades), Newton was able to show that the elongation predicted by existing theory was quantitatively far smaller than the one observed. On this quantitative discrepancy, all previous qualitative explanations of elongation broke down. Given the quantitative law of refraction, Newton's ultimate, and in this case quite rapid, victory was assured.[45] The development of chemistry provides a second striking illustration. It was well known, long before Lavoisier, that some metals gain weight when they are calcined (i.e., roasted). Furthermore, by the middle of the eighteenth century this qualitative observation was recognized to be incompatible with at least the simplest versions of the phlogiston theory, a theory that said phlogiston *escaped* from the metal during calcination. But so long as the discrepancy remained qualitative, it could be disposed of in numerous ways: perhaps phlogiston had negative weight, or perhaps fire particles lodged in the roasted metal. There were other suggestions besides, and together they served to reduce the urgency of the qualitative problem. The development of pneumatic techniques, however, transformed the qualitative anomaly into a quantitative one. In the hands of Lavoisier, they showed how much weight was gained and where it came from. These were data with which the earlier qualitative theories could not deal. Though phlogiston's adherents gave vehement and skillful battle, and though their qualitative arguments were fairly persuasive, the quantitative arguments for Lavoisier's theory proved overwhelming.[46]

These examples were introduced to illustrate how difficult it is to explain away established quantitative anomalies, and to show how much more effective these are than qualitative anomalies in establishing unevadable scientific crises. But the examples also show something more. They indicate that measurement can be an immensely powerful weapon in the battle between two

[44] J. L. E. Dreyer, *A History of Astronomy from Thales to Kepler,* 2nd ed. (New York, 1953), pp. 385-393.

[45] Kuhn, "Newton's Optical Papers," pp. 31-36.

[46] This is a slight oversimplification, since the battle between Lavoisier's new chemistry and its opponents really implicated more than combustion processes, and the full range of relevant evidence cannot be treated in terms of combustion alone. Useful elementary accounts of Lavoisier's contributions can be found in: J. B. Conant, *The Overthrow of the Phlogiston Theory,* Harvard Case Histories in Experimental Science, Case 2 (Cambridge, Mass., 1950), and D. McKie, *Antoine Lavoisier: Scientist, Economist, Social Reformer* (New York, 1952). Maurice Daumas, *Lavoisier, Théoricien et expérimenteur* (Paris, 1955) is the best recent scholarly review. J. H. White, *The Phlogiston Theory* (London, 1932) and especially J. R. Partington and D. McKie, "Historical Studies of the Phlogiston Theory: IV. Last Phases of the Theory," *Annals of Science,* 1939, 4: 113-149, give most detail about the conflict between the new theory and the old.

theories, and that, I think, is its second particularly significant function. Furthermore, it is for this function—aid in the choice between theories—and for it alone, that we must reserve the word "confirmation." We must, that is, if "confirmation" is intended to denote a procedure anything like what scientists ever do. The measurements that display an anomaly and thus create crisis may tempt the scientist to leave science or to transfer his attention to some other part of the field. But, if he stays where he is, anomalous observations, quantitative or qualitative, cannot tempt him to abandon his theory *until another one is suggested to replace it*. Just as a carpenter, while he retains his craft, cannot discard his toolbox because it contains no hammer fit to drive a particular nail, so the practitioner of science cannot discard established theory because of a felt inadequacy. At least he cannot do so until shown some other way to do his job. In scientific practice the real confirmation questions always involve the comparison of two theories with each other and with the world, not the comparison of a single theory with the world. In these three-way comparisons, measurement has a particular advantage.

To see where measurement's advantage resides, I must once more step briefly, and hence dogmatically, beyond the bounds of this essay. In the transition from an earlier to a later theory, there is very often a loss as well as a gain of explanatory power.[47] Newton's theory of planetary and projectile motion was fought vehemently for more than a generation because, unlike its main competitors, it demanded the introduction of an inexplicable force that acted directly upon bodies at a distance. Cartesian theory, for example, had attempted to explain gravity in terms of the direct collisions between elementary particles. To accept Newton meant to abandon the possibility of any such explanation, or so it seemed to most of Newton's immediate successors.[48] Similarly, though the historical detail is more equivocal, Lavoisier's new chemical theory was opposed by a number of men who felt that it deprived chemistry of one principal traditional function—the explanation of the qualitative properties of bodies in terms of the particular combination of chemical "principles" that composed them.[49] In each case the new theory was victorious, but the price of victory was the abandonment of an old and partly achieved goal. For eighteenth-century Newtonians it gradually became "unscientific" to ask for the cause of gravity; nineteenth-century chemists increasingly ceased to ask for the causes of particular qualities. Yet subsequent experience has shown that there was nothing *intrinsically* "unscientific" about these questions. Gen-

[47] This point is central to the reference cited in note 3. In fact, it is largely the necessity of balancing gains and losses and the controversies that so often result from disagreements about an appropriate balance that make it appropriate to describe changes of theory as "revolutions."

[48] Cohen, *Franklin and Newton*, Chapter 4; Pierre Brunet, *L'introduction des théories de Newton en France au xviiie siècle* (Paris, 1931).

[49] On this traditional task of chemistry see E. Meyerson, *Identity and Reality*, trans. K. Lowenberg (London, 1930), Chapter X, particularly pp. 331-336. Much essential material is also scattered through Hélène Metzger, *Les xviie à la fin du xviiie siècle*, vol. I (Paris, 1923), and *Newton, Stahl, Boerhaave, et la doctrine chimique* (Paris, 1930). Notice particularly that the phlogistonists, who looked upon ores as elementary bodies from which the metals were compounded by addition of phlogiston, could explain why the metals were so much more like each other than were the ores from which they were compounded. All metals had a principle, phlogiston, in common. No such explanation was possible on Lavoisier's theory.

eral relativity does explain gravitational attraction, and quantum mechanics does explain many of the qualitative characteristics of bodies. We now know what makes some bodies yellow and others transparent, etc. But in gaining this immensely important understanding, we have had to regress, in certain respects, to an older set of notions about the bounds of scientific inquiry. Problems and solutions that had to be abandoned in embracing classic theories of modern science are again very much with us.

The study of the confirmation procedures as they are practiced in the sciences is therefore often the study of what scientists will and will not give up in order to gain other particular advantages. That problem has scarcely even been stated before, and I can therefore scarcely guess what its fuller investigation would reveal. But impressionistic study strongly suggests one significant conclusion. I know of no case in the development of science which exhibits a loss of quantitative accuracy as a consequence of the transition from an earlier to a later theory. Nor can I imagine a debate between scientists in which, however hot the emotions, the search for greater numerical accuracy in a previously quantified field would be called "unscientific." Probably for the same reasons that make them particularly effective in creating scientific crises, the comparison of numerical predictions, *where they have been available*, has proved particularly successful in bringing scientific controversies to a close. Whatever the price in redefinitions of science, its methods, and its goals, scientists have shown themselves consistently unwilling to compromise the numerical success of their theories. Presumably there are other such desiderata as well, but one suspects that, in case of conflict, measurement would be the consistent victor.

V. MEASUREMENT IN THE DEVELOPMENT OF PHYSICAL SCIENCE

To this point we have taken for granted that measurement did play a central role in physical science and have asked about the nature of that role and the reasons for its peculiar efficacy. Now we must ask, though too late to anticipate a comparably full response, about the way in which physical science came to make use of quantitative techniques at all. To make that large and factual question manageable, I select for discussion only those parts of an answer which relate particularly closely to what has already been said.

One recurrent implication of the preceding discussion is that much qualitative research, both empirical and theoretical, is normally prerequisite to fruitful quantification of a given research field. In the absence of such prior work, the methodological directive, "Go ye forth and measure," may well prove only an invitation to waste time. If doubts about this point remain, they should be quickly resolved by a brief review of the role played by quantitative techniques in the emergence of the various physical sciences. Let me begin by asking what role such techniques had in the scientific revolution that centered in the seventeenth century.

Since any answer must now be schematic, I begin by dividing the fields of physical science studied during the seventeenth century into two groups. The first, to be labeled the traditional sciences, consists of astronomy, optics, and mechanics, all of them fields that had received considerable qualitative and quantitative development in antiquity and during the Middle Ages. These fields are to be contrasted with what I shall call the Baconian sciences, a new cluster of research areas that owed their status *as sciences* to the seventeenth century's characteristic insistence upon experimentation and upon the compilation of natural histories, including histories of the crafts. To this second group belong particularly the study of heat, of electricity, of magnetism, and of chemistry. Only chemistry had been much explored before the Scientific Revolution, and the men who explored it had almost all been either craftsmen or alchemists. If we except a few of the art's Islamic practitioners, the emergence of a rational and systematic chemical tradition cannot be dated earlier than the late sixteenth century.[50] Magnetism, heat, and electricity emerged still more slowly as independent subjects for learned study. Even more clearly than chemistry, they are novel by-products of the Baconian elements in the "new philosophy."[51]

The separation of traditional from Baconian sciences provides an important analytic tool, because the man who looks to the Scientific Revolution for examples of productive measurement in physical science will find them only in the sciences of the first group. Further, and perhaps more revealing, even in these traditional sciences measurement was most often effective just when it could be performed with well-known instruments and applied to very nearly traditional concepts. In astronomy, for example, it was Tycho Brahe's enlarged and better-calibrated version of medieval instruments that made the decisive quantitative contribution. The telescope, a characteristic novelty of the seventeenth century, was scarcely used quantitatively until the last third of the century, and that quantitative use had no effect on astronomical theory until Bradley's discovery of aberration in 1729. Even that discovery was isolated. Only during the second half of the eighteenth century did astronomy begin to experience the full effects of the immense improvements in quantitative observation that the telescope permitted.[52] Or again, as previously indicated, the novel inclined plane experiments of the seventeenth century were not nearly accurate enough to have alone been the source of the law of uniform acceleration. What is important about them—and they are critically important—is the conception that such measurements could have relevance to the problems of free fall and of projectile motion. That conception implies a fundamental shift in both the idea of motion and the techniques relevant to its analysis. But clearly no such conception could have evolved as it did if

[50] Boas, *Robert Boyle*, pp. 48-66.

[51] For electricity see, Roller and Roller, *Concept of Electric Charge*, Harvard Case Histories in Experimental Science, Case 8 (Cambridge, Mass., 1954), and, Edgar Zilsel, "The Origins of William Gilbert's Scientific Method," *J. Hist. Ideas*, 1941, 2: 1-32. I agree with those who feel Zilsel exaggerates the importance of a single factor in the genesis of electrical science and, by implication, of Baconianism, but the craft influences he describes cannot conceivably be dismissed. There is no equally satisfactory discussion of the development of thermal science before the eighteenth century, but Wolf, *16th and 17th Centuries*, pp. 82-92 and 275-281 will illustrate the transformation produced by Baconianism.

[52] Wolf, *Eighteenth Century*, pp. 102-145, and Whewell, *Inductive Sciences*, pp. 213-371. Particularly in the latter, notice the difficulty in separating advances due to improved instrumentation from those due to improved theory. This difficulty is not due primarily to Whewell's mode of presentation.

many of the subsidiary concepts needed for its exploitation had not existed, at least as developed embryos, in the works of Archimedes and of the scholastic analysts of motion.[53] Here again the effectiveness of quantitative work depended upon a long-standing prior tradition.

Perhaps the best test case is provided by optics, the third of my traditional sciences. In this field during the seventeenth century, real quantitative work was done with both new and old instruments, and the work done with old instruments on well-known phenomena proved the more important. The Scientific Revolution's reformulation of optical theory turned upon Newton's prism experiments, and for these there was much qualitative precedent. Newton's innovation was the quantitative analysis of a well-known qualitative effect, and that analysis was possibly only because of the discovery, a few decades before Newton's work, of Snell's law of refraction. That law is the vital quantitative novelty in the optics of the seventeenth century. It was, however, a law that had been sought by a series of brilliant investigators since the time of Ptolemy, and all had used apparatus quite similar to that which Snell employed. In short, the research which led to Newton's new theory of light and color was of an essentially traditional nature.[54]

Much in seventeenth-century optics was, however, by no means traditional. Interference, diffraction, and double refraction were all first discovered in the half-century before Newton's *Opticks* appeared; all were totally unexpected phenomena; and all were known to Newton.[55] On two of them Newton conducted careful quantitative investigations. Yet the real impact of these novel phenomena upon optical theory was scarcely felt until the work of Young and Fresnel a century later. Though Newton was able to develop a brilliant preliminary theory for interference effects, neither he nor his immediate successors even noted that that theory agreed with quantitative experiment only for the limited case of perpendicular incidence. Newton's measurements of diffraction produced only the most qualitative theory, and on double refraction he seems not even to have attempted quantitative work of his own. Both Newton and Huyghen announced mathematical laws governing the refraction of the extraordinary ray, and the latter showed how to account for this behavior by considering the expansion of a spheroidal wave front. But both mathematical discussions involved large extrapolations from scattered quantitative data of doubtful accuracy. And almost a hundred years elapsed before quantitative experiments proved able to distinguish between these two quite different mathematical formulations.[56] As with the other optical phenomena

[53] For pre-Galilean work see, Marshall Clagett, *The Science of Mechanics in the Middle Ages* (Madison, Wis., 1959), particularly Parts II & III. For Galileo's use of this work see, Alexandre Koyré, *Études Galiléennes,* 3 vols. (Paris, 1939), particularly I & II.

[54] A. C. Crombie, *Augustine to Galileo* (London, 1952), pp. 70-82, and Wolf, *16th & 17th Centuries,* pp. 244-254.

[55] *Ibid.,* pp. 254-264.

[56] For the seventeenth-century work (including Huyghen's geometric construction)

see the reference in the preceding note. The eighteenth-century investigations of these phenomena have scarcely been studied, but for what is known see, Joseph Priestley, *History ...of Discoveries relating to Vision, Light, and Colours* (London, 1772), pp. 279-316, 498-520, 548-562. The earliest examples I know of more precise work on double refraction are, R. J. Haüy, "Sur la double réfraction du Spath d'Islande," *Mem. d l'Acad.* (1788), pp. 34-61, and, W. H. Wollaston, "On the oblique Refraction of Iceland Crystal," *Phil. Trans.,* 1802, *92:* 381-386.

discovered during the Scientific Revolution, most of the eighteenth century was needed for the additional exploration and instrumentation prerequisite to quantitative exploitation.

Turning now to the Baconian sciences, which throughout the Scientific Revolution possessed few old instruments and even fewer well-wrought concepts, we find quantification proceeding even more slowly. Though the seventeenth century saw many new instruments, of which a number were quantitative and others potentially so, only the new barometer disclosed significant quantitative regularities when applied to new fields of study. And even the barometer is only an apparent exception, for pneumatics, the field of its application, was able to borrow *en bloc* the concepts of a far older field, hydrostatics. As Toricelli put it, the barometer measured pressure "at the bottom of an ocean of the element air."[57] In the field of magnetism the only significant seventeenth-century measurements, those of declination and dip, were made with one or another modified version of the traditional compass, and these measurements did little to improve the understanding of magnetic phenomena. For a more fundamental quantification, magnetism, like electricity, awaited the work of Coulomb, Gauss, Poisson, and others in the late eighteenth and early nineteenth centuries. Before that work could be done, a better qualitative understanding of attraction, repulsion, conduction, and other such phenomena was needed. The instruments which produced a lasting quantification had then to be designed with these initially qualitative conceptions in mind.[58] Furthermore, the decades in which success was at last achieved are almost the same ones that produced the first effective contacts between measurement and theory in the study of chemistry and of heat.[59] Successful quantification of the Baconian sciences had scarcely begun before the last third of the eighteenth century and only realized its full potential in the nineteenth. That realization—exemplified in the work of Fourier, Clausius, Kelvin, and Maxwell—is one facet of a second scientific revolution no less consequential than the seventeenth-century revolution. Only in the nineteenth century did the Baconian physical sciences undergo the transformation which the group of traditional sciences had experienced two or more centuries before.

Since Professor Guerlac's paper is devoted to chemistry and since I have already sketched some of the bars to quantification of electrical and magnetic phenomena, I take my single more extended illustration from the study of heat. Unfortunately, much of the research upon which such a sketch should be based remains to be done. What follows is necessarily more tentative than what has gone before.

Many of the early experiments involving thermometers read like investigations *of* that new instrument rather than like investigations *with* it. How

[57] See I.H.B. and A.G.H. Spiers, *The Physical Treatises of Pascal* (New York, 1937), p. 164. This whole volume displays the way in which seventeenth-century pneumatics took over concepts from hydrostatics.

[58] For the quantification and early mathematization of electrical science, see: Roller and Roller, *Concept of Electric Charge*, pp. 66-80; Whittaker, *Aether and Electricity*, pp.

53-66; and W. C. Walker, "The Detection and Estimation of Electric Charge in the Eighteenth Century," *Annals of Science*, 1936, *1*: 66-100.

[59] For heat see, Douglas McKie and N. H. de V. Heathcote, *The Discovery of Specific and Latent Heats* (London, 1935). In chemistry it may well be impossible to fix any date for the "first effective contacts between meas-

could anything else have been the case during a period when it was totally unclear what the thermometer measured? Its readings obviously depended upon the "degree of heat" but apparently in immensely complex ways. "Degree of heat" had for a long time been defined by the senses, and the senses responded quite differently to bodies which produced the same thermometric readings. Before the thermometer could become unequivocally a laboratory instrument rather than an experimental subject, thermometric reading had to be seen as the direct measure of "degree of heat," and sensation had simultaneously to be viewed as a complex and equivocal phenomenon dependent upon a number of different parameters.[60]

That conceptual reorientation seems to have been completed in at least a few scientific circles before the end of the seventeenth century, but no rapid discovery of quantitative regularities followed. First scientists had to be forced to a bifurcation of "degree of heat" into "quantity of heat," on the one hand, and "temperature," on the other. In addition they had to select for close scrutiny, from the immense multitude of available thermal phenomena, the ones that could most readily be made to reveal quantitative law. These proved to be: mixing two components of a single fluid initially at different temperatures, and radiant heating of two different fluids in identical vessels. Even when attention was focused upon these phenomena, however, scientists still did not get unequivocal or uniform results. As Heathcote and McKie have brilliantly shown, the last stages in the development of the concepts of specific and latent heat display intuited hypotheses constantly interacting with stubborn measurement, each forcing the other into line.[61] Still other sorts of work were required before the contributions of Laplace, Poisson, and Fourier could transform the study of thermal phenomena into a branch of mathematical physics.[62]

This sort of pattern, reiterated both in the other Baconian sciences and in the extension of traditional sciences to new instruments and new phenomena, thus provides one additional illustration of this paper's most persistent thesis. *The road from scientific law to scientific measurement can rarely be traveled*

urement and theory." Volumetric or gravimetric measures were always an ingredient of chemical recipes and assays. By the seventeenth century, for example in the work of Boyle, weight-gain or loss was often a clue to the theoretical analysis of particular reactions. But until the middle of the eighteenth century, the significance of chemical measurement seems always to have been either descriptive (as in recipes) or qualitative (as in demonstrating a weight-gain without significant reference to its magnitude). Only in the work of Black, Lavoisier, and Richter does measurement begin to play a fully quantitative role in the development of chemical laws and theories. For an introduction to these men and their work see, J. B. Partington, *A Short History of Chemistry,* 2nd ed. (London, 1951), pp. 93-97, 122-128, and 161-163.

[60] Maurice Daumas, *Les instruments scientifiques aux xviie et xviiie siècles* (Paris, 1953), pp. 78-80, provides an excellent brief account of the slow stages in the deployment of the thermometer as a scientific instrument. Robert Boyle's *New Experiments and Observations Touching Cold* illustrates the seventeenth century's need to demonstrate that properly constructed thermometers must replace the senses in thermal measurements even though the two give divergent results. See *Works of the Honourable Robert Boyle,* ed. T. Birch, 5 vols. (London, 1744), II, 240-243.

[61] For the elaboration of calorimetric concepts see, E. Mach, *Die Principien der Wärmelehre* (Leipzig, 1919), pp. 153-181, and McKie and Heathcote, *Specific and Latent Heats.* The discussion of Krafft's work in the latter (pp. 59-63) provides a particularly striking example of the problems in making measurement work.

[62] Gaston Bachelard, *Étude sur l'évolution d'un problème de physique* (Paris, 1928), and Kuhn, "Caloric Theory of Adiabatic Compression."

in the reverse direction. To discover quantitative regularity one must normally know what regularity one is seeking and one's instruments must be designed accordingly; even then nature may not yield consistent or generalizable results without a struggle. So much for my major thesis. The preceding remarks about the way in which quantification entered the modern physical sciences should, however, also recall this paper's minor thesis, for they redirect attention to the immense efficacy of quantitative experimentation undertaken within the context of a fully mathematized theory. Sometime between 1800 and 1850 there was an important change in the character of research in many of the physical sciences, particularly in the cluster of research fields known as physics. That change is what makes me call the mathematization of Baconian physical science one facet of a second scientific revolution.

It would be absurd to pretend that mathematization was more than a facet. The first half of the nineteenth century also witnessed a vast increase in the scale of the scientific enterprise, major changes in patterns of scientific organization, and a total reconstruction of scientific education.[63] But these changes affected all the sciences in much the same way. They ought not to explain the characteristics that differentiate the newly mathematized sciences of the nineteenth century from other sciences of the same period. Though my sources are now impressionistic, I feel quite sure that there are such characteristics. Let me hazard the following prediction. Analytic, and in part statistical, research would show that physicists, as a group, have displayed since about 1840 a greater ability to concentrate their attention on a few key areas of research than have their colleagues in less completely quantified fields. In the same period, if I am right, physicists would prove to have been more successful than most other scientists in decreasing the length of controversies about scientific theories and in increasing the strength of the consensus that emerged from such controversies. In short, I believe that the nineteenth-century mathematization of physical science produced vastly refined professional criteria for problem selection and that it simultaneously very much increased the effectiveness of professional verification procedures.[64] These are, of course, just the changes that the discussion in Section IV would lead us to expect. A critical and comparative analysis of the development of physics during the past century-and-a-quarter should provide an acid test of those conclusions.

Pending that test, can we conclude anything at all? I venture the following paradox: The full and intimate quantification of any science is a consummation devoutly to be wished. Nevertheless, it is not a consummation that can effectively be sought by measuring. As in individual development, so in the scientific group, maturity comes most surely to those who know how to wait.

[63] S. F. Mason, *Main Currents of Scientific Thought* (New York, 1956), pp. 352-363, provides an excellent brief sketch of these institutional changes. Much additional material is scattered through, J. T. Merz, *History of European Thought in the Nineteenth Century,* vol. I (London, 1923).

[64] For an example of effective problem selection, note the esoteric quantitative discrepancies which isolated the three problems—photoelectric effect, black body radiation, and specific heats—that gave rise to quantum mechanics. For the new effectiveness of verification procedures, note the speed with which this radical new theory was adopted by the profession.

APPENDIX

Reflecting on the other papers and on the discussion that continued throughout the conference, two additional points that had reference to my own paper seem worth recording. Undoubtedly there were others as well, but my memory has proved more than usually unreliable. Professor Price raised the first point, which gave rise to considerable discussion. The second followed from an aside by Professor Spengler, and I shall consider its consequences first.

Professor Spengler expressed great interest in my concept of "crises" in the development of a science or of a scientific specialty, but added that he had had difficulty discovering more than one such episode in the development of economics. This raised for me the perennial, but perhaps not very important question about whether or not the social sciences are really sciences at all. Though I shall not even attempt to answer it in that form, a few further remarks about the possible absence of crises in the development of a social science may illuminate some part of what is at issue.

As developed in Section IV, above, the concept of a crisis implies a prior unanimity of the group that experiences one. Anomalies, by definition, exist only with respect to firmly established expectations. Experiments can create a crisis by consistently going wrong only for a group that has previously experienced everything's seeming to go right. Now, as my Sections II and III should indicate quite fully, in the mature physical sciences most things generally do go right. The entire professional community can therefore ordinarily agree about the fundamental concepts, tools, and problems of its science. Without that professional consensus, there would be no basis for the sort of puzzle-solving activity in which, as I have already urged, most physical scientists are normally engaged. In the physical sciences disagreement about fundamentals is, like the search for basic innovations, reserved for periods of crisis.[65] It is, however, by no means equally clear that a consensus of anything like similar strength and scope ordinarily characterizes the social sciences. Experience with my university colleagues and a fortunate year spent at the Center for Advanced Study in the Behavioral Sciences suggest that the fundamental agreement which physicists, say, can normally take for granted has only recently begun to emerge in a few areas of social-science research. Most other areas are still characterized by fundamental disagreements about the definition of the field, its paradigm achievements, and its problems. While that situation obtains (as it did also in earlier periods of the development of the various physical sciences), either there can be no crises or there can never be anything else.

Professor Price's point was very different and far more historical. He suggested, and I think quite rightly, that my historical epilogue failed to call attention to a very important change in the attitude of physical scientists towards measurement that occurred during the Scientific Revolution. In com-

---

[65] I have developed some other significant concomitants of this professional consensus in my paper, "The Essential Tension: Tradition and Innovation in Scientific Research." That paper appears in, Calvin W. Taylor (ed.), *The Third (1959) University of Utah Research Conference on the Identification of Creative Scientific Talent* (University of Utah Press, 1959), pp. 162-177.

menting on Dr. Crombie's paper, Price had pointed out that not until the late sixteenth century did astronomers begin to record continuous series of observations of planetary position. (Previously they had restricted themselves to occasional quantitative observations of special phenomena.) Only in that same late period, he continued, did astronomers begin to be critical of their quantitative data, recognizing, for example, that a recorded celestial position is a clue to an astronomical fact rather than the fact itself. When discussing my paper, Professor Price pointed to still other signs of a change in the attitude towards measurement during the Scientific Revolution. For one thing, he emphasized, many more numbers were recorded. More important, perhaps, people like Boyle, when announcing laws derived from measurement, began for the first time to record their quantitative data, *whether or not they perfectly fit the law,* rather than simply stating the law itself.

I am somewhat doubtful that this transition in attitude towards numbers proceeded quite so far in the seventeenth century as Professor Price seemed occasionally to imply. Hooke, for one example, did not report the numbers from which he derived his law of elasticity; no concept of "significant figures" seems to have emerged in the experimental physical sciences before the *nineteenth* century. But I cannot doubt that the change was in process and that it is very important. At least in another sort of paper, it deserves detailed examination which I very much hope it will get. Pending that examination, however, let me simply point out how very closely the development of the phenomena emphasized by Professor Price fits the pattern I have already sketched in describing the effects of seventeenth-century Baconianism.

In the first place, except perhaps in astronomy, the seventeenth-century change in attitude towards measurement looks very much like a response to the novelties of the methodological program of the "new philosophy." Those novelties were not, as has so often been supposed, consequences of the belief that observation and experiment were basic to science. As Crombie has brilliantly shown, that belief and an accompanying methodological philosophy were highly developed during the Middle Ages.[66] Instead, the novelties of method in the "new philosophy" included a belief that lots and lots of experiments would be necessary (the plea for natural histories) and an insistence that all experiments and observations be reported in full and naturalistic detail, preferably accompanied by the names and credentials of witnesses. Both the increased frequency with which numbers were recorded and the decreased tendency to round them off are precisely congruent with those more general Baconian changes in the attitude towards experimentation at large.

Furthermore, whether or not its source lies in Baconianism, the effectiveness of the seventeenth-century's new attitude towards numbers developed in very much the same way as the effectiveness of the other Baconian novelties discussed in my concluding section. In dynamics, as Professor Koyré has repeatedly shown, the new attitude had almost no effect before the later eighteenth century. The other two traditional sciences, astronomy and optics, were affected sooner by the change, but only in their most nearly traditional parts.

[66] See particularly his *Robert Grosseteste and the Origins of Experimental Science, 1100-1700* (Oxford, 1953).

And the Baconian sciences, heat, electricity, chemistry, etc., scarcely begin to profit from the new attitude until after 1750. Again it is in the work of Black, Lavoisier, Coulomb, and their contemporaries that the first truly significant effects of the change are seen. And the full transformation of physical science due to that change is scarcely visible before the work of Ampère, Fourier, Ohm, and Kelvin. Professor Price has, I think, isolated another very significant seventeenth-century novelty. But like so many of the other novel attitudes displayed by the "new philosophy," the significant effects of this new attitude towards measurement were scarcely manifested in the seventeenth century at all.

Quantification in Chemistry

By Henry Guerlac*

INTRODUCTION

CHEMISTRY is universally classed among the exact sciences: that is, among those sciences making use of careful measurement, quantitative experiment, and indispensable precision equipment. The beginning student of chemistry soon becomes aware of this. He is obliged to learn the so-called *empirical formulas* which represent in symbols the quantitative, as well as the qualitative, constitution of substances; and the *empirical equations* which record (again both qualitatively and quantitatively) the interactions and exchanges between different substances. He is soon taught that these formulas and equations imply certain invariable "laws" or principles, broad quantitative assertions upon which the whole science of chemistry depends. The *Law of the Conservation of Matter* says that in chemical reactions matter is never created or destroyed, but merely transferred or exchanged; the *Law of Definite Proportions*, teaches that any chemical compound has a fixed composition by weight; and the *Law of Multiple Proportions*, states that if two or more compounds can be prepared out of the same elements, these compounds will be composed of simple multiples of the weights of the elements. The student soon learns that these "laws" can best be understood in terms of the atomic and molecular theories.

Early in his career, the chemistry student is taught the two fundamental skills of the profession: *Qualitative Analysis*, in which he learns to detect the presence of the different chemical substances by characteristic reactions; and *Quantitative Analysis* in which he learns the delicate business of determining *how much* there is of a given substance in a given mixture or compound. These are the skills by means of which the formulas and equations have been ascertained, and which lie behind the body of theory the student has learned. If he progresses further into the study of organic chemistry, he finds that these skills and these quantitative concepts are still fundamental.

But when, towards the end of his undergraduate study, he is introduced to physical chemistry, he enters a different world. The physical chemist deals partly with problems that belong to physics (but are of special interest to the chemist, like change of state, the behavior of gases and liquids, and molecular and atomic structure), partly with special types of problems (like chemical equilibria, solution theory, reaction rates, etc.) which the chemist treats in the spirit of the physicist. It is characteristic of the physical chemist that he is less concerned with the behavior and properties of *particular substances*, than he is with learning about the behavior of *wide classes of matter*, and summing

* Cornell University, Ithaca, N.Y.

up this behavior in abstract, mathematical laws. The line between chemistry and physics has nearly vanished; indeed we might define physical chemistry as that part of physics which does not primarily interest the physicist.

This sequence of chemical study pretty well recapitulates, as a biologist might say, the development of chemistry itself during the past two centuries. Inorganic (and analytical) chemistry came into its own, and emerged as a science, in the age of Marggraf, Scheele, Priestley and Lavoisier. Organic chemistry was rapidly built up in its main lines during the early and middle 19th century. Physical chemistry emerged as a separate specialty only in the last decades of the 19th century.[1]

Between inorganic and organic chemistry on the one hand and physical chemistry on the other, whether we view them historically or in terms of the curriculum, there is a theoretical and methodological hiatus. Today, in the chemical laboratory of any large university we find the inorganic, analytical and organic chemists working in a more or less traditional way. Though they have new and sophisticated techniques and instrumentation at their disposal, and though they confront problems—organic syntheses for example—of a complexity beyond the imaginings of their predecessors, we can still conceive of them as able to communicate readily, as fellow-chemists, with a Bunsen, a Liebig, a Gerhardt or a Lavoisier. But the physical chemists are a different breed; they think and work in the spirit of physics; they are concerned with establishing and refining certain general laws governing the behavior of matter. They are not primarily interested, I repeat, in different *kinds* of matter. When they study in detail the behavior of chemically unique substances, it is to find the general principles upon which chemical reactions depend.

If we are to talk meaningfully about quantification in chemistry, we should make clear which group of persons we are talking about. So I propose to leave the physical chemists aside. To discuss their use of measurement and quantitative thinking would be to discuss the practices of the physicist, as somewhat modified by a concern with a special set of problems. If there is anything peculiar and characteristic about the chemists' use of quantification, I believe it will be found in the work of the older and more traditional branches of the subject, in chemistry *proprement dite*.

QUANTITY AND QUALITY IN EARLY CHEMISTRY

Until about the middle of the 18th century, textbooks customarily described chemistry, not as a science, but as an *art*: at first the delusive art of gold-making; then, by the early 17th century, an art serving the metallurgist and, more commonly, the physician—the latter especially, for the typical 18th cen-

---

[1] This may be illustrated by the successive appearance of specialized journals for the several branches of chemistry. The earliest serial publications devoted to chemistry, established at the close of the 18th century, covered the subject as a whole. For all practical purposes, Justus Liebig's *Annalen der Chemie,* launched in 1832, became the earliest journal devoted to organic chemistry. By 1860 Dumas could argue at Carlsruhe that organic and inorganic chemistry were distinct sciences. Journals of analytical chemistry first appeared in the '60s and '70s (Fresenius' *Zeitschrift für analytische Chemie* in 1862 and the *Analyst* in 1876). The *Zeitschrift für physikalische Chemie* was founded in 1887 and the American *Journal of Physical Chemistry* in 1896.

tury chemist was likely to have been trained as a pharmacist or medical doctor.[2]

One of the most influential early textbooks, that of Nicolas Lémery, defined chemistry in the late 17th century as "an art which teaches the separation of different substances found in complex bodies."[3] Baron, in re-editing Lémery's book in 1756, described chemistry as a *science pratique* concerned with the decomposition and recomposition of substances.[4] This was scarcely an advance; but ten years later, in his famous *Dictionnaire de Chymie,* P. J. Macquer not only called chemistry a science, but suggested that its goal was theoretical knowledge. "Chemistry," he wrote, "is a science whose object is to learn the nature and properties of all bodies, by their analysis and their combinations."[5]

But if chemistry was a science, it was a science markedly different from physics. The distinction between the two sciences was clearly put by William Cullen, a Scottish physician and one of the great teachers of chemistry in his day. About 1760 he was telling his students that chemistry is "a science that shows the Particular, as Mechanics do the general, properties of bodies." And he went on to explain that while physics deals with the characteristics common to all bodies, chemistry deals with the properties of certain bodies that are peculiar to them alone.[6]

Recognized as a science, then, rather than an art, soon after the middle of the 18th century, chemistry concerned itself with distinguishing and describing the wide variety of substances found in nature or made by art. To discriminate and classify different bodies, to note, and if possible explain, their individual characteristics, powers and interactions: these were the goals of the chemist. It is understandable, therefore, that early chemistry was a qualitative science, largely if not completely devoid of quantitative *concepts* (until towards the close of the 18th century), a science which employed quantitative *procedures* chiefly in the interests of art or *techne:* for the compounding of remedies, the assaying of metals, and so on. It is my suggestion in this paper that, in the main, chemistry has retained this qualitative goal, even after the advent of the sub-science of physical chemistry. It remained, and to a large extent still remains in its older branches, a qualitative science, though possessed of an even more impressive armory of quantitative techniques, quantifiable statements, numerical constants, and what-not. These quantitative techniques serve an essentially qualitative purpose: the discrimination and classification of "chemical individuals" with ever-deepening insight and ever-increasing precision.

Is there something paradoxical about this view of chemistry as a typically qualitative and descriptive science that has found quantitative thinking in-

---

[2] See my recent paper, "Some French Antecedents of the Chemical Revolution," *Chymia, 5:* 73-111.

[3] "La Chymie est un Art qui enseigne à séparer les différentes substances qui se rencontrent dans un mixte." N. Lémery: *Cours de Chymie,* ed. Baron (Paris, 1756), p. 2. The word "mixte" had a less precise meaning with Lémery than with later chemists. See below.

[4] *Ibid.,* note (a).

[5] *Dictionnaire de Chymie,* 2 vols., (Paris, 1766), I, p. 259.

[6] MS Notes of Dr. Cullen's Lectures on Chemistry made by Dr. John White of Paisley. I am indebted to the City Library of Paisley, Scotland, for a microfilm of these lectures.

dispensable to its main classificatory goal? A moment's reflection will remind us that on a rather naive level such procedures enter into all of the admittedly descriptive sciences. Simple measurements and simple counts play their part in that most purely qualitative of all sciences, taxonomy. Botanists, as everyone knows, count the stamens of flowers or the number of cells of an ovary to establish fundamental divisions; and they separate the angiosperms into two main groups according to whether the embryo has one or two cotyledons. Entomologists, to give a less familiar example, divide a large family of ground beetles into two populous sub-families by a single, apparently trivial "quantifiable" character, the number of seta-bearing pores over each eye. Strange as it may seem, the infinitely more sophisticated weighings, volumetric measurements, etc., of the chemist serve essentially the same purpose: they assist in the process of classification, yield precise distinctions between chemical substances, and accurately characterize their properties. The aim is not, as with physics, the enunciation and verification of general laws or the precise description of generalized processes. In what follows I shall give some examples of how the chemist has used quantification to (1) characterize common substances, (2) delimit classes of substances, (3) determine the relationship of the elementary substances making up compounds, and (4) explore relations among the elements themselves.

THE CHARACTERIZATION OF COMMON SUBSTANCES

The earliest chemists were able to distinguish and characterize a substantial number of different chemical substances. Some were elements in a more or less pure state (sulphur, for example, and the common metals); others were simple compounds, like sea salt, soda, magnesia, potash, certain metallic oxides and sulphides, several vitriols, and so on. These were set apart from each other by qualitative distinctions: texture, color, odor, taste, the source from which the material was obtained, or the use to which it was put. Until the turn of the 19th century, the quantitative characteristics (physical constants) we encounter in modern descriptions were almost totally lacking, chiefly but not solely because the facts were not available. For example, measurements of the relative density or specific gravity of the common metals were made in Islamic times, using the hydrostatic balance, but when the several metals were described by authors of the 17th and early 18th centuries this property was generally omitted.[7] It was not until the closing years of the 18th century that the chemical textbooks began to describe chemical substances in terms of physical constants and *measurable* chemical properties. Thomas Thomson in his *System of Chemistry* (1802) was one of the earliest to do this as systematically as his knowledge permitted. For the metals he gave the specific grav-

---

[7] Lémery, for example, makes no reference to the specific gravity of metals in his famous textbook. The figures are supplied by Baron in his notes to the 1756 edition of the *Cours de Chymie*. The same service was performed for Caspar Neumann by William Lewis in his *Chemical Works of Caspar Neumann, M.D.,* London, 1759. Boerhaave, by contrast, prefaced his discussion of the metals in his *Elementa Chemiae* (1732) by printing a table of specific gravities based on two early papers in the *Philosophical Transactions* of the Royal Society of London.

ity, the hardness (according to a scale devised by the Irish chemist, Richard Kirwan), and where possible the melting point, according to the Fahrenheit scale or that of Wedgewood's pyrometer.[8] Moreover, he extended the procedure to other substances where the data was available; and for many of them he was able to give solubility figures; for although it was known throughout the 18th century that salts have a characteristic solubility in water at a specified temperature, no reasonably reliable measurements were made until the last years of the century.[9]

THE CLASSES OF CHEMICAL SUBSTANCES

From the earliest times, the substances known to the chemist were divided into classes or groups according to chemical properties which they shared. Thus in the 10th century, the great Arab chemist al-Razi divided the solid substances into two main divisions: (1) *bodies,* which remain fixed and withstand a moderate exposure to fire; and (2) *spirits* which are volatile. The bodies included metals, the salts and vitriols, and various "stones." The spirits were sulphur, mercury, arsenic sulphide and sal ammoniac.[10] This classification underwent profound modifications as chemistry advanced, until by the late 17th century (though there was no agreement on a single scheme) it was common to distinguish at least five member classes of the mineral kingdom: metals, demi-metals, earths and stones, sulphur and bituminuous substances, and "salts." The "salts" included all substances which are soluble in water and affect the palate with a strong taste; in this group were placed the acids, the alkalis (soda and potash) and the "neutral salts." For obvious reasons, qualitative considerations (based on chemical behavior) continued to determine the groups into which substances were placed. But in the definition of

[8] It may be interesting to compare the description of metallic copper as given by one of the most influential early chemists, the Latin Geber, with Thomson's, which is one of the first really modern descriptions. In the Geberian *Sum of Perfection,* we read that copper is "a Metallick Body, livid, partaking of a dusky *Redness,* ignible (or sustaining ignition), fusible, extensible under the hammer, but refusing the *Cupel,* and cement." See *The Works of Geber, Englished by Richard Russell 1678, a new edition with introduction by E. J. Holmyard,* (London & Toronto, 1928), p. 68. Lémery's description, though longer, is hardly in advance of this. But in Thomson we read: "This metal is of a fine red colour, and has a great deal of brilliancy. Its taste is styptic and nauseous... Its hardness is 7.5. Its specific gravity, when melted, is 8.667; but after being hammered it is 8.9. Its malleability is also considerable... Its tenacity is such, that a copper wire 1/12.6 inch in diameter is capable of supporting 546 pounds without breaking. When heated to the temperature of 27° Wedgewood, or, according to the calculation of Mortimer to 1450° Fahrenheit, it melts... When allowed to cool slowly, it assumes a crystalline form." *A System of Chemistry,* 4 vols., (Edinburgh, 1802), I, pp. 113-114. Thomson, of course, follows the physical description with a detailed account of the chemical properties of the metal.

[9] Nehemiah Grew reported (January, 1697) the first quantitative experiments on the solubility of salts in water. See his *Anatomy of Plants,* (London, 1682), pp. 296-304, and the reference in Charles Alston: *A Dissertation on Quick-Lime and Lime-Water,* (Edinburgh, 1752), pp. 53-54. The subject was again taken up by Richard Watson in a paper published in the *Philosophical Transactions* in 1770 and reprinted in his *Chemical Essays,* V, pp. 43-101. But as Fourcroy somewhere indicates, it was the rise of industrial chemistry at the close of the 18th century which inspired the first exact studies of the solubility of salts in water.

[10] For the classification of substances by al-Razi, see H. E. Stapleton, R. F. Azo and M. Hidayat Husain: "Chemistry in Iraq and Persia in the Tenth Century A.D.," *Memoirs of the Asiatic Society of Bengal,* 1922, *6:* 345-346 and 373-377.

acids we have an interesting example of how a quantitative definition eventually emerged, though only in our own time. Robert Boyle was perhaps the first to go beyond mere taste and odor, and to identify acids by a series of chemical reactions: effervescence with coral or crab's eyes; precipitation of sulphur from solution in alkalis; and by color tests, such as destroying the blue color of *lignum nephriticum* or turning syrup of violets red.[11] This was followed, a century later, by the more sophisticated attempt to define acids by some elementary constituent. Lavoisier, as everyone learns, believed all acids to contain oxygen, a view that was soon disproved, and supplanted by Davy's tentative suggestion of a hydrogen theory, which Liebig adopted when he defined an acid as a hydrogen-containing substance which will generate the gas on reaction with metals. After it was shown that acids, bases and salts are electrolytes and Arrhenius and Ostwald had developed their theory of ionization, it was agreed to define an acid as a substance which breaks down in aqueous solution to give positively charged hydrogen ions (H+) and bases as substances which give negative hydroxyl ions (OH—). This led to a clarification of the nature of strong and weak acids, and indeed yielded a quantified definition of acids and bases. Any acid HA breaks down (ionizes) to some definite degree in solution to produce hydrogen ions (H+) and its characteristic anion (A—), according to the reaction

$$HA = H+ \; + \; A-$$

The extent of the ionization reached at equilibrium is characteristic of each acid, and we can represent the general case by the relation

$$\frac{(H+)(A-)}{HA} = K_{HA}$$

where K_{HA} is the equilibrium constant for the particular acid. If the acid is strong, the reaction shifts toward the production of the ions, and the constant is (relatively) large. In the case of weak acid, the constant is smaller.

Thus a precise quantitative definition supplanted the vaguer qualitative ones. But this is a special case of defining substances in terms of their constitution and composition. It is here perhaps, more than elsewhere, that our theme can best be illustrated.

THE COMPOSITION OF CHEMICAL SUBSTANCES

The notion of quantitative chemical composition—that a given substance is composed of a certain proportion by weight of identifiable constituents intimately bound together—is fundamental to the science of chemistry. Yet it took many centuries before it was clearly appreciated that compounds could ever be said to be *composed* of precise constituents, and still longer before it was realized that these constituents always are found combined in constant weight proportions. Yet it is safe to say that this is the most fundamental *quantitative concept* of chemistry. It was also, so it would appear, the earliest to emerge.

[11] Marie Boas: *Robert Boyle and Seven-* pp. 134-136.
teenth-Century Chemistry (Cambridge, 1958),

That various common materials can be heated together, or simply mixed together in solution, to produce new substances (and sometimes substances already recognized in nature) was a commonplace of great antiquity; indeed it must have been this fact that brought chemistry originally into being. But more often than not, the complexity of these early "syntheses" obscured what was taking place. Thus the Latin Geber described the preparation of corrosive sublimate (mercuric chloride) by subliming a mixture of mercury, calcined green vitriol, common salt and nitre. Such complicated reactions, producing a number of products (from which, in this case, the mercuric chloride was separated by sublimation) could scarcely reveal what was taking place.

Gradually, however, these preparations were simplified; by the middle of the 17th century, chemists could prepare a number of substances by simple binary exchange reactions. Thus Glauber made his *sal mirabile* (sodium sulphate) by the action of sulphuric acid on common salt; butter of antimony (antimony trichloride) by treating stibnite with hydrochloric acid; or very pure nitre (potassium nitrate) by adding rectified nitric acid drop by drop to a filtered solution of potassium carbonate. Glauber was one of the first chemists, if not the first, to have a clear, though only qualitative, idea of chemical composition.[12] He recognized sal ammoniac (ammonium chloride) as a compound of spirit of salt (HCl) and *sal volatile urinae* (ammonia). That this was true, he showed by synthesizing the salt from the ammonia and HCl, but also by decomposing the sal ammoniac to yield its constituents. He asserted also that the vitriols (the sulphates) were composed of a sulphuric salt (sulphuric acid) and earths containing iron or copper (oxides of iron or copper).

These definitions, though a notable advance, were still only descriptive and qualitative. There was no attempt to give the composition in terms of the quantity of the substances entering into the final product. What lends a deceptive appearance of quantitative procedure to such preparations of early chemists is the *recipe*. Empirically it was known that certain proportions by weight of reactants had been found to give a satisfactory product, and textbooks and manuals, even those dating from very early times, commonly indicated that certain convenient or effective proportions of this or that should be employed to give the desired result. But this did not mean that these reactants were supposed to exist in the final product in those proportions. We can see that an excess of one reactant may often have been employed to force the reaction to completion. Recipes strike us today as only a sort of pseudo-quantification, or at best a first step towards a real quantification.

It was an immensely important advance to realize that substances *react* only in definite proportions by weight, and to discover in certain reactions a defi-

---

[12] For Glauber's contributions, especially his work on salts, see Paul Walden, *Salts, Acids, and Bases* (New York, 1929), pp. 38-43; also Walden's study in Günther Bugge *Das Buch der Grossen Chemiker*, reprint of 1955, I, pp. 151-172. It should be emphasized that underlying the concept of quantitative composition lay the Law of the Conservation of Matter, which was taken for granted from the time of Van Helmont onwards. Professor Parting-ton credits Van Helmont with showing that "the weights or masses of substances, recovered from compounds prepared from them, are equal to the masses originally taken." He adds that Glauber had emphasized that compounds "actually contain the substances from which they are prepared." J. R. Partington "The Concepts of Substance and Chemical Element," *Chymia*, 1948, *1*: 114-115.

nite point of saturation or neutralization of one substance by another, as in preparing salts by the interaction of acids with alkalis. Thus Glauber added nitric acid to his solution of potassium carbonate until "both disagreeable natures . . . have killed each other," a point conveniently marked by the cessation of effervescence. Newton was aware that a definite quantity of *aqua fortis* was necessary to dissolve a particular amount of copper, and that still more acid was needed to dissolve the same amount of iron. Stahl went so far as to refer to a *pondus naturae,* i.e., the proportion according to which a substance reacts. When, as in treating spirit of nitre with spirit of wine, an excess of the latter is added, no further reaction takes place. This point was brought home forcibly by the careful studies of G. F. Rouelle (1703-1770) on neutral salts, for he showed that an excess of acid or base merely mixed physically with the salt produced, and did not enter into its composition.[13]

About the middle of the 18th century, these effects were generally understood to mean that a compound substance has a definite and constant composition. This is the more remarkable when we realize how imprecise was the notion of chemical principles or elements, and how few substances—like mercury, sulphur, phosphorus and the common metals—were known in what we should call an elementary state. It would be interesting to discover which compound was first described with reasonable accuracy in terms of its quantitative composition. A good claim can be made for mercuric sulphide. Cinnabar, the ore which provided the mercury of commerce, had long been known to yield on heating, only two simple substances, mercury and sulphur. For centuries, also, chemists had known that an artificial or "factitious" cinnabar, could be produced by the combination of mercury and sulphur. According to Nicolas Lémery in his famous textbook (1675), this artificial cinnabar could be made by heating together three parts by weight of mercury with two parts of sulphur, a *recipe* that did not reflect the composition of the product, for he further reported that when this artificial cinnabar is "revivified," that is decomposed, it yields about 13 ounces of mercury for each pound of cinnabar.[14] Clearly he did not interpret his recipe as involving a *pondus naturae,* nor see that synthesis and analysis should yield comparable figures. But in 1756 his editor, Baron, said that to make artificial cinnabar, the proper proportions should be at least seven or eight parts by weight of mercury to two parts of sulphur, according to Lémery himself "cinnabar contains hardly more than a seventh of its weight of sulphur." Even Baron, it will be observed, did not go the whole distance. But ten years later, Macquer in his *Dictionary* explicitly described cinnabar as *composed of* seven parts by weight of mercury and one part of sulphur.[15]

It is obvious that few other common substances could so easily have had their quantitative composition even roughly determined in a manner satis-

---

[13] Pierre Duhem *Le Mixte et la Combinaison Chimique* (Paris, 1902), p. 53.

[14] Lémery: *Cours de Chymie,* ed. Baron, p. 181.

[15] Macquer writes that "Ce minéral est composé de mercure & de soufre. . . . En pesant exactement le cinabre qu'on décompose par cette méthode [by heating with iron filings], & le mercure qu'on en retire, on trouve que ce mercure fait à-peu-près les sept huitièmes du cinabre employé; ce qui prouve qu'il y a dans le cinabre environ sept parties de mercure, contre une partie de soufre." *Dictionnaire de Chymie,* ed. 1766, I, pp. 259-260.

factory to us. So it is surprising to find that a year before Macquer gave the composition by weight of artificial cinnabar, a reader of Diderot's *Encyclopédie* could learn that it had become a "dogme d'éternelle vérité" among chemists that compounds (*mixtes*) are composed of definite and invariable proportions of their constituents, and that only such substances as are "essentially" and "necessarily" constituted in this fashion deserve the name of *mixtes*.[16] The evidence for this sweeping, confident statement must have been scanty. Apparently it was an inference from the *point de saturation* carefully studied by Rouelle and others in the production of neutral salts, rather than from analysis and synthesis from the true elements as in the isolated case of cinnabar.

The principle of definite proportions was nevertheless widely accepted. It guided Lavoisier throughout his investigations on the chemical role of gases, as indeed it guided Joseph Black in his earlier study of *magnesia alba* and the alkalis, for Black was the first to show that a gas can enter quantitatively into the composition of familiar substances. While Black's followers, Cavendish and Priestley for example, generally ignored this important question, and were concerned to isolate and describe the different gases, Lavoisier and his disciples focussed their attention on the part that certain elementary gases, especially oxygen, played in the constitution of different compounds. This aspect of Lavoisier's accomplishment has rarely been emphasized, for it was less dramatic than his demonstration of the role of oxygen in combustion and respiration. The discovery of oxygen meant the isolation of one of the most reactive elements, one which enters into the composition of a host of common substances. Directly or indirectly, Lavoisier's study of this crucial substance led, before 1789, to establishing the composition by weight of phosphoric, nitric, and sulphuric acids; of water and carbon dioxide; and of the oxides of some seventeen different metals. It was soon shown, too, both in the case of acids and of the metallic oxides, that certain compounds containing the same elements, yet differing in properties, contained different proportions of combined oxygen. Thus nitrous acid was distinguished from nitric acid, sulphurous acid from sulphuric, and carbonic acid gas (CO_2) from carbonic oxide (CO), by the amount of oxygen in the compound.[17]

Perhaps this might have settled the matter and confirmed the view which Lavoisier and his contemporaries took as axiomatic. Instead, the principle of constant quantitative constitution was seriously questioned by one of Lavoisier's closest disciples. In the course of his study of affinity, C. L. Berthollet came to doubt this proposition, and finally asserted in his *Essai de statique chimique* (1803) that within certain limits bodies have a tendency to combine in every proportion, and that combination is never definite and invariable, except when rendered so by the operation of modifying causes, such

---

[16] Article "Mixte et Mixtion" in *Encyclopédie*, X, 1765, pp. 585-588. The author of the article was Venel, a pupil of Rouelle. The term *mixta* goes back to Beccher and Stahl, who employed it to mean the chemically irreducible substances composed of the elements or principles. Venel uses it to mean any com-pound formed of "substances simples," that is, the empirically simple substances which Lavoisier was to call "elements."

[17] See the summary table in Lavoisier's *Traité Elémentaire de Chimie* (Paris, 1789), I, p. 203. My citation is from what Duveen calls the third edition.

as cohesion, insolubility, elasticity, quantity of reactants, and the like.[18] In a series of papers the French chemist, J. L. Proust (1755-1826), working in Madrid, published careful analyses to show that Berthollet's views were incorrect. Proust agreed that the common oxides, sulphides and carbonates of the metals had the same constitution, regardless of the way they were prepared. He distinguished sharply between mixtures, with their variable compositions, and compounds; and he defined a chemical compound as "a privileged product to which nature has assigned a fixed composition." Nature, he added, never produces a compound, even through the agency of man, other than balance in hand.[19]

From this time onwards—indeed even before Proust had settled the matter[20]—textbooks of chemistry (like those of Fourcroy and Thomas Thomson), introduced each compound, not only by discussing its chemical behavior, its physical properties and its use, but where possible by giving central importance to its composition by weight. Much of the chemical work done between 1789 and 1840 consisted in efforts to determine quantitative composition of compounds with greater and greater precision.

THE ELEMENTS

What we have said about the definitions early chemists gave of familiar substances applies equally well to those substances which we now class as *elements*. Before the time of Lavoisier, only sulphur, phosphorus and the metals were known in the elementary state. These were characterized for the most part in *qualitative* terms, though, as we have seen, the weight or specific gravity of the metals was from early times sometimes included as a quantitative feature.

Yet long before Lavoisier, and certainly by the end of the 17th century, it was recognized that certain substances can be reduced to simpler ones by chemical action, and that these simpler substances could not be decomposed further. Following Beccher and Stahl, it was common practice to call these apparently simple substances *mixtes,* since it was assumed that these apparently unalterable substances were composed of such hypothetical elements as the sulphur, salt and mercury of Paracelsus, or of the Four Peripatetic Principles, earth, air, fire and water. In practice, these largely imaginary principles were ignored by chemists even before Lavoisier's day.

What Lavoisier did, when he enunciated the modern doctrine of elements,

[18] Berthollet's *Recherches sur les Lois de l'Affinité* (1801) advanced his new theory that not affinities alone, but also the masses of the reactants, determine the course of a chemical reaction. Berthollet expanded the book into the two-volume *Essai de Statique Chimique* (1803), an English translation of which by B. Lambert was published in 1804.

[19] Cited by Eric John Holmyard in *Makers of Chemistry* (Oxford, 1931), p. 237. The controversy between Berthollet and Proust is treated in most histories of chemistry; a particularly good account is to be found in Ida Freund, *The Study of Chemical Composition* (Cambridge, 1904), Chapter IV. Proust's papers in the controversy appeared in the *Journal de Physique* between 1801 and 1806. Translations of some of them appeared in *Nicolson's Journal* from 1802 to 1810.

[20] Meldrum has argued, however, that it was Dalton's atomic theory, rather than Proust's work, which led to the acceptance of the principle of constant composition. See *Memoirs of the Manchester Literary and Philosophical Society,* vol. 54, 1909-10, No. 7. The importance of analysis is stressed by Frank Greenaway, *The Biographical Approach to John Dalton* (Manchester, 1958).

was to make explicit what had been the practical assumption of chemists. Since the *mixtes* were not reducible to the so-called first principles, it seemed sensible to forget about these principles and refer to all irreducible substances as *elements* of bodies. To the list of earlier simple substances Lavoisier was able to add in 1789, from his own discoveries and those of others, four newly discovered metallic elements: manganese, molybdenum, platinum and tungsten; phosphorus and carbon; and three simple gases: oxygen, hydrogen and nitrogen (*azote*).[21]

It is interesting that he declined to include the familiar fixed alkalis (potash and soda) among the elements, though they were generally treated as simple bodies by his predecessors, for he suspected that each of them contained a metallic base which, because of a strong affinity for oxygen, could not be obtained in pure form. Yet he listed such earthy substances as lime, magnesia, baryta, alumina and silica as elements. Within a decade, two new metals, chromium and uranium, had been isolated, as well as magnesium in impure form. In the decade 1800-1810, Humphrey Davy fulfilled Lavoisier's prophecy by isolating sodium and potassium; Gay-Lussac and Thenard obtained boron; and Davy isolated barium, strontium, calcium and magnesium. In 1810 Davy proved that chlorine, a gas discovered by Scheele, was elementary.[22]

These elements or simple substances were of course still mainly defined by their appearance, and odor, taste and their chemical behavior with other substances. But already by 1802, as we saw, T. Thomson was characterizing the metallic elements by three quantitative characteristics: their specific gravity, their hardness and, where possible, their melting point. The gaseous elements (hydrogen, oxygen and nitrogen) could be characterized, in quantitative terms, by their density.

These quantitative differences served chiefly to distinguish from one another substances belonging to the same general class. What was needed was a quantitative index of chemical behavior which could be used with all classes of substances. This was found in the *combining weights* or *equivalent weights* of the elements.

Several chemists in the 18th century tried to measure accurately the amount of base required to neutralize various acids. Later workers, Wenzel and Kirwan, for example, hoped to use the weight of different bases required to neutralize a known weight of a given acid as a measure of the "affinity" of the acid for each base.[23]

A more influential series of experiments was carried out somewhat later by J. B. Richter and published between 1792 and 1802.[24] He determined the weights of various bases (lime, soda, baryta, potash and magnesia) which

[21] Lavoisier: *Traité Elémentaire de Chimie*, I, p. 203. The gases were, however, assumed to be combined with *caloric*, the weightless matter of heat.

[22] For these elements, see Mary Elvira Weeks, *Discovery of the Elements*, 6th edition, edited by Henry M. Leicester (Easton, Pa., 1956).

[23] For a discussion of Wenzel's work, see M. M. Pattison Muir, *A History of Chemical Theories and Laws* (New York and London, 1907), pp. 277-278. For Kirwan, see below note 35.

[24] For Richter see Muir, *Chemical Laws and Theories*, pp. 269-276, and Freund, *Chemical Composition*, Chapter VII.

neutralized a constant weight of each of the common acids. His experiments, to be sure, were not very accurate, and indeed he did not hesitate to correct his results to satisfy certain extravagant hypotheses of his own. But he had shown that the weight of each base which neutralizes a given quantity of an acid is constant and characteristic of the particular base. Likewise the weights of different acids neutralized by a given quantity of a certain base are characteristic of the particular acids.

In 1802 E. G. Fischer, in a note to his translation of Berthollet's *Recherches sur les lois de l'affinité*, put Richter's results in tabular form. This reference in Berthollet's important and controversial work, made Richter's results widely known and generally available.[25]

The Fischer-Richter table gave the weight equivalents of various bases that would neutralize 1000 parts of sulphuric acid. The numbers assigned to the various acids show the weights of acids necessary to neutralize the same amount of any base as could be neutralized by the 1000 parts of sulphuric acid.

Acids		*Bases*	
Hydrofluoric	427	Alumina	525
Carbonic	577	Magnesia	615
Phosphoric	979	Lime	793
Sulphuric	1000	Baryta	2222
Nitric	1409		

Here we have the first table of *equivalent weights*. For example the 525 parts by weight of alumina which will neutralize the 1000 parts of sulphuric acid, will also neutralize 577 parts of carbonic acid, 979 parts of phosphoric acid, etc.

We need hardly point out that Richter was dealing with compound substances. The full significance of his discoveries came when attempts were made to find equivalent combining weights for the *elementary* substances. It was in 1803 that the Manchester schoolmaster, John Dalton, made the discovery that was to clarify this problem. This is the *law of multiple proportions* to which I referred at the beginning of this paper. It states that if two *elements* combine to form more than one compound, the weights of one element which unite with the same weight of the other are simple multiples of one another.

We may illustrate this law by one of the instances that Dalton studied.[26] About 1804 he made an analysis of two inflammable gases, carburetted hydro-

---

[25] Berthollet included a French version of Fischer's note, with its accompanying table, in his *Essai de Statique Chimique* (1803), pp. 134-138. This was included in the English translation (*Essay of Chemical Statics*) of B. Lambert, which appeared in 1804. Fischer's table, from which the above numbers were selected for illustration, is reproduced in Henry M. Leicester and Herbert S. Klickstein, *A Source Book in Chemistry, 1400-1900,* (McGraw Hill Book Company, 1952) p. 208.

[26] For the earliest record of Dalton's experiment supporting the theory of multiple proportions, see Frank Greenaway, *op. cit.,* p. 81. The result was first reported in Dalton's "Experimental Inquiry into the proportion of the several gases or elastic fluids constituting the atmosphere," *Memoirs of the Literary and Philosophical Society of Manchester,* second series, I, p. 250.

gen (methane) and olefiant gas (ethylene), which are composed only of carbon and hydrogen, and (as later and more accurate analysis showed) in the following proportions:

	Methane	*Ethylene*
Carbon	74.85	85.62
Hydrogen	25.5	14.38

Nothing very significant emerges from these figures, which are calculated on a weight percentage basis. But if we translate them into the amounts of hydrogen which combine in the two cases with the same amount, say ten parts, of carbon, then we get:

	Methane	*Ethylene*
Carbon	10	10
Hydrogen	3.36	1.68

It is evident that marsh gas, or methane, contains just twice as much hydrogen as does ethylene. Today we give the formulas respectively as CH_4 and C_2H_4.

Dalton found other examples from his own experiments (in the case of the oxides of nitrogen, for example) and in the literature; and in 1805 stated the principle of multiple proportions and gave several examples in his first printed table of "atomic" weights.

It is not surprising that he should have presented his law of multiple proportions in the same year, 1805, in which he made his first printed reference to his atomic theory. As Berzelius later wrote in a letter to Dalton, "The theory of multiple proportions is a mystery without the atomic theory."[27] Today it is widely believed that Dalton's Law of Multiple Proportions was an inference from his atomic theory.[28] The Law, indeed, means nothing, unless it means that elements combine as separate and discrete units, each unit possessing a characteristic weight. This attribution of a definite weight to the atoms of each individual kind of element is the cardinal feature of Dalton's theory. It was surely the most important step ever taken in the quantification of chemical theory, for there is no more fundamental *quantitative theory* in chemistry than this simple notion of elementary atomic weights.

A belief in chemically distinct atoms was, of course, not original with Dalton. That matter is ultimately composed of indivisible material corpuscles, and that a mathematical divisibility *ad infinitum* does not apply to the matter of which the world is made, was one of the main tenets of the Mechanical Philoso-

---

[27] From a letter of Berzelius to Dalton, in William Charles Henry, *Memoirs of the Life and Scientific Researches of John Dalton* (London, printed for the Cavendish Society, 1854), pp. 100-101.

[28] For the origins of Dalton's atomic theory, the fundamental work is H. E. Roscoe and A. Harden, *A New View of the Origin of Dalton's Atomic Theory* (London, 1896). But see also the perceptive papers of A. N. Meldrum in the *Memoirs of the Manchester Lit-* *erary and Philosophical Society* (Vol. 55, 1910-11, Nos. III-VI and XIX). Leonard K. Nash, "The Origin of Dalton's Chemical Atomic Theory, *Isis*, 1956, *47*: 101-116, and his case study ("The Atomic-Molecular Theory") in J. B. Conant, ed., *Harvard Case Studies in Experimental Science* (2 vols., Cambridge, Mass., 1957), I, pp. 217-321. For a somewhat different interpretation, see Frank Greenaway, *op. cit.*

phy of the 17th century.[29] Throughout the 18th century, this doctrine was widely accepted by physical philosophers. In a somewhat cautious fashion— influenced by the work of Lémery, Boyle and Newton—chemists held the same view. Some writers like Boerhaave in Holland and Newton's followers in England adopted the view explicitly; but others—especially Stahl and his disciples—while agreeing that matter was ultimately corpuscular or atomic, doubted if this theory could be usefully applied to the manifold mysteries of chemical combination.[30] At least by mid-century, however, chemical atomism had made considerable headway. It was the theoretical basis of Macquer's teaching in France and of Cullen's in Scotland. Cullen, for his part, distinguished in his lectures the *physical* elements (atoms) from the *chemical* elements or principles. But unlike Stahl, to whom he was indebted for this distinction, he did not despair of making some real use of the concept of atoms in chemistry. Though he recognized that "we have never been able to reduce bodies to their Physical Elements," he taught that all changes produced in bodies by chemical experiments result from the combination and separation of these physical elements under the influence of elective attraction.[31] The *chemical* elements or principles are, by contrast, the macroscopic masses which are the end products of actual analysis in the laboratory; and these he described, in words that recall Lavoisier's later and more famous definition of elements, as the class of bodies "formed of those which have been divided as far as art can go." How the atoms of these "more practical elements" differed among themselves to account for the qualitative differences observed, Cullen was not certain, except that each kind of atom had a characteristic, and perhaps measurable, affinity or power of chemical attraction. Like Macquer, Cullen believed that these elementary atoms combined to yield corpuscles of a higher order which are the smallest physical elements to which the substance of a pure compound can be reduced.[32] These higher order corpuscles (corresponding to our modern concept of the molecule) are reducible by chemical action to the true physical elements, the indivisible atoms, of which they are compounded. In his lectures delivered after 1758, Cullen began to represent graphically these corpuscular combinations and exchanges. He seems to have been the first to do so, and in this practice he was followed by his eminent pupil, Joseph Black.[33]

[29] Marie Boas, "Establishment of the Mechanical Philosophy," *Osiris*, 1950, *10:* 413-541. See also J. R. Partington, "The Origins of the Atomic Theory," *Annals of Science*, 1939, *4:* 245-267. Still worth consulting is Ernst Bloch, "Die Antike Atomistik in der neueren Geschichte der Chemie," *Isis*, 1913, *1:* 377-415.

[30] See P. Duhem, *Le Mixte*, pp. 38-42; cf. Hélène Metzger, "La Philosophie de la matière chez Stahl et ses Disciples," *Isis*, 1926, *8:* 427-464; reprinted in her *Newton, Stahl, Boerhaave et la Doctrine Chimique* (Paris, 1930), pp. 99-148.

[31] Cullen Lectures, Paisley MS.

[32] Macquer distinguished the *parties constituantes* (corresponding to the atoms or physical elements of Cullen) from the *parties intégrantes*, or molecules. See especially the article "Aggrégation" in his *Dictionnaire de Chymie*, ed., 1766. A good summary of his views is given by Marie Boas, "Structure of Matter and Chemical Theory in the Seventeenth and Eighteenth Centuries," in Clagett, *Critical Problems in the History of Science* (Madison, Wis., 1959), pp. 499-514.

[33] For Black's diagrams, see my "Commentary on the Papers of Cyril Stanley Smith and Marie Boas," in Marshall Clagett, ed.: *Critical Problems*, pp. 515-518. For the only printed description of Cullen's scheme of graphical representation, see John Thomson,

It occurred to none of these early exponents of an atomic theory before Dalton that the distinguishing character of the different elementary atoms might be their weight, and that this differential character, if measurable, might in some way be correlated with the varieties of chemical behavior. Yet it was clear, if Stahl's strictures against the use of mechanical principles were to be refuted, and if the atomic hypothesis was to prove of real explanatory value to the chemist, that some distinguishable and, if possible, quantifiable, attribute of the particles must be found which could be correlated with the observed qualitative differences in the behavior of the different *chemical* elements.

The earliest attempt by chemists—Lémery is the classical instance—to differentiate the atoms of different substances had been by assigning them hypothetical shapes. This solution called forth the scorn of Stahl and his followers, and was equally unpopular with the followers of Newton. In the second half of the 18th century, the answer was commonly sought in the concept of a characteristic attraction or affinity, a property that appeared to admit of quantification. Cullen would seem to have been the first to explore this in systematic fashion.[34] In the diagrams he used to illuminate for his students the phenomenon of double decomposition ("double elective attraction"), Cullen used letters (or as his biographer called them, algebraic symbols) to represent the force of attraction between the corpuscles of the reactants and the resulting compounds. A great deal of misdirected effort continued to be expended up to the time of Dalton to perfect the tables of elective affinities (or elective attractions) and to assign numerical values for the affinities between pairs of substances as revealed by their places in these tables.[35]

Less familiar, probably, is the isolated attempt of Guyton de Morveau to combine a consideration of atomic shape with the problem of elective attraction, along lines apparently first suggested by Buffon. In 1765, Buffon objected in print to Newton's view that the laws of chemical attraction must be different from the law of gravitation operating in the solar system. The great naturalist insisted that the law was identical throughout the universe with respect to the roles of mass and distance, and that if different effects sometimes

---

An Account of the Life, Lectures, and Writings of William Cullen, M.D., 2 vols. (Edinburgh and London, 1859), I, pp. 44-45 and 570-571. The earliest *published* diagrams of this sort are those of William Higgins in his *A Comparative View of the Phlogistic and Antiphlogistic Theories*, 1789. Cf. Partington, *loc. cit.*, pp. 272-276.

[34] Though Macquer (in his *Elémens de Chymie Théorique*, 1749) was the first chemical pedagogue to build his basic theory on the doctrine of affinities, Cullen was the earliest to make "elective attractions," in the Newtonian sense, the fundamental doctrine of his teachings. Macquer did not become an attractionist (and then only tentatively) until the publication of his *Dictionnaire* in 1766. We may owe the phrase "elective attractions" to Cullen; he certainly used it before Tobern Bergman gave

it wide currency. The Paisley MS of Cullen Lectures, where this term is used, dates from about 1757 (certainly between 1753 and 1758) and thus anticipates the appearance of Bergman's work on affinity by about seventeen years.

[35] For the work of Kirwan and Guyton de Morveau see Muir, *op. cit.*, pp. 389-391. Kirwan used specific gravities of aqueous solutions of mineral acids to determine the weights of acid involved; he then titrated these against carefully weighed quantities of different bases. He believed the weights of alkali required to saturate a given weight of acid to be a measure of the affinity of the acid for the base. The whole problem was reviewed by Guyton de Morveau in his long article, actually a monograph, on "Affinité" in the *Encyclopédie Méthodique* (1786).

were observed, it must be because at very small distances the shape of the attracting particles exerted a pronounced effect. He suggested, therefore, that the shape of the elementary particles could be inferred if the law of attraction for different substances were determined by experiment.[36] This evidently stimulated Guyton de Morveau, a friend and disciple of Buffon, to urge in 1772 that a careful study of crystallization might disclose the shapes of atoms, and allow the forces of attraction to be calculated.[37]

None of these lines of endeavor, it is unnecessary to emphasize, provided the sought-for physical specification, let alone the quantification, of the elementary atoms. This was the achievement of John Dalton. His famous theory, it is now well established, was a by-product of his interest in meteorology and his study of the gases in the atmosphere. In 1801, having begun to investigate the behavior of mixed gases, he enunciated his Law of Partial Pressures. This law made sense only if a mixture of gases is a true mixture, and not— as many chemists believed—a loose form of chemical combination. It made sense, too, only if one assumed the elastic fluids to be made up of particles, the particles of one fluid being virtually unaffected by the presence of other particles of different kinds in the mixture. This behavior was confirmed by experiments on the diffusion of two gases through each other, and on the solubility of different gases in water. In particular Dalton believed his experiments had shown that solubility depended on the *weight* of the ultimate particles of the several gases: "those whose particles are lightest and single being least absorbable, and the others more, according as they increase in weight and complexity." Appended to this paper was a "Table of the relative weights of the ultimate particles of gaseous and other bodies."[38]

It was by a technique not differing appreciably from Richter's, using the concept of equivalent weights, that Dalton was able, from the quantitative constitution of relatively simple compounds, to infer the combining weights of *elementary substances*. Whether the work of Richter, to which Dalton later acknowledged a substantial debt, was known to him as early as the year 1803 cannot be definitely determined. But neither can the possibility be dismissed.[39] At all events the method employed may well be illustrated at this point, much as it was presented in the post-Daltonian textbooks and after reasonably accurate analyses became available.

There were obvious advantages in starting with elements like oxygen, hydrogen, or sulphur which combine with a great many other substances. By comparing the figures for the percentages compositions of different substances containing the same elements, equivalent weights can be determined.

[36] Buffon, *Oeuvres Complètes,* ed. Flourens, T. III, pp. 419-421.

[37] Guyton's discussion of crystallization as a clue to the forces of attraction was published as an essay in his *Digressions Académiques* in 1772. The significance of this work was recently pointed out by W. A. Smeaton in a paper entitled "The contributions of L. B. Guyton de Morveau to the theory of chemical affinity," which was read in September, 1959, to the *Colloque* on the History of Eighteenth Century Chemistry, held in Paris at the Conservatoire des Arts et Métiers.

[38] Dalton's paper "On the Absorption of Gases by Water and other Liquids," which contains his first printed table of "atomic" weights, was read to the Manchester Philosophical Society on 21 October 1803. When he published it in 1805 in the *Memoirs* of the Society, Dalton added a footnote stating that his conjecture about the relation of weight to solubility appeared to him "less probable."

[39] See my "Some Daltonian Doubts," *Isis* (to appear).

For example, the percentage composition of water was commonly given as:

Hydrogen	11.19
Oxygen	88.81
	100.00

Thus, reducing hydrogen to unity, 8 parts of oxygen combine approximately with 1 part of hydrogen, more accurately 7.93 parts of oxygen with one of hydrogen. But it is preferable to have a whole number for oxygen, instead of hydrogen, since oxygen occurs in many more inorganic compounds than does hydrogen.

It is thus advisable to take oxygen as 8.000 and hydrogen as 1.008, and convert all percentage compositions by weight into equivalents of the elements. The percentage compositions of two common oxides are as follows:

Lead oxide		Copper oxide	
Lead	92.83	Copper	79.89
Oxygen	7.17	Oxygen	20.11

Converted to *equivalents*, these figures yield the weights of lead and copper that combine with 8 parts of oxygen, or:

Lead	103.55	Copper	31.78
Oxygen	8.00	Oxygen	8.00

These are the combining weights of lead and copper. Similarly, by a comparison of other simple compounds, equivalent weights were established for mercury, carbon, sulphur, and all the common elements.

Dalton was convinced that his combining weights—the actual figures he gave were several times emended—were proportional to the weights of the individual atoms. He therefore published his results as a table of *Atomic Weights*, which underwent a number of revisions. Yet it was apparent that nobody could really know how many atoms in fact combined to produce even the simplest substances. Take water, for example: the atomic weight of 8 was for a time assigned to oxygen on the assumption that water was formed when one atom of hydrogen combined with one atom of oxygen. If, however, as some people suspected, there were two atoms of hydrogen to one of oxygen, the atomic weight of the latter would be 16, not 8. Yet Dalton seemed quite confident that he had determined the true atomic proportional weights. He argued on the basis of his Law of Multiple Proportions that if there is only one known compound of the substances A and B, this can be presumed to be *binary*, with one atom of A combining with one atom of B. When two compounds exist, one is probably binary (A+B) and the other ternary (either A+2B or 2A+B).

So water, which appeared to exist only as a single compound of oxygen and hydrogen, was assumed to be binary, composed of one atom of each element. Hence the weight of oxygen was taken to be 8 not 16, the value accepted today.

Dalton's theory was enthusiastically adopted by the young Swedish chemist, J. J. Berzelius. About 1807 Berzelius had been stimulated by the work of Richter—and here the influence of Richter is beyond dispute—to carry out careful analyses of various compounds. Soon after, he learned of Dalton's atomic hypothesis and adopted it fervently. His extensive and careful experiments did much to secure acceptance for the atomic theory, and his Table of so-called Atomic Weights soon took the place of Dalton's.

Some of Dalton's influential contemporaries flatly refused to accept his theory; or if they did accept it, they could not agree to the identification of these combining weights with atomic weights, for the reason I have mentioned. Gay-Lussac spoke only of "rapports" between the elements. Sir Humphrey Davy, too, was at first outspoken in opposition to Dalton, refused to use the term "atom," and referred to these combining weights as "proportional numbers." W. H. Wollaston, an early convert to the atomic theory, introduced the neutral term "chemical equivalent" or "equivalent weight" which came to have a wide currency.

The year after Dalton published Part I of his *New System of Chemical Philosophy* (1808), and set forth in some detail his atomic theory, Gay-Lussac performed a series of experiments on gases which, properly interpreted, offered a solution to the difficulty.[40] He discovered the important fact that when gases react together they do so in fixed, and sometimes multiple, proportions *by volume*. Thus hydrogen combines with oxygen in a volume ratio of 2 to 1. It seemed to follow, as Berzelius and others pointed out, that equal volumes of gases (under the same conditions of temperature and pressure) might contain the same number of atoms. If so, these combining volumes gave at once the number of atoms that combined to form a compound particle of the product. There were difficulties however, and these were not finally resolved until 1860. In this year Cannizzaro drew attention to the work of his countryman, Avogadro, who as early as 1811 had explained Gay-Lussac's results by assuming that gases were made up of diatomic particles, or molecules, not free atoms.[41] It is these molecules which exist in equal numbers in equal volumes of gases. Now it was possible, by the use of Avogadro's hypothesis, to use the combining volumes of gases (as even Berzelius had done for a few cases) to determine the number of atoms of elementary gases which combine together, and by this means to determine atomic weights having genuine validity. In consequence the Belgian chemist, Jean Servais Stas, was encouraged to devote his scientific career, from 1860 onwards, to the very accurate determination of atomic weights of the familiar, and of newly discovered, elements. Stas's results were still further refined by the improved methods devised by others, among them T. W. Richards at Harvard, beginning about 1883. Richards, like other chemists, was puzzled by the fact that the atomic weights, when accurately determined, were not always whole numbers. Thus the most pre-

---

[40] For Gay-Lussac's law of the combining volumes of gases, and a summary of his experiments, see Freund, *op. cit.*, Chapter XI, and Muir, *op. cit.*, pp. 102-106.

[41] Avogadro's hypothesis is discussed in all the principal histories of chemistry. But see also C. Graebe: "Der Entwicklungsgang der Avogadroschen Theorie," *J. prakt Chem.*, Neue Folge, 1913, *87:* 145-208.

cise methods gave an atomic weight for lead of 207.2. Independently of Soddy, Richards demonstrated that lead derived from uranium-rich ores had an atomic weight of 206, while that from thorium ores had a weight of 208. Thus ordinary lead was seen to be a mixture of these two *isotopes*, of two kinds of atoms having identical chemical properties but differing slightly in weight.

The full meaning of this discovery emerged only from a study of the so-called *Periodic Table of the Elements*, the final achievement of this early work in chemical quantification.

Just as Stas's results were yielding a highly reliable set of atomic weights, various workers were struck by certain recurring patterns and groupings observed when the elements were ordered according to their atomic weights.[42] A French geologist, Béguyer de Chancourtois, arranged the elements as an ascending spiral line traced around a cylinder. He showed that when this was done, certain chemically related elements fell in a vertical line on one side of this helix. About the same time, J. A. R. Newlands reported in the early 1860's that if the elements are arrayed according to what he called the *atomic number* (the serial number of an element in the atomic weight series), chemically related substances recur every eighth step. This was his famous "Law of Octaves."

In 1869 two distinguished scientists, Dmitri Mendeleev in Russia and Lothar Meyer in Germany independently worked out a pattern in which this recurring, or periodic, feature was clearly evident. Both tables showed what Mendeleev called the "periodic law": namely, that the properties of the elements are in periodic dependence upon their atomic weights.

Suppose you order the elements according to their atomic weights. Imagine yourself recording the symbols of the elements on a long tape, starting with hydrogen (atomic number 1) and continuing up to heavy elements like uranium, with an atomic weight of about 238. Then suppose you take a pair of scissors and cut this tape into eight or ten shorter strips and place them one after the other below each other. If the strips are of the proper length, the elements with similar chemical properties will fall into vertical columns or *groups*. The lighter elements will occupy the upper strips or periods, and the heavier elements the lower ones. The electropositive elements (the alkali metals, the alkaline earths) will fall on the left-hand side of the diagram, and the electronegative elements (the halogens for example, and sulphur and oxygen) will fall to the right. As one moves from left to right across one period, the elements at first form strongly basic oxides, then more weakly basic ones, then weakly acidic oxides (as in the case of silicon and carbon) and finally strongly acid oxides, like those of phosphorus and sulphur.

More striking is the property of the vertical columns or groups. In each, the elements closely resemble one another chemically. For example the first group or column contains elements having a valence of 1, and large atomic volumes (atomic weight / density). The second group contains elements with

---

[42] A good account is given in F. P. Venable, *The Development of the Periodic Law* (Easton, Pa., 1896), and by George Rudorf, *Das Periodische System, seine Geschichte und* *Bedeutung für die Chemische Systematik* (Hamburg and Leipzig, 1904). Freund (pp. 145-151) has a good section on the work of Stas.

a valence of 2, and smaller atomic volumes, and so on.[43] But this is not the whole story. Elements falling in the same *group* resemble one another closely in a wide variety of qualitative and quantitative characteristics: their chemical behavior, their boiling or melting points, conductivity for heat and electricity, magnetic susceptibility, appearance and texture, hardness, color of the salts in aqueous solution, and crystal form.

Even with his incomplete table, Mendeleev was able to show that this quantitative ordering yielded a most extraordinary amount of qualitative information. Most spectacularly of all, it led to the prediction of the chemical properties, the qualitative as well as quantitative characteristics, of as yet undiscovered elements.

Mendeleev noted in particular three vacant places in his table, in the groups below boron, aluminum and silicon. He called these respectively eka-boron, eka-aluminum and eka-silicon, and made bold predictions of the properties that would be observed when and if they were found. These predictions were confirmed with the subsequent discovery of scandium (1879), gallium (1874) and germanium (1885).[44] The chemical and physical properties turned out to be almost precisely as Mendeleev had predicted from his table: specific gravity and volatility; solution in acids and alkalis; formation of oxides with certain characteristics, and of salts having certain solubilities and crystal form.

What emerged most significantly from the tables of Mendeleev and Meyer was a new and highly significant numerical tag assigned to the various elements: the *atomic number*. This is simply the ordinal number marking the place of the element in the ascending scale of atomic weights. This soon turned out, when the group relationships of the table were carefully studied, to be more significant to the chemist than even the atomic weight itself. Thus Mendeleev noted that two elements, whose atomic weights had been accurately determined, appeared to fall in the wrong groups, if judged by what was known of their chemical properties. Iodine, for example, fell into Group VI with oxygen and sulphur, instead of in Group VII with the other halogens. Being a chemist, always alert to qualitative characteristics, Mendeleev interchanged the positions of iodine and tellurium in his table. The chemical relationships were thus straightened out, but at this point in the ascending order of atomic weights, a lighter element was placed after a heavier one.

It thus emerged that the *atomic number* was a quantity of profound significance. The ordering of the elements by atomic weights, and the periodizing by cutting the main strip, had served the purpose of revealing new and mysterious quantitative relationships among the elements.

Not long afterwards, because of the work of the physicists, a physical mean-

---

[43] A fuller account than was possible in this paper would have included the idea of valency, developed chiefly by Edward Frankland (1825-1899) and August Kekulé (1829-1896). The idea of a definite combining capacity could emerge when a clear distinction was made between the equivalent weight and the true atomic weight. Valency is measured by the atomic weight divided by the equivalent weight. Several chemists (among them Du-

mas, Liebig and Laurent) saw the necessity for this distinction, but the idea was first clearly put forward by Frankland in 1852. The theory of valency was primarily the achievement of organic chemists, and their most important contribution to chemical quantification.

[44] For the discovery of these elements, see Mary Elvira Weeks, *op. cit.*, Chapter 25.

ing was attached to the atomic number. Niels Bohr advanced his theory of atomic constitution which described the atom of each element as composed of a heavy positively charged nucleus, surrounded by a characteristic number of light, negatively charged electrons. The atomic weight was seen to be largely accounted for by the mass of this central nucleus, but the chemical properties depended on the electron atmosphere and on the electrical properties of the atom. The atomic number was shown to be related to the number of electrons surrounding the nucleus of a given kind of atom. This, since the electron was assigned a unit charge, was the same as the positive charge on the nucleus.

The periodic table, the final triumph of quantification in the older chemistry, was the last and most impressive consequence of a long effort to apply weighing and measurement to distinguish with ever greater precision the qualitative differences between chemical substances. This process began with the quantitative definition of chemical substances. It led to quantitative definitions of related groups and classes of chemical substances. Quantitative factors, too, provided the only reliable criteria for the purity of substances. The study of the precise elementary constitution of a wide variety of relatively simple substances, led to discovering quantitative differentia for the chemical elements, the chemical equivalents, and eventually to determining the true atomic weights of the elements. And lastly when these atomic weights were determined with sufficient accuracy and for a large enough number of substances, it emerged that chemical properties of elements could be correlated, in periodic fashion, with a quantitative index called the atomic number.

At this point the line between chemistry and physics began to fade away. On this new frontier each science required the other. To understand the structure of the atom, the physicists of the early 20th century needed to contemplate Mendeleev's table, and were obliged to take into consideration those qualitative differences which it has been the chemists' goal, during the past century or more, to quantify as thoroughly as possible.

The History of Quantification in Medical Science

By Richard H. Shryock*

ONE must introduce this theme with brief statements of what is meant by "quantification" and by "medicine." This is desirable, not to split hairs but simply to make clear what meanings are employed. Quantification here connotes the use of measurements and, in some cases, of related mathematics; though instances of what might be termed quasi quantification—without figures—will be noted.

"Medicine" and "medical science" are not easy to define. The latter, for example, may be conceived teleologically as the sum of those elements in various sciences or pseudosciences which have been used in order to maintain or restore health. This connotation, however, seems to relate medicine only to applied science, and so rules out "pure" science in such biologic disciplines as physiology and pathology. If, on the other hand, medical science is defined as all science relating to health and disease—with or without humane purposes—the concept is so broad as to limit its usefulness. Sanitary engineering, for example, relates to disease, but comment on its measurements would lure us into physical science and technology.

One falls back, then, on a quite arbitrary definition which will do well enough for the present purpose. We shall consider medical science as consisting of certain disciplines—here taken for granted—which have been deemed of value in medical education; that is, (1) anatomy and physiology, (2) pathology, (3) therapeutics, and (4) hygiene, including public hygiene. The orientation of these disciplines has been largely biologic, and attempts have long been made to equate such biology with physical science. At the other end of the medical spectrum, however, the fields noted involve social and/or psychologic considerations. The problems of measurement in some aspects of medicine are therefore those of physics or chemistry; in others, those of sociology or psychology. One may then inquire, what purpose is served by setting medicine up as a separate category?

Speaking generally, the significance of medicine in this connection lessens as we approach the present. Quantification in biochemistry over at least the last century, for example, may be largely referred to the history of chemistry. But there are two aspects of the medical story which merit attention, the one historical and the other logical in nature. Historically, prior to the nineteenth century and in some degree in even later periods, physicians pursued medical science under the impression that it was a distinct field in content as well as in purpose. Hence the subject lends itself readily to historical analysis.

* American Philosophical Society.

Logically, medical history is suggestive because it presents a single guild concerned with several of the traditional areas of knowledge. Physicians have often recognized the importance of psychic as well as of biologic factors in disease; and, over at least the last hundred years, one brave soul after another has announced that medicine "is really a social science." It is not surprising, in view of the usual role of quantification, that one of these aspects of medical science in which reliable measures became available was apt to advance more rapidly than one in which they did not, but the outcomes were sometimes surprising. Certain social aspects of medicine, for example, became susceptible to measurement earlier than did some of the physical or biologic elements.

Medical scientists have had to deal with more subtle matters than the mere spread of their interests across major fields. They have also been confronted, as individuals, with problems which simultaneously presented biologic, social, and/or psychologic components. This situation, common enough in such matters as disease causation, is usually still dealt with in nonquantitative terms and, if so, does not concern us here. But there have also been problems in which biologic or physical components seemed susceptible to quantification while the psychologic were not; and in such instances the tendency was to measure physical variables and to overlook the nonphysical—as in early studies of the force of the heart pump. Experience of this sort illustrates the confusion which may result when quantification invades one aspect of a field earlier than it does another.

The word "invades" is used advisedly here, since advocates of measurement in medicine often announced with enthusiasm that they would "take over" hitherto nonquantitative domains. Such challenges elicited an equally spirited defense of old, qualitative realms. There was much to be said for both sides, but the contest seems to have been unusually protracted in medicine—the invaders sometimes bogging down or even being thrown out, as it were, in subsequent periods. The ups and downs in this methodologic warfare were more marked in medicine than in the strictly physical disciplines, and may be explained in part by the complex content of medical science. Whether the social sciences have gone through analogous experiences is a question best left to those more familiar with these disciplines.

The primordial use of medical measures was probably in what we would term pharmacology. For all I know, primitives may have employed some sort of counting in preparing poisons or prescriptions. It is a truism that certain properties of things, such as length, weight, and volume, were early found to be measurable in terms of some common standard—eventually in numerals. Ancient records reveal extensive measurements of this sort in relation to drugs. In the Ebers papyrus of about 1500 B.C., for example, are noted almost a thousand prescriptions used in Egyptian medicine; and measures are given for about 60 per cent of those used externally, and for some 85 per cent of those employed internally.[1] Many prescriptions were compounded, but it is not clear whether exact ratios as well as data on weight or volume were involved.

Such methods in pharmacology may be taken for granted in connection with

[1] C. D. Leake, *The Old Egyptian Medical Papyri* (Lawrence, Kansas, 1952), pp. 28f.

the classical and medieval civilizations which ensued in the Western World.[2] Most of this sort of thing was doubtless empirical in origin and continued on that level; but by classical times theories about numbers or about mathematics in general at times influenced pharmacology. Perhaps there was a Pythagorean or Platonic background, for example, to Galen's elaboration of a "fantastic system" of numerical relations between drugs and the human body. Both were not only hot, cold, etcetera (in conformity with Greek physics and pathology), but each of these qualities exhibited four degrees of action—with gradations within each degree. Galen recognized the need for a point of reference in comparing heats but did not construct a thermometer. Presumably, then, he depended on his senses in observing the gradations noted.

Such an ascription of numerical values to subjective impressions, which precluded verification by others, was an approach toward quantification which, so to speak, never arrived. It continued to be popular, however, during the early Middle Ages, under the influence of neo-Pythagorean and alchemical views. Medieval physicians, indeed, quite commonly related drugs to an assumed scale of hot and cold.[3] This aided them in following the Galenic view that diseases were cured by opposites—a cold disease by hot drugs, and so on. As my colleague, Dr. Temkin, has noted, we still follow this idea in dealing with the common "cold."

Whether the fact that ancient physicians measured drugs suggested the possibility of also measuring patients is a matter of surmise. With the exception of developments at Alexandria about 300 B.C., there seems to have been no general trend in classical times toward the measurement of anatomic, physiologic, or even clinical phenomena. But Greek medical thinkers were certainly aware of such possibilities, for seemingly isolated instances did occur. A few well-known examples may be recalled in passing. In clinical matters, for example, there was in the Hippocratic literature a counting of days re the critical points in fevers. On a broader scale, crises in child health were said to occur at 40 days, at 7 months, and at 7 years.[4]

More interesting and less apt to reflect number mysticism were attempts made at Alexandria to measure physiologic behavior. Thus, about the third century B.C., Erasistratus weighed the intake and outgo of birds and found a loss of weight "perceptible only to the reason," thereby anticipating seventeenth-century work on the "insensible perspiration."[5] Here an actual discovery could be credited to measurements. The phenomenon revealed by measures was not apparent to the senses—a very early instance of this sort. Even if the Greek scientist had had an instrument which revealed perspiration to his vision, it would not have given him such precise information as did his balances. Much modern science has likewise demonstrated, through measurements and related mathematics, phenomena which are "perceptible only to the reason."

[2] See, e.g., H. E. Sigerist, "Masse u. Gewichte in den medizinischen Texten des frühen Mittelalters," *Kyklos*, 1930, *3*: 439-445.

[3] O. Temkin, "Medieval and Graeco-Arabic Alchemy," *Bull. Hist. Med.*, 1955, *29*: 141. See also A. C. Crombie, *Augustine to Galileo* ... (London, 1952), pp. 259f., 264.

[4] H. E. Sigerist, "Progress of Ideas Regarding ... Infant Mortality," *Bull. Hist. Med.*, 1940, *8*: 547ff.

[5] W.H.S. Jones, *Medical Writings of Anonymous Londiensis* (Cambridge, 1947), p. 89.

Erasistratus is also said to have devised a crude instrument for measuring respiration: his interest in applying this sort of method to body processes must have had a considerable range. That he was not unique in this respect, moreover, is indicated by the work of a fellow Alexandrian, Herophilus, who measured the rate of the pulse by use of the water clock.[6] Yet such interests lapsed thereafter, not to be revived in any significant manner until the fifteenth century A.D.

The brief appearance of physiologic measurements about 300 B.C. was but one expression of the insights of the Alexandrian "school"; Herophilus was a great anatomist, and Erasistratus a brilliant physiologist and pathologist. These facts suggest that it was only when men were doing important qualitative work that the possibility of employing measures for anything but the obvious occurred to them. It seems unlikely that the reverse was true, that is, that sudden progress was made when men measured as a matter of principle and became discoverers simply by virtue of a superior method. This question will be reconsidered when discussing the seventeenth century.

There is no need to explain here the lapse of measurements at Alexandria soon after 300 B.C., or the general decline of medicine after Galen's time in the second century A.D. But one may raise the question as to why quantification was apparently so rare throughout the whole span of classical medicine? The question is related or at least analogous to the similar one concerning experimentation. Classical scholars will have the final word, but one may make suggestions in the present context.

Among possible explanations are the following theses: (1) the records are incomplete; many instances of quantification have been lost; (2) qualitative knowledge was so meagre that phenomena susceptible to measurement could not be identified; (3) social and professional conditions inhibited research of any kind; (4) there was a conviction that measures (except of drugs) could not in the nature of the case have much bearing on the healing art.

Point one, above, does not seem promising. Point two certainly has some validity: one could hardly do blood counts when the blood cells were themselves unknown. Yet this obvious fact hardly explains why there were not further quantitative studies of the sort actually begun by the Alexandrians. Point three is also valid enough for the mass of practitioners, but does not make clear why so favored an individual as Galen did not become more intrigued by quantification. Here one turns for explanations to the so-called intellectual climate of the times; men seem to have been convinced that they could determine the function of each organ or the nature of each "clinical picture" by the use of their senses alone. Why, then, steal time from a busy practice to experiment or measure—especially when such diversions were of no apparent aid to that practice?

The outlook noted in point four is said to have appeared early in Greek medicine. The French medical authority, Cabanis, in 1798 quoted Hippocrates as having declared to practitioners:[7]

[6] F. H. Garrison, *History of Medicine*, 4th ed. (Philadelphia, 1929), p. 103. See also E. A. Underwood, "The History of the Quantitative Approach in Medicine," *Brit. Med. Bull.*, 1951, 7: 265-274.

[7] P.J.G. Cabanis, *Du Degre de Certitude de la Médecine* (Paris, 1798), p. 117.

You can discover no measure, no weight, no form of calculation, to which you can refer your judgments in order to give them absolute certainty. In our art there exists no certainty except in our sensations.

Such a statement, if authentic, implies that there were already those—perhaps inspired by Pythagorean ideas—who *wished* to measure clinical phenomena. But the Hippocratic reply reveals the view that human behavior, biologic or otherwise, eludes quantification.

This outlook, to be echoed many centuries thereafter, can hardly have encouraged medical measurements. We are also told that, later in the Greek era, the Aristotelian emphasis upon taxonomy inhibited analytic studies of biologic phenomena—and, with them, any quantification above the level of classification. The same generalization can be applied to the early Middle Ages, insofar as any original studies were carried on in the Christian world.

Most biologic research (including medical) continued in the Aristotelian tradition during the later Middle Ages, that is, was a matter of nonquantitative descriptions and classifications. But several influences—Neo-Platonism, Arabic mathematics, revived classical texts—were associated with a revolt against Aristotle in physics and mathematics. Out of this revolt emerged an interest in experiment and induction, and the idea that certain qualities of things—such as weight—could be expressed quantitatively in numerals. These procedures, applied to physics, brought statics to life in the form of dynamics, and Galileo would "take it from there."

Meantime, the same philosophers who were interested in the quantification of physics or astronomy, occasionally applied that method to biologic phenomena. These efforts were sometimes naive, as when it was assumed that the "health" of an individual was a quality even as was weight, and that the former like the latter could be measured on a scale. We now speak of "positive health" as something more than "the mere absence of disease," but no one has yet come up with a means for measuring it.

It is interesting, in passing, that the early vista of a quantitative medicine inspired something of the optimism which would become more common in the 1600's. As early as 1540, it was declared that medicine could be made as perfect as Copernicus had made astronomy. Such views were ridiculed by the humanists of the day, much as the iatrophysics of the seventeenth century would be ridiculed by *its* opponents.

More significant than this dress-rehearsal for a future controversy was the actual quantitative work done in the medical field before 1600. Notable, for example, was that of Nicholas Cusanus, who as early as 1450 included in his work on statics references to both pulse and respiratory frequency in health and disease.[8] He also urged that the purity or other qualities of body fluids—blood, urine, etc.—be tested by weight. Indeed, Cusanus was probably the source from whom later writers derived the idea of testing urine for specific gravity. In the seventeenth century, Van Helmont—an able chemist—held that such testing would throw light on the diagnosis and treatments of illness.

One notes, in this latter connection, a tendency common to much early

[8] Comment thereon will be found in N. Flaxman, "The History of Heart Block," *Bull. Hist. Med.,* 1937, 5: 115f.

quantitative work in medicine, that is, the use of measurements in a search for immediately useful means of prevention or cure. And here two circumstances joined to make quantification the servant of speculation rather than a method for checking on that process. First, the ignorance of qualitative physiology made it difficult to formulate hypotheses which were susceptible to quantitative tests. Van Helmont simply assumed that the physical properties of urine reflected supposed pathologic conditions. Second, since physicians tended to evaluate all things by their bearing on cures, they were apt to read such possibilities into any measurements which seemed feasible. They either sought measures for their immediate utility, or—if they actually measured basic processes—at once assumed that these processes could be made the bases of diagnosis and therapy.

Occasionally, quantitative tests were made to check on hypotheses in a manner analogous to procedures in physics. Van Helmont, for example, performed a so-called willow tree experiment in order to verify an old gnostic-alchemical doctrine that all body substance derives from water.[9] But here, again, the prevailing ignorance of chemistry and biology rendered the results meaningless from the modern viewpoint.

By the seventeenth century, however, the situation became more promising. The influence of predecessors who had sought to measure body substances or processes—of Cusanus, Van Helmont, and also Paracelsus—led to increasing efforts at quantification by such physicians as the Englishman Fludd. At the same time, quantitative advances in physics exerted an influence on medical thought which has continued to operate ever since that time. In Harvey's research on the circulation, partly quantitative in nature, there was a genuine check on hypotheses based on a long accumulation of necessary qualitative knowledge of anatomy and related physiology. Garrison remarks that Harvey's research (1628) was the first in biology to involve mathematical proof and exact calculations.

Quantitative advances in physics and astronomy, it will be recalled, revived a Greek view that all Nature could be interpreted in terms of matter and motion. Since there were no such distinctions between scientific fields as now obtain, the mechanistic outlook appeared almost if not quite as early in medicine as in the physical sciences. In some cases the same leaders applied their talents to both areas. Galileo, for example, measured the pulse and body temperature; and Descartes, who was a physiologist, provided a model for mechanical medicine in his concept of the animal machine.

Meantime, advances in chemistry, from Van Helmont and Paracelsus to Boyle, inspired an analogous chemical orientation, in which the animal body was viewed as a glorified retort rather than as a machine. One may sum up this whole outlook in the words of the Italian physician, Baglivi, who declared in 1696 that "the human body ... is truly nothing else but a Complex of Chemico-Mechanical Motions."

Hence there developed among the so-called "moderns" enthusiastic expectations of what mechanical or chemical approaches, combining experiments

---

[9] I am indebted to Dr. Walter Pagel of London for comments on Cusanus and Van Helmont. See also Crombie (note 3, above), 264, 268.

with measures and calculations, could achieve in the medical as well as in the physical sciences. Descartes declared that if mankind was perfectible, it would be through medicine that means to this end would be found.[10]

In due time there arose self-conscious "schools" of iatrophysics and iatrochemistry, which focused their interests at first on anatomy and physiology. In the case of the iatrophysicists, for example, the heart was viewed as a pump, the stomach as a churn, the muscles as levers, and so on. Qualitative anatomy had reached a point which rendered these views plausible and which, in the case of the heart, made it possible to check its function in a partly quantitative manner. The demonstration of the circulation led to further physiologic research, and its value was therefore not limited to this one discovery.

When, however, the mechanists moved on to more difficult problems—such as that of the force of the heart pump—their results were widely diverse and consequently confusing.[11] We may say now that they failed to allow for all variables, and also that they lacked adequate devices and techniques.

In other cases, even of genuine discoveries, quantitative findings seemed isolated. This was true, for example, of Santorio's ingenious weighings of the invisible perspiration. In a sense, these confirmed the early work of Erasistratus, but what then? One knew that there was such a thing as invisible perspiration but this fact did not fit in with any general knowledge of physiology. The aftermath, as usual, was much speculation about the role of this excretion in pathology and its consequent bearing on therapy.[12] Subsequent studies of the same sort, such as those of Dr. Lining in South Carolina, seem to have been motivated by a direct search for means of preventing or curing disease, rather than by an interest in physiology as such.

If one examines the writings of iatrophysicists, moreover, the various diagrams or computations—such as those representing muscular levers or calculations of the force exerted by a single muscle—do not suggest the need for new theories or confirm old ones. Or, if hypotheses are suggested, they are speculative ones not themselves susceptible to experimental checks. Apart from such speculation, the quantitative data given are largely descriptive and point in no particular direction.[13] One gets the impression that these men were at times measuring for the sake of measuring: that the means had become an end in itself.

Perhaps such procedure may occur in any field. But it is to be expected especially in an area wherein a demand for quantification arises before qualitative preparation has been adequate. And that situation may arise if quantification in a prepared field is so successful that it is imitated in an unprepared one. This was, to a considerable degree, the case with physiology and pathology in the seventeenth and early eighteenth centuries.

Learned physicians were trained in mathematics, and were often aware of

[10] E. S. Haldane, *Life of René Descartes* (London, 1905), p. 126.

[11] Sir Gilbert Blane, *Elements of Medical Logic* (London, 1819), pp. 73ff.; Sir Michael Foster, *Lectures on the History of Physiology* (Cambridge, 1924), pp. 73ff.

[12] A. Castiglioni, *A History of Medicine*, translated and edited by E. B. Krumbhaar

(New York, 1941), p. 537.

[13] See, e.g., J. A. Borelli, *De Motu Animalium* (Hagae, 1743), (first ed., 1679), *passim*. For detailed analyses of the work of such iatrophysicists as Baglivi, Borelli, Pitcairne, etc., see Charles Daremberg, *Histoire des Sciences Médicales* (Paris, II, 1870), pp. 735-953.

the progress made in astronomy and physics via mathematics and measurement. They also realized, in some cases, just wherein the advantage of these methods lay. Thus Giorgio Baglivi explained to physicians in 1696 the reasons for striking progress in astronomy. There had been in that field, he noted, various hypotheses on which astronomers differed. But they all agreed on the prediction of eclipses, since there was no refuting of verifiable, numerical data. Ergo, medical men should seek similar data, in order to minimize their divergencies in theory and to arrive at dependable knowledge.[14]

The prospect was attractive and it is not strange that it appealed to those who hoped to bring order and certainty into medicine. Baglivi pointed out that body motions would best lend themselves to quantification and here some progress had already been made. But, whereas dynamics had brought a new order into astronomy as a whole, in physiology and pathology it had more limited implications. It threw light on the circulation but not, at least by any methods then available, on digestion, nervous action or other physiologic processes.

Even those who wished to measure had to speculate on some aspects of physiology and on most problems in pathology. I say "had to" because, as mentioned, physicians usually assumed that their work must be justified, ultimately, by its applications to hygiene or therapeutics. Suspended judgment was not for them; what they could not demonstrate was supplied by theoretical assumptions.

Iatrophysicists, like other physicians, therefore maintained divergent theories anent the nature of body processes and the nature of disease. Through much of the seventeenth century, their speculations still involved astrology and occult notions: even Harvey employed such concepts. By the eighteenth century, the occult was repudiated and one type of imponderable was thus removed; but oversimplified and unverifiable theories continued to flourish in naturalistic terms. Pathology, for example, was viewed either in generalized or in localized terms, and as relating either to the body fluids (humoralism) or to nervous-vascular tensions (solidism). In view of all the uncertainties, it is not strange that the ancient debate over the relative merits of "experience" and of "reason" continued unabated.

The reactions of conservative physicians against mechanical views were prompt and more persistent than was the case among physical scientists. In the few instances in which medical discoveries were based on exact experiments and measurements (as in blood circulation), opposition did crumble rapidly even as in physics; but since verifiable, quantitative data were lacking in other medical areas, critics could make the most of all the uncertainties involved. The latter may have been motivated by devotion to ancient authorities or by the assumption that—in the the absence of proof to the contrary—qualitative distinctions were the easiest ones to employ. But, in any case, they ridiculed the conflicting or meaningless nature of quantitative findings. What, they inquired, could be done with tables of medicines "accurately graduated to the square of the [patient's] constitution"?[15]

[14] De Praxi Medica (Rome, 1696); English translation of second ed. (London, 1723), pp. 131, 134.

[15] T. Childs, Rational Medicine: Its Past and Present... (New York, 1863), pp. 17, 18.

Contrary to what one might now expect, vitalism in medicine—which was assumed by many biologists to explain purposeful behavior in organisms—was not necessarily in opposition to mechanical outlooks. From Descartes on, vitalists were often enthusiastic mechanists—their mystical principles simply kept the mechanisms in motion. But, quite apart from this philosophical problem, the extreme claims of iatrophysicists induced at the opposite pole of medical thought an equally extreme denial of the possibilities of measurement.

Opposition to iatrophysics gained momentum in the eighteenth century, and was expressed at the time as well as in subsequent writings. Measurement, declared so distinguished an authority as Goethe, could be employed in strictly physical science, but biologic, psychologic and social phenomena necessarily eluded the profane hands of those who would reduce them to quantitative abstractions.[16] Here one detects the feeling that measurement somehow robs human phenomena of all mystery or beauty, and denies to investigators the satisfactions of age-old sense impressions and of intuitive understanding. Such feeling usually appears within any discipline when it is first threatened, as it were, by quantification. Dr. Stevens terms it, in relation to current psychology, "the nostalgic pain of a romantic yearning to remain securely inscrutable."[17]

Goethe's general views were echoed in clinical medicine by Cabanis, whose appeal to Hippocratic tradition has been quoted. In medicine, the French physician declared in 1798, nearly everything depends on what is seen and on a certain instinct for interpretation; the outcome depends more on the artist's sensations than on any principles in the art.[18] For the many "practical" men who held such views, to turn from patients to experiments and measurements was a flight from reality. Their professional hero was the English clinician Sydenham, who largely confined his work to inexact, bedside observations.

Such reactions were so common that they help to explain a curious phenomenon, namely, that even such medical measurements as were feasible were largely ignored after they were first introduced. This was true, in the clinical world, of pulse-timing and temperature-taking. Both of these had been advocated, with appropriate instruments, before or by the 1600's, but neither came into general use until the mid- or even the later nineteenth century. When the Scottish-American James Currie wrote on clinical thermometry in 1797, for example, his work was viewed dimly in England, and a German translator cited it as illustrating the backwardness of British medicine.[19] Helmholtz later reported that, as late as the 1840's in Germany, the older physicians thought it hardly in good taste to time the pulse with a watch.[20]

The final indictment of the iatrophysics of 1600-1750 was expressed by some medical thinkers during the first half of the nineteenth century. Thus, a French authority, Auber, declared in 1839 that (1) this "school" had been arrogant in claiming that quantification alone permitted of judicious reason-

[16] Paul le Gendre, "Goethe et les Sciences Medicales . . . ," *Bull. de la Soc. Francaise d'Histoire de la Médecin*, 1932, *26:* 276f.; Paul Diepgen, "Goethe u. Die Medizin," *Klin. Wochens.*, 1932, *11:* 1611ff.

[17] S. S. Stevens, "Measurement and Man," *Science*, 1958, *127:* 385.

[18] Note 7, above, p. 117.

[19] William Osler, "Currie's Journal," *Annals of Med. Hist.*, 1919, *1:* 81.

[20] *Vorträge u. Reden*, II, 179, cited in J. T. Merz, *History of European Thought in the Nineteenth Century*, 2 ed. (London, 1904), II, 388.

ing; (2) that many physiologic and pathologic phenomena were unmeasurable, since that process could give numbers but not the qualities of things; and (3) that the iatromathematicians—by claiming too much—had done more harm than good in medicine.[21]

Yet today we cannot read iatromathematical literature without recognizing therein the prophets and, in some cases, the precursors of all the quantitative work which has so greatly advanced physiology and clinical medicine over the past century. Much of their work was indeed visionary but the dreams eventually came true![22]

Obviously, the mechanical approach to medicine, 1600-1750, was in a sense premature. It was premature because iatrophysicists were misled by the success of physics into being overconfident in medicine. They attempted shortcuts across areas of unrecognized complexity, and not until more knowledge was secured could it be realized how little was really known. Hence they overlooked the need for much qualitative research as a prerequisite to future quantification.

Meantime the antimechanists, though extreme in their scepticism about measurements, were on sound ground in urging the need for continued, qualitative studies. Despite theoretical confusion, moreover, they were groping toward a more effective conceptual basis for such research. By the early 1800's, interest shifted from a generalized (humoral) to a localized (structural) pathology, and to a focus on specific diseases.[23] Generalized problems continued to exist but were forgotten or just ignored as not susceptible to objective study; whereas localized pathology was manageable through clinical observation and autopsies—both qualitative procedures at the start. Once it was possible to identify diseases, then quantitative studies could be undertaken on a firm basis. Then and not before, for example, could statistics be applied to reveal the incidence of a given entity, or to show the effectiveness of particular drugs in the treatment thereof.

The only exceptions to this last statement related to those few diseases—chiefly epidemic in nature—which were so striking as to be recognized in ordinary practice. Statistical data on the incidence of two such entities, the plague and smallpox, were collected as far back as the late seventeenth century. More than this, it was in the case of smallpox that mathematical calculations were first successfully applied to clinical procedures. Inoculation was introduced at Boston in 1721 by the Rev. Cotton Mather, who was a convinced mechanist as well as an authority on witches. Both he and Dr. Boylston employed a simple calculus of probabilities, based on mortality statistics, to prove that prospects were better for inoculated patients than for those who contracted smallpox "in the natural way."[24] Mathematics here served medical practice; but it is interesting to note that medicine thereafter provided—

[21] T.-C.-E. Auber, *Traité de Philosophie Médicale* ... (Paris, 1839), pp. 87-92.

[22] See, e.g., the judgment of J. H. Baas, *History of Medicine,* translated by H. E. Handerson (New York, 1889), pp. 503f.

[23] This trend was actually complex and protracted. For a brief interpretation see R. H. Shryock, "Nineteenth Century Medicine: Scientific Aspects," *Jour. World Hist.* (UNESCO), iii, 1957 *3:* 885-892.

[24] R. H. Shryock, *Development of Modern Medicine* (New York, 1947), p. 136; O. T. Beall, Jr. and Shryock, *Cotton Mather* ... (Baltimore, 1954), p. 108.

in inoculation—one of the means or incentives for the further development of the calculus noted.[25] Medicine, even as physics before it and social science at the same time, called for a new mathematics in connection with new problems.

Mather and Boylston employed mortality data as a matter of course, since statistics were already "in the air" by their time. There were ancient precedents for the enumeration of peoples and of their property; and continuing vital records were kept in European towns from at least the fifteenth century. "Bills of mortality" were issued by the 1600's, in order—it was said—that emerging dangers could be detected and that the genteel would "know when to leave town."

Meanwhile, with the growth of commerce and of nationalism, the welfare of society began to be identified with the welfare of the state; and increasing interest was taken in the collection and interpretation of numerical data concerning the resources of the state—that is, "statistics." One of the resources was obviously a healthy population, while, conversely, disease lessened the value of the population and numerical measures of its prevalence were therefore of concern to governments. Thus interests of both individuals and of society promoted the collection of vital as well as of economic statistics.

As early as 1602, Sully established a bureau of statistics in Paris; and from about 1660 on, the subject began to be taught in German universities.[26] Pioneer studies of both economic and mortality data were published in England, at about the same time, by William Petty and by John Graunt. In the latter's work on the bills of mortality (1662), statistics were employed as the equivalent of an instrument of observation in order to bring out, again, phenomena "perceptible only to the reason." Thus early, for example, it was observed that deaths from certain diseases bore a constant ratio to total mortality, that death rates varied with the seasons, and that urban mortality exceeded the rural. Graunt subjected his data to critical analysis, noting the need for more systematic and reliable compilations.

In 1669, stimulated by Graunt's work and using mortality data, Huygens attempted to determine life expectancy at given ages; and in 1693, Edmund Halley prepared from certain Continental bills a life table which was used by the first life insurance companies in London during the next century. Interest in insurance, both life and voluntary health insurance, encouraged the development of a calculus of probabilities—a field in which Pascal and other mathematicians had already shown some interest. In 1713 appeared Jakob Bernoulli's work, developing the theory of such a calculus and suggesting its application to "moral" and economic matters.[27]

These possibilities subsequently aroused much enthusiasm; in France, for example, the statesman Turgot foresaw the application of the calculus to social data, and so also did the *philosophe* Condorcet. It will be noted that

[25] See, for this interesting counter-influence on mathematics, E. Netto, "Kombinatorik, Wahrscheinlichkeitsrechnung," u.s.w., in M. Cantor, ed., *Vorlesungen über Geschichte der Mathematique*, IV (Leipzig, 1908), pp. 221ff.

[26] M. Block, *Traité Théorique et Practique de Statistique*, 2 ed. (Paris, 1886), p. 25; quoted in J. T. Merz, n. 20, above, pp. 555ff.

[27] On the development of statistics and the calculus, see such standard works as Netto (n.25, above); V. John, *Geschichte der Statistik* (Stuttgart, 1884), pp. 98ff.; T. Todhunter, *History of Probabilities* (London, 1865), pp. 57ff.

mathematicians were here suggesting the possibilities of quantification in social fields, even as they had encouraged it in medicine during the preceding century. But the development of statistics and of the calculus as late as the 1700's was also significant to medicine, since vital data had medical as well as social implications.

In the medical setting, the growing interest in statistics might conceivably have been viewed as a continuation of the iatrophysics of the 1600's. The latter, however, sought laws of the usual type in physiology, whereas public health studies were pointed toward statistical laws not applicable to individual cases. In this respect and also in the personnel involved, the two trends seem distinct. They both reflected the quantitative enthusiasms of the era; but the first pertained to biologic medicine, the second to the medical aspects of social phenomena. Only in the case of inoculation was the calculus applied to biologic data, and this effort ended abruptly with the introduction of vaccination about 1800.

What apparently happened was that some disillusionment set in by the later 1700's concerning quantitative "air castles" in physiology and related therapeutics, at the very time when vital statistics began to throw light on public health. Süsmilch and other writers elaborated earlier works, in such a way as to emphasize the value of statistics in revealing problems in public hygiene and possible remedial actions.

It is true that the calculus was not yet employed on public health problems in any systematic fashion. Calculations on life expectancy within different social environments, for example, had to await the next century. But, meantime, simple mortality data in terms of age, sex, and "causes of death" brought out the dangers of infant diseases and the values of child hygiene, as well as the threat of certain supposed entities such as "consumption." Moreover, the revelation of high urban mortality provided a focus for the public health programs of the next century.[28]

As more efforts were made to study vital statistics, the more the demand arose for the collection of complete and reliable data. In this respect Sweden and to some extent Prussia led the way in the eighteenth century, while the English-speaking countries were backward. The ensuing efforts to improve statistical services carried over into the nineteenth century, and were relatively successful in certain countries by or before 1860.

Data on French cities, for example, were complete enough by the 1820's to enable Villermé to calculate the relative life expectancy of workers as contrasted to that of the upper classes. The latter were shown to have much the longer expectancy.[29] No doubt Villermé expected these results because of common (qualitative) observation; otherwise he would hardly have thought of the analysis involved. His procedure was, in this respect, similar to that often followed—as Dr. Kuhn points out in his paper in this volume—in the

[28] The impact of statistical studies on public-health interests is discussed in R. H. Shryock, *Development of Modern Medicine* (New York, 1947), pp. 135-144; in G. Rosen, *A History of Public Health* (New York, 1958), pp. 111-114; and in such national histories of this field as Fischer (n. 30, below).

[29] See L. R. Villermé, "Mémoire sur la Mortalité en France, dans la Classe Aisée et dans la Classe Indigente," *Mémoires de l'Acad. Roy. de Méd.*, i, Paris, 1828, *1*: 51ff.

physical sciences. But in demography, as in physics or chemistry, a qualitative generalization was debatable; whereas one confirmed in quantitative terms was—as far as it went—irrefutable. Assuming the reliability of his data, no one could argue against Villermé's conclusion that the public health was endangered by the social environment. As a matter of fact, his findings were confirmed by similar studies made in Prussia and in England during the 1830's and '40's.[30]

It followed, logically, that the health of workers would approach that of the upper classes, just in the degree that their living standards and environment were made to approximate those of "their betters." Statistical studies and calculations thus became an effective argument for environmental betterment, or, in medical terms, for sanitary reform. This was all the more true because such data not only inspired reforms but could later confirm their value by comparisons of "before and after."

Qualitative considerations also played a role here, and reformers often supplemented their numerical findings with human appeals—with "horrible examples" of individual cases. But the frequent citation of death rates and of expectancy calculations in the public health literature of 1830-1870 shows how potent quantitative abstractions were thought to be—even in a romantic age.[31]

In a word, vital statistics and calculations not only provided means of observation in public hygiene—as they had done since the late 1600's—but also had much to do with the direction taken by such hygiene after 1820. Curiously enough, the resulting sanitary program was quite nonspecific—it was directed against no diseases in particular—at the very time when pathology was becoming engrossed with disease specificity. In consequence, public health almost ceased to be a medical field—sanitary programs could be, and often were, directed by statisticians and engineers, rather than by physicians.

While public hygiene was becoming more and more a statistical field (1750-1850), physiology benefited from both qualitative and quantitative research in chemistry. Despite the more naive aspects of iatrochemistry or of iatrophysics and the sharp reaction against these "schools," one can observe an apparent sequence in the study of body functions from the seventeenth into the nineteenth century. In the case of respiration, for example, the line runs from the work of Boyle, Lower and Mayow in the later 1600's (re the relation of air in the lungs to respiration and to the blood), through Black's discovery that carbon dioxide is given off in breathing (1757) and Priestley's isolation of oxygen, into Lavoisier's demonstrations (1775-1790) that (1) respiration involves combustion $(C+O_2=CO_2)$, and (2) that such combustion is the source of body heat.

The studies done in the 1600's, however, now look as though they should have led directly into those of Lavoisier. But the former were largely nonquantitative, so that it was possible thereafter to elaborate the theory of a

[30] A. Fischer, *Geschichte des deutschen Gesundheitswesens,* II (Berlin, 1933), pp. 425.

[31] By the mid-nineteenth century, statisticians were even attempting to express laws true for all public health in mathematical form. Thus, William Farr declared in 1844, that "if the population be the same in other respects, an increase in density implies an increase in mortality; and that the ratio of increase, . . . is as certain roots of density" $m:m^1::^6\sqrt{d}:^6\sqrt{d^1}$, *Prov. Med. and Surg. Jour.,* 7:441.

fire-substance (phlogiston) without any exact checks on it. This concept apparently impeded discovery of the nature of combustion for some seventy-five years. Its final refutation and the substitution of a verifiable theory was made possible only by the thoroughly quantitative nature of Lavoisier's proofs. Subsequent theories concerning the locale of bodily combustion in the tissues, and the role of the blood in taking oxygen to and removing carbon dioxide therefrom, were confirmed by the similarly quantitative work of Magnus in 1837.[32]

In the case of digestion, also, there was some lag between pioneer studies of the 1600's and the final solutions of the problems involved. In the investigation of pancreatic juice, for example, nothing seems to have been accomplished between the nonquantitative research of de Graaf (1664) and the quantitative work of Claude Bernard nearly two centuries later! Scientists continued to debate the relative merits of chemical and physical views of digestion well into the 1700's. Beginning with Boerhaave, however, both processes were taken into account, and Réamur showed that gastric juice was a solvent of most foods. Quantitative research in this area was introduced by Spallanzani (1780), who demonstrated that the rate of solution was proportional to the volume of gastric juice acting on a given quantity of food.[33]

Similar summaries could be given of the history of research on other body processes. Generally speaking, these advanced with progress in chemistry and subsequently in physics; and since both these fields were essentially quantitative by or before 1800, physiology tended to follow similar methods.[34] But the importance of much qualitative work in physiology after 1800—as in Beaumont's work on gastric digestion—is not to be overlooked.

In the central medical field of pathology, research continued to be largely qualitative until after the mid-nineteenth century; indeed, much of it remains so at the present time. Between about 1800 and 1860, interest centered largely in morbid anatomy, wherein the chief object was the identification of specific diseases through clinical observations and autopsies. This was a taxonomic problem, and like most taxonomy it was pursued in what might be termed the Aristotelian tradition. But it may be repeated that this taxonomy was basic to the whole structure of medical science built upon it after about 1870— basic not only to bacteriology, for example, but also to such a quantitative, biochemical field as endocrinology.

Though the pathologists of 1800-1860 rarely used measurements, it is not too much to say that they took over their objective attitudes from the quantitative sciences. This was illustrated by their resort to new instruments of observation such as the stethescope, which provided data of a more exact nature. By the 1850's, several such instruments were invented; and the most remarkable of all, the x-ray machine, became available in the '90's. The use of these devices made it less necessary to depend—as in public hygiene—on statistical data as a means of observation.

In certain instances, pathologists did resort to enumerations. Attempts were made, for example, to count the number of cases of a supposed disease which

[32] See J. Fulton, *Physiology,* Clio Medica Ser. (New York, 1931), pp. 50-59.

[33] *Ibid.,* pp. 67-78.

[34] A brief summary of quantitative physiology after *ca.* 1850 is given in R. H. Shryock, "Nineteenth Century Medicine: Scientific Aspects," *Jour. of World History* (UNESCO), 1957, *3:* 894-900.

exhibited a particular symptom or lesion—the implication being that a sufficiently high ratio would establish the features of a given entity.[35]

After mid-century, quantitative studies occasionally threw direct light on disease identifications. Reports on the percentage of cases of pareses which were associated with syphilitic infection, for example, suggested the identity of these two supposed entities. Final proof of this relationship came with Noguchi's qualitative demonstration, after 1900, of the organisms common to both diseases. This sequence illustrates, by the way, a truism which may have been obscured by the emphasis here accorded to measurement, that is, that research did not always proceed from the qualitative to the quantitative. The latter method often opened up possibilities for further qualitative investigations.

Pathologic physiology lagged behind the related anatomy until after mid-century. Perhaps this can be explained by such circumstances as the logical relationship between structure and function, and the fact that the chief contributions in physiology as a whole were often made by men who were primarily chemists or physicists rather than physicians. And such men were not usually interested in pathology as such. For their part, physicians and biologists tended, during the early 1800's, to view physiologic experiments as random procedures. They held that functions were best revealed by morphologic studies.

Such views, which may have reflected the reaction against earlier iatrochemistry and physics, inhibited work in morbid as well as in normal physiology. The most sweeping reaction against physical and chemical approaches to medicine—or, at least, to the application of quantitative methods derived from those fields—appeared between 1810 and 1830 in the *Naturphilosophie* of the German schools. As applied in "romantic medicine," this philosophic idealism involved stimulating ideas but preferred to soar on the wings of thought rather than to plod along with prosaic investigations—quantitative or otherwise.[36]

After 1830, however, German medical men swung back to objective research with all the enthusiasm of those released from philosophic restraints. There followed marked advances in both biochemistry and biophysics, at their hands and also in those of Bernard. In these fields, qualitative and quantitative work went on simultaneously and led eventually to important pathologic discoveries, for example, in endocrinology and in nutritional disorders.[37]

Little has been said up to this point about the field of chief concern to physicians, namely, clinical medicine. Iatrophysicists had applied their theories to this area, but the reaction against their speculations has been noted. Advances in pathology after 1800 did depend in part on more exact clinical observations; and in this connection numerical measures—as in pulse-timing and in thermometry—were finally introduced into general practice after 1850.

Measurements of other phenomena of clinical significance also began to be

[35] The pathologic anatomy of 1800-1850 is best illustrated in the history of "the Paris school"; see, e.g., M. Fosseyeaux, *Paris Médicale En 1830* (Paris, 1930), pp. 97ff., or any standard history of medicine.

[36] See, e.g., P. Diepgen, *Deutsche Medizin vor 100 Jahre...* (Leipzig, 1923), *passim*.

[37] Shryock (n. 34, above), pp. 896-900.

made in this period. Thus, the clinician Andral weighed fibrin, corpuscles, and the albumen in blood serum; and Marey applied graphic representations (first employed in the late Middle Ages), which would later be used in cardiographs and the like. Graduated, hypodermic needles were introduced in the 1840's; and as early as 1852, Vierordt was making "blood counts." Later, in 1887, S. Von Basch invented a practical instrument for measuring blood pressure, the use of which is said, somewhat cynically, to have introduced new diseases.[88]

Much of this clinical work, however, was directed more toward the identification of diseases than toward their cure. The clinician-pathologists of 1800-1850 became sceptical about therapy, and their research took on many of the characteristics of "pure" science. M. Broussais of Paris remarked of his colleague M. Louis that the latter was more interested in performing autopsies than in preventing them![89] At this point, clinicians came into conflict with practitioners, who still held that *something* must be done for patients.

One of the bases for the clinical scepticism of 1830-1870 was the rather late introduction of quantitative methods in therapeutics. With all the enthusiasm of the iatrophysicists for measurement in principle, and with all the controversies about *this* treatment or *that*, one might have expected numerical checks long before 1800. Did not many physicians, as Pierre Louis later noted, claim that a given drug was best because "most" of their patients benefited from it? And could not means for reducing such vague quantification to exactitude be found in the statistical approach already so common in public hygiene—or, more immediately, in the statistical studies made for decades after 1720 on inoculation, which was close to a clinical procedure?

Yet the record before about 1830 was very meagre in this respect. It has been said that the pathologist Morgagni recognized the need for clinical statistics by the 1750's, but was unable to collect them. Benjamin Rush wrote a friend, "I could send you ... 100 cases that establish the value of salt as a drug," but he did not mention the need for controls. Other physicians assembled statistical data on given diseases but did not apply them to test the efficacy of the means by which these were treated.

One of the few attempts made to do this before 1800 was that of the Englishman William Cobbett, a layman who claimed that Dr. Benjamin Rush's treatment of yellow fever in Philadelphia (1793) was killing rather than curing the patients. In order to prove this, Cobbett analyzed the bills of mortality, thus using them as if they were the equivalents of clinical data.[40] Obviously, crude death rates were not adequate for his purpose; but it is interesting that a layman saw the need for such quantitative checks at a time when physicians just ignored it.

One explanation of this attitude involves the antipathy to quantification as such which has already been noted. Physicians disliked the idea of submitting their insights and cumulative wisdom to prosaic, numerical tests. As late as

---

[88] Shryock, *Development of Modern Medicine*, pp. 165f.

[89] F.J.V. Broussais, *Examen des Doctrines Médicales* (Paris, 1821), p. 717.

[40] Cobbett, *The Rush Light* (New York, Feb. 28, 1800), p. 49. Rush's own reference to "100 cases," quoted above, comes from T. Percival, *Medical Essays*, 4th ed. (London, 1789), p. 344.

1844, a prominent American physician remarked that it would be surprising if a well-informed "doctor" could:[41]

> come into the presence of a sick man without discerning, by a sort of intuition almost, what is wrong in his system, what is wanting for the treatment.

Even more significant were professional circumstances. Clinical data of value could only be collected in a relatively large hospital service, and such services hardly existed until after 1800. It has just been remarked that Morgagni found no way to collect statistics of this sort, and that Cobbett, finding none, had to make the best of mortality figures.

A final difficulty related to the state of contemporary pathology. It was necessary to identify a disease with reasonable certainty before any studies could be made on methods of treating it. Statistics concerning such categories of the time as "convulsions" or "decay" would have been quite meaningless.

We can now see, however, that prospects for clinical statistics improved during the decades between 1800 and 1830. Clinicians, seeking to study disease objectively, realized their need for hospital services and secured them on a much enlarged scale. This was notably the case in the hospitals of Paris, reorganized after the Revolution. Boerhaave's eighteenth-century clinic had possessed only 12 beds; but by the 1820's, Bouillaud of Paris claimed to have seen 25,000 cases in five years![42] Such numbers had possibilities for statistical analysis.

In the course of the clinical-pathologic studies which flourished in Paris after 1800, clearer pictures of distinct diseases were emerging by the 1820's. More entities which were potentially measurable, in relation to therapy as well as to epidemiology, thus became available.

Paris also happened to be a center of mathematical interests. It was here that Laplace published in 1810 his classic formulation of the calculus of probabilities, in which he called attention to ways in which this could be employed in medical research.[43] Such suggestions probably influenced Pinel, who attempted, 1809-1820, to use statistics and even the calculus in a study of mental-hospital populations,[44] and also Villermé, whose analysis of life expectancies (1828) has been mentioned.

In these several ways, the medical stage was set by about 1830 for a full presentation of clinical statistics. The chief actor was the physician Pierre Louis, whose personal experience had focused attention on therapy as well as on pathology, and who had given seven lean years to "full-time" research. The major formulation of his "numerical method" appeared in his work on the effects of bloodletting (1835). In this, Louis presented some 100 cases of pneumonia in which bleeding had been employed, along with a control group, and so demonstrated statistically how uncertain were the values of this age-old procedure. Unlike his predecessors, moreover, Louis ridiculed the vaguely

[41] C. D. Meigs, *Lecture Introductory to His Course of Lectures for 1843-44* (Philadelphia, 1843), p. 14.

[42] E. H. Ackerknecht, *Short History of Medicine* (New York, 1955), p. 134.

[43] *Théorie Analytique des Probabiliés, 3* ed. (Paris, 1920), pp. 420-424.

[44] P. Pinel, *Traité Médico-Philosophique sur l'Aliénation Mentale* (Paris, 1809), pp. 423, 450; *Médecine Clinique* (Paris, 1815), pp. 460-462; *Nosographie Philosophique* (Paris, 1818), p. lxxvii.

quantitative judgments of his contemporaries and made clear the merits of numerical exactitude.[45]

Louis' views promptly elicited both support and opposition—even as had the appearance of iatrophysics in general more than a century before. In the very year that Louis' work appeared, a debate on the uses of the calculus was held in the French Academy, and in 1837 a similar discussion was held in the Paris Academy of Medicine.

The most obvious criticism of clinical statistics was that, like all statistics dealing with populations, their averages could not be applied to individual cases. And was not therapy, necessarily, an individual matter? This difficulty, which, by the way had been noted as early as the thirteenth century,[46] led many to fear that the concept of *l'homme moyen* would lead to indiscriminate, routine treatments.[47] Louis replied that he could "allow" for such differences, but the debate continued.

More serious was the criticism that Louis' method involved only simple enumeration. It offered no criterion for judging what was a significant number of cases, and made no allowance for the limit of possible error. These technical difficulties were pointed out by Gavarett in 1840, who noted the need for applying the calculus to raw data.[48]

There were, finally, certain strictly medical criticisms of the "numerical method." Was not the identification of the entities measured so objectively, itself a *subjective* procedure based in some instances only on the clinician's senses? If so, the validity of the entities measured (that is, the diagnoses) was open to question.

More sweeping was the denial that these entities (specific diseases) existed at all, except in the pathologist's imagination. Broussais referred scathingly to "the maladies created by M. L——."[49] Here one was involved in the basic distinction between the older, generalized pathology (to which Broussais adhered) and the newer, specific concepts.[50] If the former view had been maintained, clinical statistics would have had no meaning, since there was no use in measuring the nonexistent. Reversing this logic, one may now say that one of the virtues of the concept of specificity was that it provided entities which were subject to measurement.

During the 1840's, further efforts were made to check on the value of various treatments by statistical means. It also appeared that, in some cases, this method could throw light on the casual factors or means of transmission of infectious entities. American physicians, for example, sometimes used epidemiologic statistics in order to show that certain diseases were "caused" by living organisms. In this case, however, the statistical approach was not conclusive: the "germ theory" was later demonstrated by laboratory research which was largely nonquantitative in nature.

[45] *Recherches sur Les Effets de la Saignée* (Paris, 1835), pp. 85ff.

[46] Crombie, *Augustine to Galileo,* p. 228.

[47] See, e.g., Quetelet, *Sur l'Homme et la Developpement de ses Facultés,* II (Brussels, 1836), p. 281; Auber, *Traité de Philosophie Médicale* (Paris, 1839), pp. 87-92.

[48] J. Gavarett, *Principes Généreaux de Statistique Médicale* (Paris, 1840), *passim.* It was here (p. 49) that Morgagni's interest in clinical statistics was noted.

[49] Broussais, *Examen des Doctrines Médicales,* II (Paris, 1821), p. 726.

[50] See Shryock (n. 34, above), pp. 889, 894.

More convincing, in the long run, was the demonstration by Semmelweis that puerperal (childbed) fever was carried by physicians themselves from one patient to another. Proof was provided in elaborate clinical and mortality tables.[51] These now seem irrefutable, though the disinclination of many doctors to admit such a charge led to vigorous denials at the time. It is interesting, in passing, that some of this opposition also claimed statistical justification.

After 1835, despite the criticisms of Louis' views, the value of clinical statistics was accorded increasing recognition. Various leaders expressed their approval in terms almost as optimistic as those used by iatrophysicists in an earlier day; indeed, one can almost speak here of a second wave of quantitative enthusiasm.

Bouillaud of Paris declared in 1836 that statistical method was revolutionizing medicine: a conjectural art was becoming an exact science.[52] Henry Holland of London stated, four years later, that "through medical statistics lies the most secure path into the philosophy of medicine";[53] and by 1842, J. F. Double of Paris claimed that all critics had come to admit the value of such data in therapeutic studies.[54] Last but not least, W. P. Alison of Edinburgh assured British scientists in 1855 that many of the most important questions in medicine could be investigated by statistics "and in no other way."[55]

The English astronomer Herschell reported about 1850 that:[56]

> Men began to hear with surprise, not unmixed with some vague hope of ultimate benefit that not only births, deaths and marriages, but ... the comparative value of medical remedies, and different modes of treatment of disease ... might come to be surveyed with the lynx-eyed scrutiny of a dispassionate analysis.

The other side of this picture was the limited extent to which statistical methods were actually used, in clinical and pathologic studies, for some decades after 1835. Even when problems seemed to call for such methods, considerable inertia and ignorance had to be overcome. Quetelet complained in 1846 that medical data were usually "incomplete, incomparable, suspected, heaped up pell-mell ... and nearly always it is neglected to inquire whether the number of observations is sufficient to inspire confidence."

Yet it seems significant that few voices were raised after 1850—as they were in the 1700's—to condemn measurement in principle. In this respect, the second wave of quantification did not recede as had the first but, rather, swept over much of the medical world in a lasting manner. Dr. Oliver Wendell Holmes was hardly exaggerating when he declared to a medical audience in 1860:[57]

[51] Semmelweis, *Die Ätiologie, der Begriff, u. die Prophylaxis des Kindbettfiebers* (Wien, 1861), *passim*.

[52] J. Bouillaud, *Esai sur la Philosophie Médicale* ... (Paris, 1836), pp. 96f.

[53] "On Medical Evidence," *Medical Notes and Reflections,* 2 ed. (London, 1840), p. 6.

[54] Cited in P. V. Renouard, *History of Medicine,* transl. by C. G. Comegys (1842), pp. 569f.

[55] "Notes on the Application of Statistics to Questions in Medical Science," Brit. Asso. for Advancement of Science, *Report for 1855,* pp. 155ff.

[56] In the *Edinburgh Rev.,* 1850, *92:* 12.

[57] *Currents and Cross Currents in Medical Science* ... (Boston, 1861), p. 12.

The two dominating words in our time are *law* and *average* ... Statistics have been tabulated on everything—population, growth, wealth, crime, disease. The positive philosophy of Comte has only given expression to the ... computing mind of the nineteenth century.

By that decade, physiology and public hygiene were largely quantitative fields, though the latter was about to be invaded by nonquantitative bacteriology. Even anatomy, in the case of physical anthropology, was soon to take on statistical forms. Pathology and clinical medicine were still largely qualitative fields, but were resorting to numerical data and calculations wherever this seemed feasible.

In a word, medical science since the mid-nineteenth century has continued in some areas to be of a basically qualitative nature, but has in other fields permanently taken over quantitative methods. And the trend in medicine, as in other sciences, has been to gradually reduce to measurement problems previously considered unmeasurable.

In summing up medical experience, one notes that quantitative methods were, usually, first suggested—and sometimes introduced—by mathematicians or physical scientists. The resulting enthusiasm for iatrophysics after 1600 proved premature in many ways, and anti-quantitative reactions ensued in relation to medical biology. In the social aspects of medicine, however, statistical approaches were increasingly employed, and quantification was subsequently introduced on a firmer basis in both physiology and clinical medicine.

In a general way, then, the tradition that quantification came over into medicine from the physical sciences—but with less immediate success than in those sciences—seems to be valid. In this sense, medicine has been viewed as following the lead of the physical disciplines.

The relative lag in developing medical quantification is usually ascribed, rather vaguely, to the complexity of biologic phenomena. More specifically, one notes that certain problems in quantification were encountered in medicine long before these arose in "the exact sciences." Earlier than in physics, for example, medicine occasionally found itself dealing with phenomena which were "disturbed" by the process of observation itself. And, in common with social fields, clinical medicine and public hygiene found it necessary to use statistical averages not applicable to individual units—a situation which appeared in physics, or at least was recognized in physics, only in a later period.

APPENDIX

Additional comments here will be related, first, to certain of the other papers, and, second, to the general discussions.

With regard to Dr. Wilks' statements on the need for precise quantification, it is obvious that when units measured in medicine were identified only by the observer's senses, precision was lacking. An example is that of Galen's "degrees" of heat in the patient's body (pathology), which were judged without a thermometer.

Such imprecision has persisted into our own times in clinical statistics, insofar as diagnoses are based on subjective judgments. Certain diagnostic signs are now usually measured by relatively exact instruments (temperature, pulse, etc.), but diagnoses also depend on non-quantitative judgments concerning lesions and/or causal factors. As in Galen's case, moreover, certain apparent measures have really been subjective in nature.

About 1920, e.g., a diagnosis of syphilis was often based on the Wasserman test, wherein a technician, observing the degree of cloudiness in a fluid, judged it on an assumed scale of "—; +; ++." Only the latter symbol indicated a "positive" diagnosis, yet two observers could disagree as to a "+" or a "++." Clinical statistics on a large scale were based on such diagnoses. The danger here—that subjective elements may lurk behind a façade of statistical exactitude—was noted by the French authority J. Gavarett when clinical statistics were first being advocated in the 1830's.

Dr. Wilks' statement concerning the "validity" of quantification can be illustrated by many instances of invalidity in medical measures. This was the case whenever a supposedly measurable "property" of the human body corresponded to no observable reality, e.g., early attempts to measure a patient's "health" or "constitution." Whether such generalized concepts can ever be so defined as to make them susceptible to valid measures is an open question. The problem seems analogous to that in psychology—as pointed out, I believe, by Dr. Boring—of attempting to measure general intelligence (I.Q.).

In clinical statistics, or those for "causes of death" in public health, the units measured corresponded to observable realities. But these realities were often so ill-defined that figures concerning them lack validity from the present standpoint; e.g., statistics on "fevers" as a cause of death would now be considered meaningless. But they *were* considered meaningful in 1860. Conversely, data on "cancer" as a cause of death are now thought to be more or less valid; but if the day comes when this concept is broken down into several distinct entities, our present data will then be viewed as misleading.

A major illustration of quantification once considered valid but no longer so viewed, is afforded by the history of medical astrology prior to 1700. Dr. Price noted during the discussions that this theme was not adequately recognized in the original paper. The point was well taken, since medical astrology was mentioned only in passing and yet it did involve quantification over a long period.

The validity of astrologic measurements was, however, completely repudiated after 1700, whereas, in such a matter as measures of the causes of death, their meaning was modified but not abandoned as more discriminating criteria became available. Perhaps there is a remote analogy here to changes in standards for the "margin of error" in physical sciences, which followed the introduction of more discriminating instruments—as noted in Dr. Kuhn's paper.

Implicit in this same paper was the suggestion that the "image" which social scientists have formed of quantification in "the exact sciences" may not correspond to the actual role which this method has played in physics. Certainly, in the case of seventeenth-century medicine, this "image" seems to have been an over-simplified one which made quantification almost an end in itself. I do not recall, however, any attempt to analyze just what medical men of that era *did* think was the role of measurement in physics, and such a study might be worth while if feasible. The same may be said of a corresponding study of social scientists of a later period. The difficulty would be that an "image" of quantification in physics is usually implicit rather than explicit in the writings of either physicians or social scientists.

The long delay in finding measurable units in medicine may be ascribed to different circumstances in different fields. In physiology, for example, the model of physics led to rapid advances *re* the circulation, but was inapplicable to respiration and digestion. The latter functions could not be well studied quantitatively until, as noted in Dr. Guerlac's discussion, chemistry was able after *ca.* 1790 to provide a pertinent, quantitative model.

The even longer delay in finding measurable units in clinical medicine and public health resulted from the peculiar difficulty in identifying disease entities. The very existence of such entities was often denied—a situation for which I find no parallel in the papers on other sciences. Thus, no one questioned the reality of pendulums or falling bodies in physics, or of distinct species in biology.

Physicians who *did* accept "the ontologic concept" of the reality of diseases, moreover, had great difficulty in finding criteria for their identification. Three criteria—symptoms, lesions, casual factors—were eventually worked out in that order, but the process occupied more than 200 years (*ca.* 1650-1875) and has indeed never been made complete. For all its difficulties, the identification of biologic species seems to have been easy in comparison. The difference here may be ascribed in part to the relatively elusive nature of disease entities, in contrast to biologic species which may be observed as units by the senses.

It is also true that biologic taxonomy, as was noted in the discussions, makes some use of quantification (as in counting plant parts), whereas, with occasional exceptions (as noted in my original paper) quantitative methods have usually not proved feasible in disease identification except in relation to symptoms. If symptomology had alone been adequate for disease identification (as was hoped in the 1700's), the situation would have paralleled that in botany. But it proved necessary to pursue diseases on the non-quantitative, pathologic and etiologic levels as well as on the symptomatic.

There were also, of course, purely social or professional reasons for the slow development of medical taxonomy. These circumstances related, as Dr. Merton pointed out during the discussions, to the sociology of science. Until recent decades, developments in medicine seemed to have a more obvious and vital bearing on human welfare than did those in any of the other sciences; hence medical research was subjected to peculiarly potent, extraneous pressures. When pathologic anatomy became essential to surgery and later to disease identification, for example, studies were handicapped by moral aversions to dissection.

Less obvious, but perhaps more important, was the professional fact that medical research was assumed to be primarily a function of physicians (practitioners). Comte once said that this was as bad as assigning astronomic studies to sea captains, but a more modern analogy would be that of turning over sociology to the "social workers." In medicine, the arrangement not only limited the time which could be spared for research, but often led investigators off on tangents relating to pathology and therapy. The tradition that *something* must be done for patients was not seriously questioned until about the 1830's, and it was noted in my original paper that this tradition encouraged therapeutic speculation beyond the limits of verification.

In the light of the discussions, quantification in medicine—outside those fields absorbed into the physical sciences (biophysics, biochemistry)—seems to have served largely, in effect, as an instrument of observation. This was true in physiology (as in the discovery of invisible perspiration); occasionally in pathology (as in the relation between paresis and syphilis); in clinical medicine (as in observing the effects of therapy); and notably in public health (in revealing the incidence of disease, mortality rates, etc.).

On the other hand, quantification has rarely if ever revealed in medicine what Dr. Kuhn terms "crises," or means of resolving them. There have been situations in medicine which might be called crises, for example, the growing conviction by about 1820, that generalized theories in pathology were inadequate to explain the specificity of localized lesions. But such a crisis was not revealed or resolved by quantification: there were rarely any decisive measurements. In these respects, I would think that quantification served much the same purpose in medicine that it has in psychophysics and in social science.

Conversely, medicine—unlike the social but like the physical sciences—also employed actual instruments of observation (microscopes, stethoscopes) as well as measuring instruments (watches, thermometers). Query: what procedures in social science, if any, are analogous to direct observation with a microscope—interviews or questionnaires?

While on this matter of possible parallels between medicine and the social sciences, I am not yet clear as to how far the latter fields exhibited analogies to medicine *re* (1) early, extreme claims for quantification as such, (2) a resulting, premature resort to that method, (3) opposition to it in principle, etc. My impression, based on our recent discussions as well as on general reading, is that there *were* such analogies; if so, it would be interesting to see them dissected out from the narrative history of quantification in these fields. I realize, of course, that this may be difficult, since opposition to quantification may be expressed merely by indifference, rather than by explicit statements.

The Beginning and Growth of Measurement in Psychology

By Edwin G. Boring*

A SCIENCE has to undergo a good deal of development before it is ready to be founded, before it can be recognized as a distinct social institution with its separate books, journals, and appointments, as an independent enterprise to which some men devote their lives. A science, once founded, develops and changes, and sometimes the changes involve the addition of new fields to the old science, new fields that have histories of their own that were not part of the history of the science as it stood previously. In this way the history of psychology changes as psychology's present becomes enlarged, and it is not always clear just which events in the history of science belong to psychology. For instance, there are those who feel nowadays that psychology, as it moves over into the field of linguistics, should claim part of that history for its own, and there are others, but by no means as yet a majority, who think that psychology has now moved so far from physiology that it ought to give back some of its older history to the physiologists. Be those things as they may, there is, nevertheless, a pretty clear history of the entry of measurement into psychology and into those activities that eventually became psychology, and these events we find falling naturally into four fairly independent histories.

(1) In the first place, there is the history of *psychophysics,* which may be thought of as founded in 1860 with the publication of Fechner's *Elemente der Psychophysik,* but which goes back nearly a hundred years more to the measurement of sensitivity and of the discriminatory capacity of the senses as accomplished by physiologists and other natural philosophers.[1]

(2) Then there is the history of *reaction time,* which is at first the astronomer's learning to measure and take account of the personal equation in the observation of stellar transits, and then, when the discovery of galvanic electricity and electromagnets had made chronographs and chronoscopes available, the determination of actual individual differences in reaction times. First the physiologist Donders[2] (1862) used these procedures to measure, as he thought, the times of various mental acts, and then the psychologists built an elaborate mental chronometry on these methods, generating an excitement about mental measurement that collapsed after thirty years.[3]

(3) There had been no quantitative measurement of *learning* or *remember-*

* Harvard University

[1] E. G. Boring, *Sensation and Perception in the History of Experimental Psychology* (New York: Appleton-Century, 1942), pp. 34-45, 50-52.

[2] F. C. Donders, "Die Schnelligkeit psy- chischer Processe," *Arch. Anat. Physiol.,* 1868: 657-681.

[3] E. G. Boring, *A History of Experimental Psychology,* 2 ed. (New York: Appleton-Century-Crofts, 1950), pp. 134-153.

ing until Ebbinghaus[4] in 1885, stimulated by Fechner's achievement in psychophysics, described the first measurements. In its early days this new field of endeavor flourished with no awareness of Pavlov's work on conditioning in Russia at the turn of the century. Along about 1913, however, the two sets of activity were brought together in America, coming presently to dominate the field of experimental psychology. Skinner introduced operant conditioning early in the 1930's.[5]

(4) And then finally, under the aegis of Francis Galton, there was the beginning of the measurement of *individual differences,* mostly by means of the mental test. This trend was generated in the enthusiasm caused by Charles Darwin's theory of evolution. Galton, Darwin's cousin, undertook to establish the fact of mental inheritance in 1869 by the publication of his *Hereditary Genius.*[6] Later in his *Inquiries into Human Faculty*[7] (1883), he established the facts of great differences in individual capacities. He devised simple tests of these capacities which James McKeen Cattell[8] in America named *mental tests,* promoting them vigorously. Binet's tests of intelligence came just after these initial efforts, and thereafter the testing of individual capacities became one of the primary undertakings of the rapidly growing American psychology.

Here, however, we have an instance of another new development that is not independent, the emergence of *statistical method.* The roots of modern statistics lie in mathematical probability theory with Jacques Bernoulli[9] (1713) and other great men, including Laplace and Gauss. The father of statistics is Quetelet[10] (1835), and Galton got from him his idea of measuring hereditary genius (1869). It was Galton who invented the concept of "co-relation," and Karl Pearson who, taking the problem over, developed the methods of correlation. The early work in biological statistics was concerned chiefly with the establishment of relationships, and it was not until about 1908 that the methods for computing the significance of differences came into vogue. Ever since Galton, statistical method and the psychology of individual differences have developed in mutual support.[11]

Before we proceed further with our four histories of quantification, it is worth while to note here the nature of some of the very early scientific contributions that belong in psychology's history and were nearly, though perhaps not quite, measurements.

The astronomer Kepler in 1604 reinforced the opinion, already held by some, that the crystalline body in the eye is not a sensitive receptor but a lens which must, Kepler noted, form on the retina an inverted image of the external world. How is it, he asked, that we see rightside up when the immediate

[4] Hermann Ebbinghaus, *Über das Gedächtnis* (Leipzig: Duncker & Humblot, 1885).

[5] Boring, *History (op. cit.),* pp. 386-392, 431f., 625-631, 636-638, 650-652; Gardner Murphy, *Historical Introduction to Modern Psychology,* 2 ed. (New York: Harcourt Brace, 1949), pp. 174-183.

[6] Francis Galton, *Hereditary Genius* (London: Macmillan, 1869).

[7] Francis Galton, *Inquiries into Human Faculty* (London: Macmillan, 1883).

[8] J. McK. Cattell, "Mental tests and measurements," *Mind,* 1890, *15:* 373-381.

[9] I. Todhunter, *A History of the Mathematical Theory of Probability* (New York: Chelsea Publishing Co., 1949), pp. 56-77.

[10] Adolphe Quetelet, *Sur l'homme et le développement de ses facultés, ou essai de physique sociale* (Paris: Bachelier, 1835).

[11] E. G. Boring, "The logic of the normal law of error in mental measurement," *Amer. J. Psychol.,* 1920, *31:* 1-18; *History (op. cit.),* pp. 468-488, 498-501, 532-540, 548f., 560f., 570-578, 581-583.

source of our information is upside down? Descartes supported Kepler by fixing the excised eye of a bull in a hole in his shutter, scraping off the sclerotic coat at the back of the eye, and letting you see on a paper at the back of the eye-ball the inverted image of the world outside. Was not this measurement? Is it not a kind of measurement to show that the image is inverted, that the top goes to the bottom, and the bottom to the top?[12]

Then in 1638 Galileo published his measurement of the relative frequency of the different pitches. Pythagoras had already shown how pitch is dependent on the length of the plucked string that sounds the pitch, and that too was measurement. What Galileo did was to run an iron chisel across a brass plate so that it made a whistling noise. He judged by ear the musical relation of two tones thus produced and then counted the relative frequencies of the successive "streaks" which the chisel made on the brass as it "screeched" across. This observation, added to Pythagoras's, established the frequency theory of pitch and the octave relation.[13]

There seems to be no reason why these discoveries—the inversion of the retinal image, the frequency of pitch—should not have been made earlier. In general, though, the Zeitgeist had been against experimentation. Archimedes thought of pure reason as the highest human endeavor and was contemptuous of his own use of physical knowledge to achieve practical ends, and that view had continued through medieval times. It takes originality, the determination of genius sometimes, to transcend the Zeitgeist; yet every time genius breaks through, it becomes easier for others to resist the standard values of the time, and the growth of this habit of experimenting with nature is clearly a part of how science entered into civilization and did so much to form it.

1. PSYCHOPHYSICS

It is usually not easy to say what determines a trend in the Zeitgeist, what establishes a steady change in the values that affect science. The trend progresses slowly and steadily and is more often recognized after it has progressed for some time than while it is in progress. If it does not persist, it is not even seen as a trend.

In the seventeenth and eighteenth centuries, natural philosophy was becoming more and more experimental, and the study of the functions of the human body advanced with the rest of science. It is surprising how much Albrecht von Haller[14] (1757-1766), who is sometimes instead of Johannes Müller called the father of experimental physiology, had to say about sensation. Especially were the phenomena of vision, stimulated by Newton's *Opticks*[15] (1704), the subject of description. The big names are William Porterfield[16] (1759), Joseph Priestley[17] (1772), and Thomas Young[18] (1807). In the

---

[12] Boring, *Sensation and Perception* (*op. cit.*), pp. 222-225.

[13] *Ibid.*, pp. 322-324.

[14] Albrecht von Haller, *Elementa physiologiae corporis humani*, 8 vols. (Lausanne: M.-M. Bousquet, 1757-1766).

[15] Isaac Newton, *Opticks* (London: printed for Samuel Smith and Benjamin Walford, 1704).

[16] William Porterfield, *A Treatise on the Eye, the Manner and Phaenomena of Vision* (Edinburgh: Miller, 1759).

[17] Joseph Priestley, *The History and Present State of Discoveries relating to Vision, Light and Colours* (London: printed for J. Johnson, 1772).

[18] Thomas Young, *A Course of Lectures on Natural Philosophy and the Mechanical Arts*, 2 vols. (London: printed for J. Johnson, 1807).

nineteenth century the poet Goethe,[19] turned natural philosopher in his bitterness against Newton's theory of color, polemized on vision (1810), and then there were Purkinje[20] (1819-1825) and Johannes Müller[21] (1826), whose early researches were on vision.[22] Some people said that this flurry in research upon sensation was due to the discovery that the motor and sensory nerves are different—the law of the spinal nerve-roots (Bell,[23] 1811; Magendie,[24] 1822)—that now sensation as well as movement needed to be studied. It is, however, more likely that this discovery, made independently by Sir Charles Bell (1811) and Francois Magendie (1822), was itself a natural function of the Zeitgeist; someone else would have made it if they had not.[25]

Now you can not describe visual phenomena and optical systems without being quantitative and making measurements. There were, however, certain early experiments which are especially interesting because they were thought —at least later—to have measured sensation.

Bouguer in 1760 performed an experiment that anticipated Weber's Law. He had two lighted candles and a vertical rod, and he moved one candle away from the rod until its shadow on a screen was only just noticeably different (jnd) from the background on which both candles shone. Then he determined another pair of distances for another jnd and finally concluded that two illuminations are just noticeably different when they differ by about 1/64. This ratio for the jnd was independent of the total illumination.[26]

In 1815 Fraunhofer[27] undertook to measure the relative brightness of the spectral colors. He used a divided field and matched in brightness a band of the spectrum in one-half of the field with a variable white light in the other half. The resulting curve with its maximum in the yellows is the ancestor of the modern luminosity curve.[28]

It was in 1834 that the physiologist, Ernest Heinrich Weber,[29] discovered what was later to be called Weber's Law. He concluded that for pressure on the skin, the jnd is a constant fraction (about 1/30) of the weight, so that you may speak of 29 and 30 being just noticeably different without saying whether you mean ounces or drams. Weber extended his views in 1846,[30] and immediately others began trying to establish Weber's Law for senses other

[19] J. W. von Goethe, *Zur Farbenlehre*, 2 vols. (Tübingen: J. G. Cotta, 1810).

[20] J. E. Purkinje, *Beobachtungen und Versuche zur Physiologie der Sinne*, 2 vols. (Prague: J. G. Calve'sche Buchhandlung, 1819-1825).

[21] Johannes Müller, *Zur vergleichenden Physiologie des Gesichtssinnes* (Leipzig: Cnobloch, 1826).

[22] Boring, *History* (*op. cit.*), pp. 96-115.

[23] Charles Bell, *Idea of a New Anatomy of the Brain* (London: Strahan & Preston, 1811).

[24] François Magendie, "Expériences sur les fonctions des racines des nerfs rachidiens," *J. physiol. expér. Pathol.*, 1822, 2: 276-279; "Expériences sur les fonctions des racines des nerfs qui naissent de la moëlle épinière," *ibid.*, pp. 366-371.

[25] Boring, *History* (*op. cit.*), pp. 31-33.

[26] Pierre Bouguer, *Traité d'optique sur la gradation de la lumière* (Paris: Guerin & Delatour, 1760), pp. 51f.; Boring, *Sensation and Perception* (*op. cit.*), pp. 136f.

[27] Joseph von Fraunhofer, "Bestimmung des Brechungs- und Farbenzerstreuungs-Vermögens verschiedener Glassarten in Bezug auf die achromatische Fernröhre," *Denkschr. Acad. Wiss. München* (math.-nat. Cl.), 1815, 5: 193-226.

[28] Boring, *Sensation and Perception* (*op. cit.*), pp. 176-182.

[29] E. H. Weber, *De pulsu, resorptione, auditu et tactu: annotationes anatomicae et physiologicae* (Leipzig: Koehler, 1834).

[30] E. H. Weber, "Der Tastsinn und das Gemeingefühl," in Rudolph Wagner, ed., *Handwörterbuch der Physiologie* (Braunschweig: F. Vieweg und Sohn, 1846), vol. III, pt. ii, pp. 481-588.

than touch and for dimensions other than intensity. Weber's Law was quantitative. It was a measurement in the sense that it measured in terms of the stimulus a sensory distance judged quantitatively. It did not, however, imply a sensory scale.[31]

It was Fechner who turned Weber's Law into a psychological scale and into what is nowadays called Fechner's Law. He made the assumption that all just noticeable differences are equal. You count up jnd to find the magnitude of a sensation, its distance above the sensory zero, which is, of course, the absolute threshold. If S is the magnitude of the sensation and I (intensity) the magnitude of the corresponding stimulus, then Fechner's Law is $S = k \log I$. Weber's Law is $dI/I = \text{constant}$, where dI is the stimulus value of the jnd. The former comes from the latter via Fechner's assumption of the equality of all jnd.[32]

Fechner's experiments on sensory measurements during the 1850's were published in his *Elemente der Psychophysik*[33] in 1860, the book that some think marks the beginning of the new experimental psychology because it brought sensation, the representative of impalpable, immaterial, unextended consciousness, under the requirements of measurement. The three methods of measuring absolute thresholds, differential thresholds, sensory equivalents, and sensory distances that Fechner established are still the three fundamental methods today. Fechner did indeed introduce measurement formally in the new psychology, and he helped in this way to found a new science—for it was thought that the fact of being able to measure phenomena secured the status of an activity as scientific.

In the 1860's and 1870's there was, principally in Germany, great activity in measuring sensation, in establishing Weber's and Fechner's Laws. There was also great controversy, interminable Teutonic polemical talk, which led William James in 1890[34] to make his well-known satirical summary of it all:

> "And what good came of it at last?"
> Quoth little Peterkin.
> "Why that I cannot tell," said he,
> "But 'twas a famous victory!"

The other objections were three:

(1) The facts do not support the laws. Often Weber's Law seems to hold fairly well in the middle range of intensities, but fails at the extremes, especially at low intensities. If Weber's Law fails, so does Fechner's. Yet many held fondly to them because they had nothing else so good with which to replace them—the horror vacui in scientific theories.

(2) The assumption that all jnd are subjectively equal was denied. That was fair enough, and Fechner's Law was vulnerable because of this assumption. The way out was to measure supraliminal sense distances directly without reference to the jnd, but there were few such measurements available in

[31] Boring, *Sensation and Perception* (*op. cit.*), pp. 495-498.

[32] Boring, *History* (*op. cit.*), pp. 284-296.

[33] G. T. Fechner, *Elemente der Psycho-physik* (Leipzig: Breitkopf & Härtel, 1860).

[34] William James, *Principles of Psychology* (New York: Henry Holt, 1890), vol. I, pp. 533-549.

the nineteenth century. Today we have plenty, and we know that jnd of intensity do not correspond to equal subjective increments.[35]

(3) The third objection was introspective and was called the quantity objection. Sensations do not, it was argued, have magnitude. They differ only in quality. "Our feeling of pink," said William James, "is surely not a portion of our feeling of scarlet; nor does the light of an electric arc seem to contain that of a tallow candle within itself." "A low tone," said Ebbinghaus, "sounds different from a high tone, and in like manner a loud tone different from a soft." The objection was vigorously urged and at the time no one seemed to see that the argument against sensation can be applied equally well to the stimulus. True that a scarlet does not look more complex than a pink, but neither is a heavy weight more complex than a light one, or a bullet more complex than a cork.[36] After the turn of the century, this argument lapsed with the demise of introspective psychology and the rise of operationism.

The measurement of supraliminal sense-distances would be the way to determine whether the Fechner function were the logarithmic relation of the Fechner Law or something else. Psychologists seemed to be slow in taking up these determinations. Plateau[37] in the 1850's asked artists to paint a gray half way between black and white. He did not report his results until 1872, and then the next year he got Delboeuf[38] to undertake and publish experiments on the bisection of sensory distances. Delboeuf reported again on this work in 1883,[39] G. E. Müller[40] lent the weight of his prestige to the procedure in 1903, and then Titchener[41] coined the phrase *sense-distance* in 1905. The standard procedure was bisection. You had a faint sound a and a loud sound c, and you varied the intensity of an intermediate sound b until $ab = bc$. Then you could divide ab in half, or bc, and so on to any degree of fineness of scaling. Is such a sensory scale a logarithmic function of the scale of the stimulus? No, it is not.

Psychology had already been facing the problems of scaling human abilities. They came in at the turn of the century with the effort to establish scales of intelligence and to rate individual differences by mental tests. Mostly the scales for the tests were ordinal scales; they ranked people in order without indicating what intervals on the scales were equal to each other. It was Stevens' interest in psychophysics, beginning in the 1930's and carrying on to the present, that made psychologists aware of the various kinds of scales and of the possibility of purely subjective scales, which could, in a test of the Fechner function, be studied in relation to physical scales.

Stevens holds that there are three kinds of scales, or better four if you

[35] S. S. Stevens, "On the psychophysical law," *Psychol. Rev.,* 1957, *64:* 153-181.

[36] E. G. Boring, "The stimulus-error," *Amer. J. Psychol.,* 1921, *33:* 451-460.

[37] J. A. F. Plateau, "Sur la mesure des sensations physiques," *Bull. Acad. Belg. Cl. Sci.,* 1872, 2 sér., *33:* 376-388.

[38] J. R. L. Delboeuf, "Etude psychophysique," *Mém. Acad. R. Belg.,* 1873, *23:* nr. 5.

[39] J. R. L. Delboeuf, *Eléments de psycho-physique générale et spéciale* (Paris: G. Baillière, 1883).

[40] G. E. Müller, "Die Gesichtspunkte und die Tatsachen der psychophysischen Methodic," in L. Asher & K. Spiro, eds., *Ergebnisse der Physiologie* (Strassburg: J. F. Bergmann, 1903), vol. II, pt. ii, pp. 267-516.

[41] E. B. Titchener, *Experimental Psychology* (New York: Macmillan, 1905), vol. II, pt. ii, pp. 194-232.

include the initial limiting case. (1) The *nominal scale*, the beginning of quantification, is a labelling of items without ordering them, as is done for football players. (2) The *ordinal scale* places the items in rank-order, as in the raw data of mental tests. (3) The *interval scale* ranks the items and also arranges them so that the intervals between different pairs can be compared in magnitude. The method of bisection, of equal sense-distances, yields an interval scale. So does thermometry when it results in Fahrenheit or Celsius scales. These scales admit of statements about the differences between magnitudes, but, having no true zero, they do not admit of statements about the ratio of one magnitude to another. (4) The *ratio scale* is the most powerful of all, having all the properties of the others and also a true zero, which allows us to make statements about the ratio between two magnitudes. The ratio scale is familiar in physics (length, absolute temperature) but its introduction into psychophysics was a great step forward.[42]

To measure subjective intervals directly, you ask a subject to say which of two intervals appears greater to him, or else to change one until the two are equal. To measure ratios subjectively, you ask the subject to state how great one magnitude is in relation to another, or else to vary one magnitude until it has a given relation to another (is twice as great or half, or ten times as great).

Stevens did not originate the ratio scale for subjective magnitude. It seems to have been an innovation of Merkel's[43] in Wundt's Leipzig laboratory in 1888, but it had almost no use until the 1930's, when the development of electronics had made possible the control of the loudness of tones and at least eight researches between 1930 and 1936 employed ratio judgments of loudness. The one in 1936 was Stevens'.[44]

You would think that interval-scaling and ratio-scaling for the same sensory magnitudes would give consistent results, that the latter procedure would simply supply the missing zero for the scale of intervals, and Stevens presumably thought so too. He soon found, however, that the two procedures set up different attitudes in the subject and that the results do not agree. Interval judgments may, under some conditions, give results consistent with the old Fechner function, $S = k \log I$, but the outcome is generally less curved than a logarithmic function. Stevens has found for a very large number of different sensory modalities and dimensions that ratio judgments yield scales that can be described by a power function, $S = k I^n$, where n is a constant whose value varies with the sense department and with conditions of stimulation. Since the ratio scale has much more meaning than the interval scale, and since the observed data from many experiments can be described by a simple formula, Stevens[45] thinks of the power function as the true form of the function sought

[42] S. S. Stevens, "Mathematics, measurement, and psychophysics," in S. S. Stevens, ed., *Handbook of Experimental Psychology* (New York: John Wiley, 1951), pp. 30-44; "Measurement and man," *Science*, 1958, *127*: 383-389.

[43] Julius Merkel, "Die Abhängigkeit zwischen Reiz und Empfindung," *Phil Stud.*, 1888,

4: 545-547, 562-565; *ibid.*, 1889, *5*: 245-291, 499-557; *ibid.*, 1894, *10*: 203-248.

[44] S. S. Stevens, "A scale for the measurement of a psychological magnitude: loudness," *Psychol. Rev.*, 1936, *43*: 405-416.

[45] Stevens, "On the psychophysical law," *op. cit.*

by Fechner. It almost looks as if this problem might at last be regarded as settled, a full century after the publication of Fechner's *Psychophysik* in 1860.

What we have been saying about psychophysics does little more than indicate the temper of the times. The new experimental psychology may be said to have been founded by Wundt because he played the role of entrepreneur for it. The novel science was begun formally about 1860, with Fechner's *Psychophysik* and Helmholtz's monumental three volumes on physiological optics[46] (1867) and his classic on tones[47] (1863), which showed how scientific and quantitative the field could be. The researches—not the system of concepts but the experiments—grew out of experimental physiology, and Wundt actually called the new science *physiological psychology* and represented it as a Zwischenwissenschaft between physiology and philosophy. Naturally then the early phase dealt with the physiology of consciousness, and that meant with sensation and perception, topics which lent themselves readily to measurement. Later complaints were to be heard that the new psychology was nearly all physiology and had skimped learning and the cognitive mental processes; but of course that was the way it had to be. Experimental psychology had to begin somewhere, and the historical fact was that sensory physiology was there to draw upon.

Eventually, before the end of the century, there were available many measurements in every department of sense, quantitative data on quality, intensity, duration (the so-called "time-sense"), and on spatial relations for vision and touch. There was a big body of measured fact to show before Ebbinghaus brought learning under measurement in 1885, and even before there had grown up the chronology of higher mental processes which were based upon reaction times.

2. REACTION TIMES

Psychology's self-conscious effort to become "founded" as a new experimental science, an effort that derived from Wundt but was reinforced by Helmholtz, Ernst Mach, and some of the great or soon-to-be-great investigators of the 1860's, produced in Germany a group that was trying hard to advance quantitative investigation, that was on the lookout for psychological variables that are measurable. It was not so much that measurement intruded itself upon psychology as that these new psychologists were seeking out psychic measurables and dragging them triumphantly into psychology. Those were the circumstances under which both the mental chronometry and the experimental psychology of learning began.

The reaction times came from astronomy. In 1796 the Astronomer Royal at the Greenwich Observatory dismissed his assistant because his observations of stellar transits had been half a second in error and increased to nearly a whole second when he was admonished to improve—at least such was the difference in time between the measurements of the Astronomer Royal and of his

[46] Hermann von Helmholtz, *Handbuch der physiologischen Optik* (Leipzig: L. Voss, 1867).

[47] Hermann von Helmholtz (1863), *Die Lehre von den Tonempfindungen als physiologische Grundlage für die Theorie der Musik* (Braunschweig: F. Vieweg und Sohn, 1913).

assistant. Since the calibration of the Observatory's clocks depended upon this kind of observation, the discrepancy was serious.

In 1820 F. W. Bessel,[48] the astronomer at Königsberg, undertook to compare his own observations of stellar transits with those of another equally eminent astronomer. He knew about the incident at Greenwich. He was interested in errors of observation and had been talking to Gauss about them. The difference of his own observations from the other astronomer's turned out to be so large that he set about getting still other comparisons made as astronomers visited each other's observatories. There was great variability in the results; no one astronomer's deviation stayed constant. Nevertheless a great many of these discrepancies were recorded, and the phrase *personal equation* was introduced. The equation, "A-S = 0.202 sec.," means that on the average Argelander observed transits 0.202 sec. later than Struve. These personal equations are relative. No one knew at that time, moreover, why there should be these individual differences.

Later the development of electrical knowledge made possible the invention of the chronoscope (1840) and the chronograph (1859), so that the measurement of absolute personal equations became possible. You let an artificial star make the transit of a cross-hair in the field of view and measure electrically the elapsed time before a subject has pressed a key as soon as he observes the transit. These measures are, of course, reaction times. Since these personal "constants," like the relative equations, also showed too much variability to satisfy the astronomers' need for accuracy, they developed other means of observation, yet not before the psychologists had discovered that the personal equation is measuring a psychological phenomenon.[49]

Wundt was aware of this problem of variability in reaction time and spoke about it at a meeting of astronomers in 1861.[50] In 1863 he discussed it in his *Vorlesungen über die Menschen- und Thierseele*.[51] Because the transits were determined by the observer's listening to a clock ticking seconds while watching the star move across the hair-line and his estimating the fraction of a second at which the transit occurred, Wundt called this observation a *complication*, a term that Herbart had used for a perception that is composed of elements from more than one department of sense. In Wundt's laboratory the "complication experiment" was standard for a good many years, and complication clocks were built to provide the conditions under which a subject could determine the subjective synchronism of a sound and a sight, or a touch and a sight, or a sound and a touch.[52]

The more important development was, however, the way in which the absolute personal equation became a reaction time, and further the manner in which the Dutch physiologist, F. C. Donders[53] (1862), established what came to be called the subtractive procedure. Donders proceeded to complicate the

[48] F. W. Bessel, *Astronomische Beobachtungen auf der Königlichen Universitäts-Sternwarte zu Königsberg* (Königsberg: R. Leupold, 1823), vol. 8, pp. iii-viii.

[49] Boring, *History (op. cit.)*, pp. 134-142.

[50] E. B. Titchener, "Wundt's address at Speyer, 1861," *Amer. J. Psychol.*, 1923, *34*:

311.

[51] Wilhelm Wundt, *Vorlesungen über die Menschen- und Thierseele*, 2 vols. (Leipzig: L. Voss, 1863).

[52] Boring, *History (op. cit.)*, pp. 142-147.

[53] Donders, *op. cit.*

simple reaction, the immediate response to a stimulus by the movement of a finger. First, he added several stimuli but limited the response to a single movement for only one of the stimuli. He called this reaction Discrimination. It took longer than the simple reaction and the difference in time was, he thought, the time that Discrimination takes. Then he complicated the reaction still further by using several stimuli with a different finger to react to each stimulus. This was Choice, and the time that Choice takes he got by subtracting from the total time the time for Discrimination.

The Leipzig Institute under Wundt took up this procedure and the 1880's saw an elaborate development of what some called *mental chronometry*. We can put everything together into a table to show what the maximal complication at Leipzig was at one time thought to be. This table is a hierarchy. The total time for each reaction included the time of the process at the right, which is added by the conditions of the experiment, to the preceding reaction. In other words the time of each process alone is got by subtracting from the total time for the reaction the total time for the preceding reaction.

Reaction	*Conditions*	*Process*	*Subtraction*
1. Reflex	Inherited reaction	Reflex	(1)
2. Automatic action	Learned automatic action	Voluntary impulse	(2-1)
3. Simple muscular reaction	One stimulus, one movement, attention on movement, stimulus perceived	Perception	(3-2)
4. Simple sensorial reaction	One stimulus, one movement, attention on stimulus, stimulus apperceived	Apperception	(4-3)
5. Cognition reaction	Many stimuli, each apperceived, one movement	Cognition	(5-4)
6. Association reaction	Cognition reaction with association added	Association	(6-5)
7. Judgment reaction	Association reaction with judgment added	Judgment	(7-6)

Discrimination and choice were obtained by different complications.

For more than a decade this manner of measuring the time of conscious processes was one of the excitements of the new psychology. Measurement had come into the new psychology in a grand way to give it unassailable scientific status. Then Külpe[54] in 1893 leveled against the subtractive procedure a criticism that presently deflated the balloon. He appealed to introspection, the same introspection that had said that a scarlet is not so many pinks, that sensations, since they are not complex, lack magnitude. Külpe noted that the change of conditions, indicated in the second column of the table, means a change in the attitude of the subject and in the whole conscious process. For

[54] Oswald Külpe, *Grundriss der Psychologie* (Leipzig: Englemann, 1893).

instance, you do not add apperception to perception, you substitute it for perception; and so with the others. It may seem odd that so grand a dream of measurement could have been so easily dispelled, but it must be noted that nothing important emerged from these measures of reaction times. It was also true that the times for the various processes were not constant. Not even the sacred 0.1 sec. for the time of Apperception (4-3) was reliably substantiated. So, between the verdict of introspection and the unreliability of the times, the dream of measurement faded. What was left was the method of measuring reaction time, used in a hundred different ways in psychological research ever since.[55]

3. LEARNING

The new experimental psychology was born in the mid-nineteenth century of two parents: physiology and philosophy. Sense-physiology, as we have seen, furnished the experimental research on sensation and perception with both facts and methods. Philosophy contributed British empiricism, which seemed to make the study of sensation especially appropriate for an understanding of the mind, and British associationism, which grew out of empiricism and constituted at first the fundamental synthetic principle for the new science.

The development of the doctrine of association, from John Locke[56] (1690), through Bishop Berkeley[57] (1710) and David Hume[58] (1739-1740), to Alexander Bain[59] (1855) and Herbert Spencer[60] (1855), took up Aristotle's four principles for remembering the forgotten and made them into formal laws of association. Two ideas become associated so that the recurrence of one evokes the recurrence of the other, when the objects of the two are similar or contrasting or are together in space or in time. Ultimately it was seen that contrast is a form of similarity, since disparates do not even contrast, and that spatial contiguity is a form of temporal contiguity, since objects can not be together in space unless they are also together in time. When William James was writing his *Principles* (1890), the four laws had become reduced to two psychological ones: similarity and temporal contiguity, with the former debated and the latter pretty generally accepted. Two ideas that once concur in thought tend to recur together, either evoking the other—such was the basic law.

Nevertheless that law can not be universal. The recurrence of one idea can not arouse every other idea that has ever concurred with it. There are too many. There has to be selection, and for this reason philosophers, beginning with Hume, came more and more to think of associations as having different strengths dependent on the frequencies of the past contiguities. When you

[55] Joseph Jastrow, *Time-Relations of Mental Phenomena* (New York: N. D. C. Hodges, 1890) ; Titchener, *Experimental Psychology* (*op. cit.*), vol. II, pt. ii, pp. 356-392; Boring, *History* (*op. cit.*), pp. 147-153.

[56] John Locke, *Essay concerning Human Understanding* (London: Basset, 1690).

[57] George Berkeley (1710), *A Treatise concerning the Principles of Human Knowledge* (London: printed for Jacob Tonson, 1734).

[58] David Hume, *A Treatise of Human Nature: Being an Attempt to Introduce the Experimental Method of Reasoning into Moral Subjects*, 3 vols. (London: printed for John Noon, 1739-40).

[59] Alexander Bain, *The Senses and the Intellect* (London: J. W. Parker, 1855).

[60] Herbert Spencer (1855), *Principles of Psychology*, 2 ed., 2 vols. (London: Williams and Norgate, 1870-72).

heard about the law of contiguity and the law of frequency, what was meant was the law of the frequency of contiguity. Although the philosophers spoke of associative strength as depending upon the frequency of concurrences, they never got around to actual measurement, to using frequency as a measure of association. That advance waited for Ebbinghaus in 1885.[61]

In the late 1870's, Ebbinghaus picked up at a Paris bookstall a second-hand copy of Fechner's *Psychophysik*. He was fascinated by it. He saw that Fechner by measuring sensation had made psychology scientific, but that measurement had not yet been applied to the higher mental processes. So he undertook to make the application to learning and memory, working out the requirements carefully, with his eye on Fechner, Quetelet, and theory of probabilities. You can measure, he noted, the difficulty of learning a material, like prose or poetry, by counting the number of repetitions it takes to learn it. Thus he set up repetition as a measure of learning. Because prose and poetry, being in the culture, are already partly learned by those who know the language and its literature, he invented the nonsense syllable—two consonants with a vowel between, like *zat, bok, sid,* not a word—and taught himself lists of these nonsensical and thus more uniform materials. He counted the number of repetitions necessary just completely to master nonsense series of different lengths. He compared the difficulty of poetry, prose and nonsense. He studied repeated learning of the same material. He measured the strength of backward associations by observing how many repetitions were necessary to learn backwards a series that had just been learned forwards; and by a similar rearrangement he measured the strength of remote associations (syllables next but one, next but two, and so on). He measured forgetting by seeing how many repetitions were required to relearn, after different lapses of time, a series that had originally just been learned perfectly. His classical forgetting curve shows the losses of learning (repetitions necessary to relearn) for intervals varying from 20 minutes to 31 days.[62]

Ebbinghaus' contribution was a scientific break-through. He did not follow up his success but left that to others, of whom the most distinguished in the early days was G. E. Müller.[63] Methods and research multiplied rapidly, producing too huge a literature to outline here. The present writer in 1920 listed 15 standardized, approved, almost classical methods for measuring learning and memory. All depended on the same simple relationship.

If W is the amount of work done in learning, usually measured by the number of repetitions, and if M is the degree of mastery achieved, usually expressed as a percentage, and if D is the difficulty of the material learned (nonsense, prose, poetry, long materials or short), then the relation between these variables is $DM/W = a$ constant. You can keep anyone of these three variables constant, vary a second as the independent variable to be measured, and use the third, the dependent variable, as the measure. Ebbinghaus' method of complete mastery kept M constant at 100 per cent and measured D by observing W. The method of retained members measures learning in terms of M, the per cent learned, when D is varied and W is constant. How many of 10 words

[61] Ebbinghaus, *op. cit.*   *History (op. cit.)*, pp. 386-392.
[62] Murphy, *op. cit.,* pp. 174-181; Boring,   [63] *Ibid.,* pp. 371-379.

can you remember as compared with 10 nonsense syllables, when you have only five repetitions of each? The method of memory span uses D as a measure: how long a series of syllables or digits can you remember perfectly (M = 100 per cent) with 1 repetition, with 2, and so on?

These methods have tended to die out in the last three decades as American psychology has been becoming more and more behavioral in its outlook and the concepts and terminology of conditioning have been replacing the concepts and terminology of association.

The observation of what was called the conditioned reflex began in Russia with Pavlov about 1902.[64] He had been working on digestive secretion—in fact he received in 1904 the Nobel Prize for this research—and he arranged to observe the secretion of these digestive glands by turning their ducts around to open on the surface of the experimental animal's body. Thus he observed that the secretions begin when the animal perceives food. Why? Because the secretory reflex, which is an inherited response to ingested food, has now become "conditioned" to the sight of food, for the reason that the sight has been so often associated with the ingestion. This is association by frequency of contiguity. Pavlov called it *conditioning* because he wanted no truck with the vocabulary of the psychologist-mentalists. He was a thorough-going materialist, getting his view specifically from Sechenov's objective psychology of 1863,[65] but presumably more generally from the Russian Ortgeist.

At first this work on conditioning did not become very quantitative. You found the salivary reflex conditioned upon the sight of food, and then you found that by accompanying the sight with a tone you could get the tone by itself to make the saliva flow. You found that, when the normal stimulus to the reflex is eliminated, the conditioned response becomes less frequent and finally disappears, is *extinguished* as the phrase is. Nor was this work extensive until the Americans learned about it in 1914,[66] just after John B. Watson,[67] founding behaviorism (1913), adopted Pavlov's method as a behavioristic substitute for the introspectionists' association. Presently, however, there were being established learning curves, plotted against repetitions of the contiguity, and extinction curves, and then curves of generalization which showed how specific is the response to a stimulus (if the dog is conditioned to 1012 cps will he also respond to 1000 cps or does he discriminate between the two tones, or can he be taught to discriminate?).[68]

There is another development in the psychology of learning which has resulted today in a great quantity of measurement. It began in 1898 with Thorndike's work on learning in animals. He found that cats can learn to perform a fixed series of acts in order to escape confinement in a "puzzle box," a box with

[64] I. P. Pavlov, *Conditioned Reflexes: An Investigation of the Physiological Activity of the Cerebral Cortex* (London: Oxford University Press, 1927); *Lectures on Conditioned Reflexes* (New York: International Publishers, 1928).

[65] E. G. Boring, "I. Sechenov's Selected Works," *Psychol. Bull.*, 1949, 46: 309-311.

[66] Sergius Morgulis, "Pavlov's theory of the function of the central nervous system and a digest of some of the more recent contributions to the subject from Pavlov's laboratory," *J. Anim. Behav.*, 1914, 4: 362-379.

[67] J. B. Watson, "Psychology as the behaviorist views it," *Psychol. Rev.*, 1913, 20: 158-177.

[68] E. R. Hilgard & D. G. Marquis, *Conditioning and Learning* (New York: Appleton-Century, 1940).

trick catches and buttons that have to be operated in a given order to open the door. Thorndike[69] concluded that the pleasantness of escape for the animal fixed, in the process of learning, the movements that had just preceded it. Later it was discovered that rats in learning a maze learned first the movements that lead directly to the food-goal. Learning is slower the more remote it is from the goal. That is the *goal gradient*. It is a measurement. You can plot it.

This retroactive effect of success upon learning was named by Thorndike the *Law of Effect*,[70] but nowadays it is simply called *reinforcement*. In the current scene the work of B. F. Skinner and his students measures, with modern electric recording-apparatus, the operant responses of rats, pigeons and other subjects. The *operant response* (Skinner's word) is a response that is reinforced after its occurrence by reward (success).[71] The recent book by Skinner and Ferster[72] (1957) is a huge manual of 912 sets of curves which measure the conditions and variation of operant responses. Actually this research moves over toward the measurement of motivation, for the learning curves that depend on schedules of reinforcement are really descriptions of how certain different kinds of motivation work for a pigeon.

4. INDIVIDUAL DIFFERENCES AND STATISTICAL METHOD

In the excitement occasioned by the publication of Darwin's *Origin*[73] in 1859, there stand out the contributions of Darwin's cousin, Francis Galton, on mental inheritance and the measurement of human faculties. Darwin himself did not at first have much to say about the origin of man, and, even before he had published *The Descent of Man*[74] (1871) and *The Expression of Emotions in Man and Animals*[75] (1872), Galton had, in 1869, brought out *Hereditary Genius*,[76] his elaborate study of the degree in which human ability, as indicated by public reputation, runs in the same English families.

Galton noted that it is apparent that idiots and men of genius occur with comparative rarity in a population, whereas average ability is quite common. For this reason he took over from Quetelet[77] (1835) the normal law of error, which Quetelet regarded as the law of the distribution of the natural magnitudes that vary by chance—as if Nature were shooting at a target and missed the bull's eye, often a little to one side or the other, but only seldom by a great amount. Quetelet supported this application of the law to human dimensions by showing that it held approximately for the girths of chest of 5738 Scotch soldiers and for the heights of 100,000 French conscripts. Galton assumed that it would hold for genius too and posited a scale of seven grades

[69] E. L. Thorndike, "Animal intelligence," *Psychol. Monogr.*, 1898, 2: no. 4 (whole no. 8).

[70] E. L. Thorndike, *Animal Intelligence: Experimental Studies* (New York: Macmillan, 1911).

[71] B. F. Skinner, *The Behavior of Organisms: An Experimental Analysis* (New York: Appleton-Century, 1938).

[72] B. F. Skinner & C. B. Ferster, *Schedules of Reinforcement* (New York: Appleton-Century-Crofts, 1957).

[73] Charles Darwin, *On the Origin of Species by Means of Natural Selection* (London: J. Murray, 1859).

[74] Charles Darwin, *The Descent of Man, and Selection in Relation to Sex* (New York: D. Appleton, 1871).

[75] Charles Darwin, *The Expression of the Emotions in Man and Animals* (London: J. Murray, 1872).

[76] *Op. cit.*

[77] Quetelet, *ob. cit.*

of superior ability $(A, B, C, \ldots G)$ and seven of inferior ability $(a, b, c, \ldots g)$ with the average the most frequent, lying between A and a. Using Quetelet's form of the probability table, Galton could assert that natural ability A would occur in one man among four, whereas ability G would be found only once among 79,000 men, and an ability greater than G only one time in a million. He had, of course, no direct scale for the measurement of ability, but he hoped that the frequencies, interpreted in accordance with the probability function, would give him a scale of equal intervals of genius. It was a good attempt at measurement and it was a long time before it came to be generally realized that you can not assume a priori that the normal law applies to nature's magnitudes. You have to measure first and then see whether it applies. Those who sided a little with Quetelet and Galton have called it a "law of insufficient reason" (*Princip des mangelnden Grundes*), a law that holds in spite of there being insufficient reason for it,[78] whereas others have ridiculed it as a law of "the equal distribution of ignorance"[79] which is just what it is until empirical evidence for its application has been found.[80] And there was another slip in Galton's measurement of ability: reputation is not a good index of genius, not when genius is equated to natural ability.

Galton was an indefatigable measurer. His classical *Inquiries into Human Faculties and Its Development*[81] of 1883 is packed full of measurements and attempts at measurement of the phenomena that he met as he lived his life. He used to carry a paper cross and a little needlepoint, arranged so that he could punch holes in the paper to keep count of whatever he was at that time observing. A hole on the head of the cross meant *greater*, on the arm *equal*, and on the bottom *less*. He "measured" individual differences in imagery in all the sense departments. He carried a "Galton" whistle on a cane to poke through the bars at the Zoo to see how high a pitch the different animals can perceive. He measured many abilities in sensory discrimination and motor precision and proposed to inventory the English nation for their capacities as tested in this manner. Thus he was really the inventor of the mental test, although that term was coined in America by Cattell[82] (1890) in an article to which Galton appended an approving note.[83]

Galton's studies of *Natural Inheritance*[84]—the book by that title came out in 1889—showed that it is often necessary to measure the "co-relation," as he called it, between two variables, as between the statures of fathers and sons. He went far enough to see that this relationship involves two "regressions toward mediocrity"—the fathers of the sons are nearer the average than their sons, just as the sons of the fathers must also be nearer the average than their fathers. But Galton was no mathematician. He had to have help and presently turned over the problem to Edgeworth[85] (1892), who renamed the "index of co-relation" or "Galton function," as it was being called, the "coefficient of

[78] Johannes von Kries, *Die Principien der Wahrscheinlichkeitsrechnung* (Freiburg: J. C. B. Mohr, 1886).

[79] George Boole, *An Investigation of the Laws of Thought* (London: Macmillan, 1854).

[80] Boring, "Normal law of error," *op. cit.*; "Statistical frequencies as dynamic equilibria," *Psychol. Rev.*, 1941, *48*: 279-301.

[81] *Op. cit.*

[82] Cattell, *op. cit.*

[83] Boring, *History* (*op. cit.*), pp. 476-488.

[84] Francis Galton, *Natural Inheritance* (London: Macmillan, 1889).

[85] F. Y. Edgeworth, "Correlated averages," *Phil. Mag.*, 1892, 5 ser., *34*: 190-204.

correlation," with the symbol *r* for *regression*. After that Karl Pearson[86] took over, developing the products-moments method of linear correlation (1896) and founding with Galton and Weldon *Biometrika* in 1901.

From this point on the development of statistical methods and their use in psychology is too huge a topic to consider here. Let me nevertheless make four comments.

(1) The early work in biometrics was largely the study of relationships by methods of correlation. The problem of the significances of differences, and thus of experimental control, did not emerge until Gosset[87]—for so many years known only under his pseudonym, "Student"—raised it in 1908 and provided the first mathematics for what is now, since R. A. Fisher revolutionized modern statistics, a *must* in nearly every statistical investigation.

(2) The a priori assumption that the normal law applies to biological and psychological variables, and thereby provides a device for changing ordinal scales into equal intervals, has continued well into the present century. The scaling of mental tests in terms of standard deviations or some fraction thereof (standard scores, T-scales, stanines) in some ways preserves this ancient fallacy.

(3) Although Fechner in 1860 made use of the normal law of error in his method of right and wrong cases, and Galton in 1869 used the same tradition for measuring human ability, the development of psychophysics and of statistics remained quite separated until the two were brought together in the same handbook in England by Brown and Thomson[88] (1921) and later in America by Guilford (1936).[89]

(4) The great current interest in psychological scaling developed independently in psychophysics and in mental testing. In psychophysics it was held back by the preoccupation with Fechner's Law and the dubious assumption that the jnd provides a unit of subjective magnitude. Progress had to wait for the increase of interest in the "direct" methods for producing, first, equal-interval scales, and then, ratio scales.[90] In mental testing, progress has been slower, for standard scores—the use of variability (discriminal dispersion) to determine equal intervals—are still quite generally employed, although Thurstone[91] (1925, 1927, 1928) has shown that alternative procedures are possible for the tests. Both histories exhibit the persistence of an ancient habit of thought that, in spite of demonstrated error, continues by its acceptance to hinder progress.

[86] Karl Pearson, "Regression, heredity and panmixia," *Phil. Trans.*, 1896, *187A*: 253-318.

[87] W. S. Gosset ("Student"), "The probable error of a mean," *Biometrika*, 1908, *6*: 1-25.

[88] William Brown & G. H. Thomson, *The Essentials of Mental Measurement* (Cambridge, England: University Press, 1921).

[89] J. P. Guilford, *Psychometric Methods* (New York: McGraw-Hill, 1936).

[90] S. S. Stevens, "On the theory of scales of measurement," *Science*, 1946, *103*: 677-680; "Mathematics, measurement, and psychophysics," *op. cit.*; "Measurement and man," *Science*, 1958, *127*: 383-389.

[91] L. L. Thurstone, "A method of scaling psychological and educational tests," *J. educ. Psychol.*, 1925, *16*: 433-451; "The unit of measurement in educational scales," *ibid.*, 1927, *18*: 505-524; "Scale construction with weighted observations," *ibid.*, 1928, *19*: 441-453.

HOW MEASUREMENT BEGINS AND PROGRESSES

The foregoing pages have been given over to showing how measurement began and progressed in psychology's four major quantitative efforts. Let us now see if we can extract from these histories any generalities about the kinds of emergence and advance that normally occur in scientific progress.

There are, it may be said, five kinds of progressive change in scientific quantification. These categories are neither rigid nor mutually exclusive, but consideration of them serves, nevertheless, to make clear the general nature of the history of quantification in science.

(1) *Quantification is adopted because it is more adequate to the description of phenomena.* Qualitative accounts are cumbersome, usually limited to verbal distinctions and thus to discrete states rather than to continuous functions. The scientist often moves over into quantification in order to avail himself of a language more adequate to what he would report. Galileo's measurement of the relative frequency of pitches (1638) is such an instance, as is Bouguer's determination of the relative jnd for illumination (1760). Here belong Pavlov's devices for measuring amounts and rates of glandular secretion, the work that led later to the discovery of the conditioned reflex.

(2) *Quantification is favored by the desire of investigators to claim the prestige of science for their research.* Especially has this motivation operated among the psychologists, insecure because of their unscientific heritage from philosophy, and thus repeatedly insisting on the scientific validity of their new experimental psychology. Both Fechner and Helmholtz asserted the scientific status of psychology, and Wundt and Titchener devoted their lives to this demonstration. Fechner's triumph was that he had shown that sensation can be measured. Ebbinghaus, stimulated by his reading of Fechner, noted that although sensation had been measured, no higher mental process had; so he set about the task of measuring learning and memory. Galton's attempted measurement of genius by use of the normal law of error was a case of his wanting to make genius amenable to scientific rigor, though he was not then being a propagandist for the new psychology. The furor about mental chronometry in the late nineteenth century, after Donders had established the subtractive procedure for reaction times, was due to the excitement of bringing apperception, cognition, discrimination, choice, association, and judgment under scientific measurement. Science was conceived as having captured one of nature's last hold-outs, the human mind.

(3) *Sometimes progress in quantification is quick because of a sudden insight into a new possibility.* In general, scientific progress is continuous and gradual and even the crucial insights have had usually to wait upon the changing Zeitgeist before they can occur. Nevertheless there have been some quick changes. What were some of them in psychology? Weber's establishment of the law of the jnd. Fechner's measurement of sensation. Bessel and the personal equation. Ebbinghaus' measurement of learning and forgetting. Pavlov's seeing that conditioned secretion would measure perception and cognition. Thorndike and the law of effect. Gosset and the significance of a difference.

Skinner and operant conditioning. Stevens and the ratio scales. Most of these insights are not brand new. They had their backgrounds and anticipations. Nevertheless they represented a time of rapid change of interest and of subsequent scientific activity, stimulated by a new insight or method or fact, whichever it was.

(4) *Quantification may depend on historical preparation.* Fechner's originality depended upon Weber, Herbart, and even to some small extent on Gauss, just as the subsequent excitement about Weber's and Fechner's Laws depended on Fechner. Stevens and the others who work now with equal-interval scales have their roots in the investigations of Plateau, Delboeuf, and Titchener. Quetelet prepared the way for Galton to measure genius, and Galton the way for Pearson and the new statistics, and that for Gosset and Fisher and the significance of differences. Skinner needed Thorndike's law of effect as his anticipation.

(5) And then, of course, there is ordinary progress. *A new line of investigation is established and everyone joins in the new pursuit.* Mental chronometry after Donders. Psychophysics after Fechner. Learning and memory after Ebbinghaus. Conditioning after Pavlov. Scaling and operant conditioning nowadays.

Scientific progress is not, however, solely the consequence of facilitating situations and events. Progress has its deterrents and inhibitors. Here are a few that have been noted in this paper.

(a) Sometimes *progress seems to be checked by a failure of what might be considered a normal incidence of insight.* Some trends are so obvious to the historian looking back; why was the next step not seen at the time? It is impossible, however, to separate these cases from those in which a positive inhibitor can be specified or at least indicated, the cases which we consider next. Why, for instance, did not Wundt's active Institute at Leipzig take up the measurement of learning? Why was that advance left for Ebbinghaus? Was the failure at Leipzig merely because no one thought of how to do it, or was it because the Leipzig Ortgeist favored the measurement of sensation and tended to shut everything else out?

(b) Certainly the *Zeitgeister and Ortgeister work both as facilitators and inhibitors.* It is hard to go about measuring the velocity of the nerve impulse when all your colleagues of distinction are so sure it can not be done. Yet Helmholtz did. Why was any considerable effort to measure equal sensory intervals by direct comparison instead of indirectly by reference to the counting of just noticeable differences, why was this productive undertaking deferred, in general, until seventy years after Fechner's *Psychophysik?* Why was the acceptance of the normal law of distribution as something given in nature, a natural law of randomness or of human ignorance, why has it persisted to confuse statistical measurement so long? Both these instances are of the Zeitgeist. The climate of opinion was set for a long time against what seems at the present moment to be inevitable progress.

These cases are ones in which the Zeitgeist worked pretty much unconsciously. What was really resistance to progress remained inarticulate, imperceptible in currently accepted habits of thinking. The Zeitgeist can, however, become articulate, and here follow three such cases.

(c) The *quantity objection* to the measurement of sensation grew out of psychology's philosophical heritage, which supported introspectionism, the study of consciousness, as the proper business of psychology. Now actually the observation of equal sense-intervals is not inconsistent with introspectionism, but the quantity objectors asserted that introspection does not reveal sensory magnitudes. They were less wrong in their introspection than in their conception of what a psychological or physical magnitude is, but their Teutonic contentiousness must have held psychophysics back during the latter part of the nineteenth century.

The same kind of objection was raised against the mental chronometry of the reaction times, but in this case the Zeitgeist helped to shut off a development that was already doomed to failure.

(d) The same Geist that objected to psychology's measuring sensation and the times of mental processes *opposed the mental tests* because they were behavioral and not made dependent on the control of conscious processes. Since the tests in company with statistical measurement moved along fairly rapidly, it is impossible to say how much effect this explicit opposition had; but the opprobrium in which the "mental testers" were long held by the "orthodox" psychologists was strong, and it seems that it must have had some deterrent effect.

(e) Against Galton and the measurement of mental inheritance, and thus ultimately against the tests, was the *opposition to the new theory of evolution,* an opposition stronger in Great Britain than in functionally minded America. It too was a conscious phase of the Zeitgeist acting as inhibitor.

So opinion—sometimes within scientific awareness, sometimes in spite of scientific unawareness, operates to aid or hinder progress, and you may not know which it is, any more than you know at the moment whether progress has got itself into a blind alley or is going straight with a clear course ahead.

And that is the way quantification in science comes about, is pushed ahead or held back—at least it is the way these things seem to me to have happened in psychology.

APPENDIX

Dr. Price comments, if I understand him, that the important things for us to be considering are the general principles that illustrate the emergence of measurement in the respective sciences and not the actual history of quantification itself. I am at a loss to answer him. The final 1500 words of my paper consider the ways in which quantification emerged in scientific psychology in respect to the four earliest kinds of measurement which are the ones I have chosen for illustration. These conclusions do not, however, make sense unless the facts upon which they are founded are known, and with this audience I could hardly assume that knowledge in order to content myself with allusions instead of historical description.

Dr. Lazarsfeld regrets that I have not dealt with the measurement of attitudes and thus of intervening variables. Well, I could not deal with everything and I chose the earliest four with the thought that they would best fulfill the intentions of the Conference. The earliest measurement of attitude was, as a matter of fact, the finding that reaction times depend on the *Einstellung* or set or attitude out of which the reaction emerges.[92] My paper mentions briefly how Külpe made this clear. I could have gone on to show how later Külpe in the Würzburg School[93] showed that the course of thought is predetermined by attitude, by what he called the "determining tendency." The intervening variable[94] which follows on in this development, is more of a theoretical concept than a measured quantity. What I did was to discuss the emergence of quantification in my own special field; Dr. Lazarsfeld asks for a discussion of early quantification in his field, which came into quantification much later. One can not discuss everything here.

Dr. Lazarsfeld also wished I had discussed Karl Bühler's[95] use of the *Ausfragemethode* in Wundt's Laboratory (1907) as the ground from which the method of interviewing grew up. That is an interesting idea about which I know nothing. Again it is the topics in Dr. Lazarsfeld's own field that he wants to have focal.

Finally, there is Dr. Lazarsfeld's question as to why more is not made of Kraepelin's relation to Wundt, since Kraepelin took his doctorate with Wundt, being one of Wundt's earliest students, ahead of Münsterberg and Catteleven. I do not know the answer to this question. Wundt would hardly have been interested in Kraepelin's work on fatigue, concerned as Wundt was with establishing the new psychology as the study of consciousness. Bright students are apt to break away from the master, as did Helmholtz, du Bois Reymond, Ludwig, and Brücke from Johannes Müller, or for that matter Külpe from Wundt.

[92] Ludwig Lange, "Neue Experimente über den Vorgang der einfachen Reaktion auf Sinneseindrücke," *Phil. Stud.*, 1888, *4:* 479-510.

[93] Narziss Ach, *Über die Willenstätigkeit und das Denken* (Göttingen: Vandenhoeck & Ruprecht, 1905).

[94] E. C. Tolman, "Operational behaviorism and current trends in psychology," in *Proceed-*ings *of the Twenty-Fifth Anniversary Celebration of the Inauguration of Graduate Studies at the University of Southern California* (Los Angeles: University of Southern California Press, 1936), pp. 89-103.

[95] Karl Bühler, "Tatsachen und Probleme zu einer Psychologie der Denkvorgänge," *Arch. ges. Psychol.*, 1907, *9:* 297-305.

On the Progress of Quantification in Economics[†]

By Joseph J. Spengler*

"And I
Found Number for them, chief device of all."
Aeschylus, in *Prometheus Bound*
"Deus fecit omnia in pondere, in numero, et mensura."
Pascal, in *De l'esprit géométrique.*
"The irregularities of a curve apprise us more
of its true nature than does its shape."

Tobias Dantzig, in *Number, the Language
of Science.*

I HAVE organized this paper in terms of answers to questions posed by Professor Shryock and his committee, there being too little space in which to present both a detailed history of the introduction of quantitative method into economics and answers to these questions.[1] For the sake of convenience of exposition, however, I have departed somewhat from the arrangement suggested by the committee. I have neglected relatively recent quantitative developments (e.g., game theory, input-output models, activity analysis, and linear programming); in fact I have not included much matter relating to the post-1920 period.

INTRODUCTION

The empirical manifestations with which economics attempts to deal, together with the concepts and relations of which economics makes use, are quantitative or quantifiable in character, and, as a rule, are susceptible of representation in cardinal or in ordinal terms. The economist himself is interested in the discovery of "causal" or functional relations (which may be either essentially uni-directional or multi-directional and reciprocal) as well as of the patterns of movement present in temporally or spatially arranged economic data.

Quantification has assumed two main forms in economics. (a) It has assumed statistical forms which have ranged from simple, numerical descriptions to complex multi-variate analyses. For purposes of description and even of loose inference, uni-dimensional numerical indicators of economically-oriented phenomena may suffice; but for purposes of careful interpretation

† Research underlying this paper was made possible by a Rockefeller Foundation grant.
* Duke University, Durham, N.C.
1 Some of the issues raised in this paper are dealt with in "Quantification in Economics: Its History," in Daniel Lerner, ed., *Quantity and Quality* (Glencoe, Ill.: Free Press, 1960.)

and analysis (e.g., the discovery of trends, concurrence, sequence, co-variation, movement-patterns, etc.) both multi-dimensional and uni-dimensional indicators, together with appropriate techniques, may be required. (b) Quantification may assume the form of models which have been contrived to represent interrelations reflective of the manner in which certain elements are connected in the underlying world of economic reality. These models may be arithmetically illustrative in nature, or they may be more generally mathematical (i.e., geometrical, algebraic, and so on) in character. Such models tend to be quite abstract, since one of their functions usually is to explain much by little;[2] certainly they will be far more abstract than are statistical forms of quantification which usually reflect economic reality relatively closely. Historically, quantification was descriptively statistical in character before it assumed more abstract arithmetical or mathematical forms. Presumably, analysts could not imagine models until after they had acquired an adequate understanding of the economic-behavioral tendencies of individuals, enterprises, or communities, and crude statistical inquiry could and did contribute to this understanding.

Forms (a) and (b) usually are combined, for statistical treatments of data can yield little beyond description unless they are based upon models or sets of hypotheses; and the expositive or predictive power of models cannot be effectively assessed unless they are subjected to verification which commonly assumes a statistical form. Forms (a) and (b) were not consciously and effectively combined, however, until late in the nineteenth century, even though the composite character of the task of hypothesizing and verifying was appreciated already in the eighteenth century and received varying amounts of attention, empirical and otherwise, in private and public inquiries at all times in the nineteenth century.[3] The economic theorist has always insisted, however, that it is at least as important to check "statistical inductions by abstract reasoning" as it is to verify "abstract reasoning by statistics."[4]

---

[2] E.g., see M. Friedman, *Essays in Positive Economics* (Chicago, 1953), p. 14. E. Rotwein's critique of Friedman's approach is not applicable to the above point. See Rotwein, "On 'The Methodology of Positive Economics,'" *Quarterly Journal of Economics,* 1959, *73:* 554-575.

[3] According to the Report of the General Secretaries of the Royal (then called London) Statistical Society in the Society's *Journal,* 1838, *1:* 322, political economy then remained in the "inductive" stage, thus resembling astronomy in the period "before the discoveries of mechanical philosophy" had enabled philosophers to use astronomical observations to test "the great primal truths of physical philosophy" and help to "explain, and even to predict, the varied motions and phenomena of the earth and heavens." So long as economics remained in this "inductive" stage, there was need for "observation without premature speculation." T. C. D. Lawson insisted, however, as did other economists, that political economy

"points out the proper object of statistical inquiry and draws conclusions from their results." See "On the Connexion between Statistics and Political Economy," *ibid.,* 1843, *6:* 322. Even J. M. Keynes restricted "the business of statistical technique" to "preparing the numerical aspects of our material in an intelligible form, so as to be ready for the application of the usual inductive method"; it was not concerned with turning "its results into probabilities." See *A Treatise On Probability* (London, 1921), p. 392.

[4] E.g., see P. G. Wright's criticism of H. L. Moore's statistically derived, upward-sloping demand curve for producers' goods in "Moore's Economic Cycles," *Quarterly Journal of Economics,* 1914-15, *29:* 638; also A. A. Young's critique of F. C. Mill's argument that statements of economic tendency are but statements of what has been arrived at inductively. See *Economic Problems New and Old* (Boston, 1927), pp. 241-244.

Since much of this paper has to do with post-1800 developments, it needs to be noted that economics developed quite slowly, not beginning to deal with exclusively mundane issues until several centuries of mercantilism and nationalism had dissipated most of the ethical and other-worldly orientation given to economic discussion in the Middle Ages. Economics itself did not assume a relatively stable form until the second half of the eighteenth century when the works of Quesnay and Adam Smith in particular gave it shape and bounds. Both authors made use of quantitative data to describe aspects of the behavior of the economy which each viewed as a kind of machine made up largely of owners of productive services whose individual pursuit of self-interest was regulated and conciliated by competition. Smith made rather more use of statistical data than did Quesnay, employing them particularly to describe longer-run trends and fluctuations and to support various of his inferences. Quesnay's use of quantitative materials was more analytical, however, than was Smith's; for example, he employed statistical data to discover which mode of agriculture was most productive. Moreover, partly on the basis of his statistical account of the French economy, he contrived an arithmetical model descriptive of economic circulation in France,—a model whose potential usefulness, apparently first remarked by Marx, is still appreciated. The work of both Quesnay and Smith would suffer greatly were it stripped of its quantitative content. Furthermore, its indicator of welfare—per capita output instead of the mercantilists' aggregate output or Bentham's utilitarian greatest good of the greatest number—would become blurred.

The predecessors of Smith and Quesnay fall largely into two classes, the mercantilists, together with their critics, and the political arithmeticians. The methodological approach of the mercantilists and their critics, viewed as a group, may be described as crypto-quantitative. Few of them made a great deal of use of quantitative data; yet they often were concerned with more and less and with determinants of changes in economic magnitudes, and they may be described as quite favorable to a quantitative approach. Richard Cantillon, considered by some to have been the founder of political economy despite his endorsement of certain mercantilist views, based a number of his findings upon an extensive and detailed statistical inquiry, the copies of which have been lost.

The political arithmeticians were much more quantitatively oriented than were the mercantilists; in fact they rested many of their conclusions (even as did Cantillon who might well be included with them) upon quantitative observations. Moreover, when they were concerned with such matters as building annuities upon mortality experience, they proceeded in a manner that helped give rise to the nineteenth-century view that regularity and uniformity characterize social phenomena. They were essentially empiricists, however. For example, Gregory King confined his efforts to preparing what was long the best estimate of the income of any country, England or otherwise. William Petty went further in that he derived his conclusions largely from analysis of the statistical data available and anticipated the view that statistical investigation might take the place of experimentation. The political arithmeticians did not proceed generally, as did Smith and Quesnay, to utilize a body of organized theory to suggest tentative findings that might be subject to empirical verification. This approach emerged only with the transformation of diverse economic observations and presuppositions into an organized body of essentially scientific knowledge in the late eighteenth century.

THE DETERMINANTS OF QUANTIFICATION

While the introduction of quantitative methods into economics was governed by both external and internal factors, the pace of their introduction seems to have been governed more by internal than by external factors. Of course, since some of these determinants are hard to categorize, their description as exclusively external or internal is somewhat arbitrary, even though it does not appreciably distort our analysis of their impact.

Among the external determinants, we may include the state of mathematics and statistics, the degree of acquaintance of economic writers with quantitative methods, the cultural *Weltanschauung*, the example of other sciences, the availability of data, and the role of the state in economic affairs. Of these only the second and the last two seem, at particular times, to have limited recourse to quantification.

While quantification must always have been retarded, as it still is, by deficiencies in the mathematical and statistical training of economic analysts, it was not retarded by laggardness in the development of relevant mathematical and statistical techniques. With few exceptions (e.g., linear programming) progress in these techniques seems to have kept more than abreast of progress in the demands made on mathematics and statistics by economists, even though economic applications began to be made of algebra, calculus, and advanced statistics as early as the eighteenth century. Furthermore, by the closing years of the nineteenth century, some economists had acquired enough proficiency in mathematics and statistics to invent appropriate techniques or to accommodate existing techniques to the analysis of problems under consideration. Until relatively late in the nineteenth century, however, and long after the age of enthusiasm (1830-1850) when many statistical societies and some journals were established, the emphasis of statistics (already nominally two centuries old) remained upon the accumulation, organization, and careful presentation of numerical data; and yet, as J. A. Schumpeter observes, economists still failed as they long had failed to avail themselves of even the "most primitive devices for presenting figures."[5] This conclusion is borne out both by what one finds in almost all of the treatises on statistics and by the contents of

[5] *History of Economic Analysis* (New York, 1954), p. 526. William Playfair's skillful use of pie diagrams and of bar, line, and circle graphs in works on economic trends exercised little influence, as did the use of co-ordinate paper around 1800, Lalande's use of logarithmic grids in 1843, and the occasional use of other devices. W. A. Jevons, exponent of the use of rectangular grids and first economist to employ arith-log grids, exercised little influence on graphical presentation, even in "the age of enthusiasm in graphics" (i.e., 1860-1900). As late as 1885 A. Marshall and E. Levasseur, in discussions of graphics, neglected arith-log graphs, and as late as 1917 they remained little known and used. See papers by Marshall and Levasseur in the *Jubilee Volume of the Statistical Society* (London, 1885), pp. 218-62; I. Fisher, "The Ratio Chart for Plotting Statistics," *Publications of the American Statistical Association*, 1916-1917, 15: 577-601; H. G. Funkhouser, "Historical Development of the Graphical Representation of Statistical Data," *Osiris*, 1937, 3: 269-404.

articles appearing in representative economic and statistical periodicals.[6] The early efforts of Quetelet to extend the "law of error" and the "law of great numbers" to social phenomena had not yet appreciably and directly modified the practice of economists who made use of statistics. But they must have been preparing the way for Francis Galton and Karl Pearson and their associates—men who contributed greatly, as did the brilliant economist, F. Y. Edgeworth, to the development and/or the application of various statistical techniques of which economic analysts began to make use in and after the closing years of the nineteenth century. Still, the foundations of these techniques had long been made known, having been largely originated in the seventeenth and eighteenth centuries; and sampling was relied upon in the second half of the eighteenth century to furnish estimates of national populations. Moreover, men had come to conceive of the universe and of human behavior as quite regular in the large and hence amenable to quantitative analysis. By the very early nineteenth century, probability theory, together with the normal curve and various measures of dispersion and deviation, had been firmly established by Laplace, Gauss, and Legendre; and the findings of these men were being given wider currency by their students and followers. In 1837 S. D. Poisson made known his curve of distribution, believing it to be an expression of "the Law of Great Numbers"; and in 1846 Bravais anticipated the idea of correlation, later developed by Galton and Pearson and extensively used by economists after if not in the 1890's. It should be noted that economists as well as analysts interested in economic data were much more empirically oriented than were the mathematicians. They were interested in knowing about those conditions in the world of man and nature which gave rise to various types of distribution (normal and otherwise), in developing measures of dispersion and central tendency which would facilitate empirical inquiry, in isolating the several movements present in empirical patterns, and in devising and fitting curves, etc.[7]

---

[6] Illustrative of the conception of statistics usually obtaining about the time the great development of this subject was initiated in the 1890's by English, Italian, and certain other scholars is A. Meitzen's *History, Theory, and Technique of Statistics* (translated by R. P. Falkner), supplement to Vol. I of the *Annals* of the American Academy of Political and Social Science (Philadelphia, 1891). Exceptional was A. Gabaglio's *Storia e teoria generale della statistica* (Milan, 1880). The best of current statistical theory was incorporated in Edgeworth's "Methods of Statistics," in the *Jubilee Volume of the Statistical Society* (London, 1885), pp. 181-217. Therein Edgeworth dealt with the comparison of means, the law of error and its genesis and use, the determination of the spread of the normal curve as indicated by its modulus (i.e., the standard deviation multiplied by $\sqrt{2}$), and the application of the calculus of probabilities to anthropometrical, vital-statistical, banking, and other data, and to concatenations of comparisons. A. L. Bowley's *Elements of Statistics* (London, 1901), incorporated much of the best of the current economic-statistical techniques. Yet economists were slow to make use of the new and improved techniques. See Bowley's address, reported in the *Journal of the Royal Statistical Society*, 1906, 69: 541, 548; also W. M. Persons, *Forecasting Business Cycles* (New York, 1931), chap. 16.

[7] On Edgeworth's statistical contributions see A. L. Bowley, *F. Y. Edgeworth's Contributions to Mathematical Statistics* (London, 1928). Edgeworth's and Pearson's systems are contrasted in *ibid.*, pp. 81-85. For accounts of the development of statistics see V. John, *Geschichte der Statistik* (Stuttgart, 1884); Helen Walker, *Studies In The History of Statistical Methods* (Baltimore, 1929); F. F. Stephan, "History of the Uses of Modern Sampling Procedure," *Journal of the American Statistical Association*, 1948, 43: 12-39; H. Westergaard, *Contributions To The History of Statistics* (London, 1932). According

Undoubtedly the progress made by physics, mechanics, and mathematics in the seventeenth century facilitated the introduction of quantitative methods into the study of social and economic phenomena. Yet, how important was this influence in the short and in the longer run remains to be established. Certainly, social theorists abandoned teleologism, hierarchism, etc., and began to look upon social phenomena as something to study rationally and objectively. Society began to be looked upon in mechanistic terms and its behavior began to be thought of in terms of equilibrium and balance.[8] The resulting shifts in natural philosophical emphasis were at least potentially quite favorable to the quantification of economic inquiry, in and after the seventeenth century; even non-quantitative writers (e.g., Bacon and Hobbes) helped establish a philosophical or heuristic basis for quantitative inquiry. The work of political arithmeticians and others reflects this new influence and its increasing emphasis upon objective empirical research, in part because wide currency was given to the new views and the *Weltanschauung* associated therewith.[9]

A detailed comparison of the introduction of mathematical and statistical techniques into economics in England and Italy with its apparently more laggard introduction in Germany might also reveal the impact of cultural differences, though differences in conceptions of economics probably were most responsible for the lag. Comparison of economics with the other social sciences suggests that post-1800 economics, since it underwent quantification more rapidly than did other social sciences, could not derive much inspiration from these sciences (with the partial exception of vital statistics). Economics therefore had to draw largely upon its own resources, tentatively inferring principles or sets of propositions and subjecting them to mathematical or other quantitative analysis. It is possible, of course, that economists draw some inspiration from astronomy and its problems, of which A. Smith and others were aware, and that knowledge of meteorology may have influenced others than Jevons who got therefrom his view of economic cycles.

The progress of quantification in economics, as in other social sciences, was conditioned by the availability of data and hence by the magnitude of the economic role assumed by the state, together with the amount of data purport-

---

to Walker (*op. cit.*, pp. 25-30), J. F. Encke's treatise, published in 1832 and the basis for later textbooks, "reads much as though it had come from the Pearson laboratory in an early day." While Condorcet and Laplace were interested in problems of elections, they did not relate their analyses to problems of economic welfare. See Duncan Black, *The Theory of Committees and Elections* (Cambridge, 1958), pp. 159-185.

[8] P. A. Sorokin, *Contemporary Sociological Theories* (New York, 1928), pp. 4-13. In the preface to Sir Dudley North's *Discourses Upon Trade* ([1691], Baltimore, 1907, p. 11), Descartes is accredited with having formulated the method ("so much approved and accepted in our Age") that permitted the reduc-

tion of economic discussion to terms of "principles." Until such was done there was little scope for models. North (*ibid.*, p. 11) specifically rejected principles of Aristotelian origin, apparently because he found them empirically irrelevant.

[9] A. C. Crombie's study of medieval mechanics leads me to infer that social scientists might well have gotten therefrom a conception of equilibrium adapted to economic analysis. See Crombie, *Augustine to Galileo* (Cambridge, 1953), pp. 83-87. Undoubtedly lack of familiarity with medieval mechanics, together with the then orientation of economic discussion, contributed to the neglect by economic writers of the example of medieval mechanics.

edly required to fulfill this role. For, at least until recently, the social sciences were not able (as are natural sciences) to supply much of their own quantitative data; they found it necessary, therefore, to work with what was at hand. It is true, of course, that, even before 1850 when data were more sparse, economists did not make as much use of the data available as they might have done. But it is also true that data, though available, were not always readily accessible, or to be had in a form suited to answer particular questions. Sampling theory, though anticipated by Laplace, does not begin to be expounded until near the close of the nineteenth century, and even then very little practical use was made of it; in fact, use of economic samples apparently did not become widespread until in or after the 1930's, under the impact of depression and (later) of war. Economists therefore had to accommodate their inquiries to the kinds of data available; thus they could study (as did Tooke, for example) changes in the purchasing power of money, since a variety of price data had become available, but they long could not, as Cournot had hoped,[10] utilize readily available data to construct demand curves; and they sometimes proceeded as if they were sampling by drawing conclusions from what were really unrepresentative collections of price or wage or other data.[11] Even so, the amount and the accessibility of data increased as time passed, in part because economists declared data to be useful and indicated what sorts were needed. Most responsible, nonetheless, for improvement in the quantity and quality of economic data was increase in the economic role, regulatory and otherwise, of the state. Frequently data were assembled and analyzed in reports done by or for governmental agencies. Furthermore, an increasing number of bureaus (with actual or potential duties requiring statistical information) were established and these became collectors and repositories of quantitative information respecting many aspects of economic life. Yet, not until after World War I and the rise of macro-economics in the wake of the Great Depression was the economy viewed as a totality whose condition and behavior might be continually revealed through the assembly, organization, and publication of a variety of income, employment, and other statistics.[12]

The rate at which economics was quantified was governed principally by

[10] A. A. Cournot observed that price observations might be obtained and, "by the well-known methods of interpolation or by graphic processes," converted into an "empiric formula or a curve." See *Researches into the Mathematical Principles of the Theory of Wealth* (translated by N. T. Bacon) (New York, 1929), pp. 47-48. Because he lacked such data, Cournot proceeded to construct a function generally compatible with experience. On sampling, see Stephan, *op. cit.*

[11] On factual work in economics in 1790-1870 see J. A. Schumpeter, *op. cit.,* pp. 519-526. For some time the data-supplying function now carried on by governmental publications was performed at least in part by such journals as that of the Royal Statistical Society.

[12] We have G. King's estimate of England's income as of 1688, A. Young's for 1770, and 18

estimates for the nineteenth century; not until in the second quarter of the present century did estimates begin to be made annually. See Phyllis Deane, "The Industrial Revolution and Economic Growth: The Evidence of Early British National Income Estimates," *Economic Development and Cultural Change,* 1957, *5:* 159-174. While the problems generated by the Great Depression increased the demand for macro-economics, its development, as well as its quantification and algebraizing was facilitated by the contributions of W. I. King, W. C. Mitchell, S. Kuznets, A. F. Burns, and others, to national income accounting. Some of the early income estimates, together with the materials presented therein, are dealt with by Paul Studenski in his *The Income of Nations* (New York, 1958).

conditions endogenous to the science, largely because (as we show below) the several schools of economists conceived of economics in terms not then considered very susceptible of extensive quantification. As has been noted already, many of the empirical manifestations with which economists are inclined to deal are actually or potentially quantitative in nature. This was recognized in part even by Aristotle and later by his scholastic followers who dealt with commutative justice in somewhat quantitative terms, even though they did not concern themselves with such available accounting records as related to the public or to the private sectors of economies, or with wage, tax, price, and other existing quantitative data. During the period when mercantilism was ascendant (especially in sixteenth and seventeenth centuries) and interest in economic affairs was steadily increasing, economic writings reflected awareness of such quantitative data and of various commonsense categories (e.g., interest, wages, taxes, duties, imports, exports, etc.) in terms of which such data tended to be organized. Even so, economics could not experience effective quantification until enough of its categories had gotten conceptualized (as they did in the eighteenth century if not somewhat earlier) in terms susceptible of arithmetical or mathematical treatment. Yet, though mathematics was employed in economics nearly ten times before 1800, though most economists made some use of statistics, though a few made use of arithmetical models (if seldom as effectively as did Ricardo), though about forty mathematico-economic items had been published by 1838 when Cournot's great work appeared, and another sixty items had appeared by 1871 when Jevon's *Theory* was first published, Jevons still could properly complain that the use of mathematical methods was being neglected.[18] By 1888 another 106 mathematico-economic methods had appeared; and within another two years the influential works of Marshall and of Auspitz and Lieben, each containing much mathematical matter, had been published, to be followed within six years by Pareto's *Cours* in which the Lausanne mathematical tradition initiated by Walras in 1874 was continued and elaborated.

DIFFERENTIAL PROGRESS IN QUANTIFICATION

Despite the fact that the methods employed in the various branches of economics had much in common, quantification did not always proceed at the same rate in all its branches, in part because in some, more data were available or quantification was easier, and in part because the interest of economists in various branches of economics varied in time. Even so, the tendency for one aspect of a science to be quantified before another apparently was far less pronounced in economics than in other social sciences or in some of the biological and life sciences.

[18] See Appendices III–V and prefaces to editions one through five, included in *The Theory of Political Economy*, 5th ed. (New York, 1957). I have been told that as late as 1900 only about 50 copies of the original printing of Cournot's work (see note 10 above) had been sold. Cournot's work is in the highly abstract and purely mathematical tradition while J. H. von Thünen's is in the empirico-quantitative tradition. Von Thünen translated empirical and experimental findings into mathematical terms whereas Cournot inferred his conceptions of functional relationships from postulates and crude observation of man's economic behavior.

Availability of data and techniques, together with the development of interest in problems, had much to do with the selection of areas for statistical inquiry. Thus Jevons's concern with the changing value of gold gave rise in the 1860's to his interest in the removal of seasonal and cyclical variations while Poynting's interest in the connections obtaining between price and import movements led him to originate the variate difference method in 1884. Methods adapted to the study of the correlation and the periodicity of time-series—periodigrams, harmonic analysis, etc.—got little attention until after 1914, even though the necessarily quantitative character of the study of economic fluctuations had been recognized since at least the middle of the nineteenth century. Lack of interest in the trade cycle as a phenomenon (probably fostered by the construction put upon Say's Law), together with failure to develop or adapt suitable techniques, accounted in considerable part for this lag. With the development, in and right after the 1890's, of correlation and other techniques designed to uncover associations, economists began to inquire into the connections obtaining between divers economic variables (e.g., prices, imports, employments, etc.) and between economic and non-economic variables (e.g., marriage rates); but they apparently did not begin to make at all extensive use of the new techniques until the second decade of the present century. Although index numbers did not come into general use until after 1900, far more than a century after price indices had first been used, understanding of the advantages and disadvantages associated with alternative forms steadily increased, especially after 1850, with the important contributions coming from economic theorists rather than from statisticians.[14] Work on wage movements lagged behind that on price movements, in part at least because data were less accessible. Effective work on the behavior of employment was not begun in England until the 1890's, not many years before the state undertook to provide unemployment "insurance." Composite economic-activity indices did not begin to replace simple measures until after World War I. Despite Verhulst's work (1838-47) on the logistic curve, very little attention was given to growth curves until after World War I; reliance was placed in simple, linear, relatively short-run projections. Measures of the distribution of income and wealth commanded much informed attention in and after the 1890's, probably because of increasing controversy respecting the actual and the prospective distribution of the fruits of that economic progress of which most Westerners had become aware.

Quantifiable economic phenomena, as envisaged by economists before World War I, may be grouped roughly as follows: (a) response of prices to changes in the quantity of money; (b) response of "utility" to changes in the quantity of utility-producing means at an individual's disposal; (c) response of purchases and (later) supplies to price or income changes; (d) response of entrepreneurial profit to changes in volume of goods sold or in quantity of factors hired; (e) conditions of general equilibrium, together with the process of equilibration; (f) phenomena whose study resulted in a merger of mathematical and statistical approaches. Of these groups (a) and (b) were the first to command considerable interest. In time, however, categories (c) and (d),

---

[14] On this last point see Schumpeter, *op. cit.,* p. 1093.

with which problems of tax incidence should also be grouped, came to command more interest than did (a) and (b). Interest in (e) and (f) developed somewhat later than that in (c) and (d).

(a) As a result of the inflow of treasure from the New World, it was noted at least as early as 1568 that price movements depend in part upon the movement of the volume of money, and crude algebraic expression was given to this relationship as early as 1694, though velocity apparently was not introduced into so-called "quantity" equations until 1811. By the 1840's, however, a Fisherine type of equation was being developed. (b) The earliness with which utility was quantified may be attributable to the importance attached to utility as a criterion of worth already in the eighteenth century; and continuing interest in its quantification reflected both the belief that utility afforded a basis for evaluating rational economic activity and the inference that economic analysis and economic planning called for something like diminishing utility. Bernoulli utilized calculus and probability theory in a discussion of utility in the 1730's; and in and after the 1840's, when an explicit quantitative approach again replaced a verbal though implicitly quantitative approach, utility (then confined largely to riskless situations) was dealt with, as was "consumer's surplus," in arithmetical, geometrical, and other mathematical terms.[15] (c) Demand and supply were treated as functions of price by Cournot as early as 1838, but this mode of expression, though sometimes employed thereafter, did not become popular until Marshall's *Principles* appeared in 1890, and it was not given effective empiric expression in the form of statistical curves until the early 1900's seven decades after Cournot had called for such expression. Walras's statement that demand for a commodity is a function of both its price and other prices was disregarded, as a rule, but on grounds of expositive convenience. While considerable work was done on personal and family income and expenditure, in and after the 1850's, it was not translated into terms of income-elasticity of demand, probably because income changes were not considered important enough in the short run to be significant causes of changes in rate of consumption.

(d) Use of differential calculus enabled Cournot in 1838 to determine how much an enterprise, bent upon maximizing its profit, might offer for sale under varying conditions of demand and competition; it thus also permitted him to define competition (a term long in use) precisely. His attainment of an equilibrium solution recalls Bernoulli's use of calculus a century earlier to represent diminution of the marginal utility of income and thus make possible a solution of the St. Petersburg Paradox. In 1850 Von Thünen made explicit the fact that, with the imputed product of factors of production tending to diminution at the margin, it paid the entrepreneur to hire additional factors only up to the point where a factor's hire-cost coincided with its capacity to add to the firm's revenue.[16] Out of the work of these writers came the pre-

---

[15] L. J. Savage, *The Foundations of Statistics* (New York, 1954), pp. 91-104. Savage touches upon the history of utility in both riskless and risky situations.

[16] As early as 1815 Georg von Buquoy had shown that it paid the agriculturist to plow only up to the point where the marginal cost of plowing equalled its marginal contribution to a farm's revenue. On his and other early uses of calculus to discover points of equilibrium when the derivative of one or both functions is increasing or decreasing, see

cision with which economists subsequently sought to express themselves when dealing with firms operating under various conditions of competition. They could envisage and quantify the problems under consideration correctly, however, because, unlike most of the classical economists, they clearly identified the decision-making enterprises and specified what rational behavior entailed. Out of the work of Von Thünen, together with the imputation theory developed by the Austrian and Lausanne schools, came lines of inquiry which involved use (in and after 1894) of Euler's theorem in the analysis of functional distribution and, some 25-30 years later, use of production functions to facilitate empirical analysis of functional distribution.[17]

(e) While Isnard was the first (1781) to describe mathematically the interdependence of economic quantities, and while Cournot noted this interdependence, it remained for L. Walras to give it remarkably complete and full expression in 1874, for Cassel to popularize it (after 1900), and for Marshall, Pareto, and others to give currency to the general idea that prices are interrelated much as are marbles situated in a bowl. Even so, empirical economic analysis seems not to have been much influenced by Walras's contribution, in part because it was difficult to apply empirically and in part because reasonably satisfactory results could be gotten when particular prices, or sets of prices, were abstracted from the price system and studied in isolation. The interdependence of macro-economic quantities, though dealt with verbally by the classical economists, was not treated quantitatively and systematically until in and after the 1930's, the theoretical work of Keynes and others, together with the growing availability of data, having finally made this approach much more feasible than when Marx sought to apply Quesnay's concept of circular flow to the study of intersectoral balance.

(f) Empirical and statistical modes of quantitative analysis did not begin to be effectively integrated with the use of abstract models until the close of the nineteenth century. For example, in the work of W. S. Jevons (1835-1882), the first great English economist to stress the quantitatively empirical as well as the abstractly theoretical, the two approaches are imperfectly blended. Around and not long after the turn of the century, however, we find such economists as Pareto, H. L. Moore, Irving Fisher, and W. M. Persons beginning to combine more or less effectively the use of abstract models with that of advanced statistical techniques. Inasmuch as each of these economists was animated by strong empirical interests, it may be inferred that the quantitatively empirical is most likely to be combined with the quantitatively abstract when the economist has strong empirical interests as well as technical proficiency.

STAGES IN QUANTIFICATION

The quantification of economics may be said to have passed through several stages of development, though some are not very conspicuous. The writings

---

R. M. Robertson, "Mathematical Economics Before Cournot," *Journal of Political Economy*, 1949, *57:* 523-536.

[17] E.g., see G. J. Stigler, *Production and Distribution Theories* (New York, 1941). I have made use in this paper of many of Stigler's excellent papers on quantitative aspects of economics, but for lack of space have not cited them.

of the mercantilists, of the anticipators of Quesnay and Smith, and of Quesnay and Smith themselves, were essentially qualitative in character, though often sprinkled with statistical information and occasional quantitative discussions. Still, it became possible to render economics mathematical only in proportion as the concepts required for economic analysis became well defined and demarcated and hence translatable into quantitative or quantifiable terms. In consequence, quantification always lagged behind qualification, and this lag was accentuated by the fact that effective quantification presupposed not only a clarification of concepts but also the transformation of these concepts into an engine of analysis. At some point always, in the course of this process of qualitative conceptualization and integration, however, attempts at quantification began to result in clearer definitions of concepts, with the further result that transformation of these concepts into an analytical system got effectively and rapidly under way: witness Cournot's clarification of the meanings of demand, market, competition, duopoly, monopoly, etc.; or Walras's specification of an economic system; or the mathematical economist's definitions of marginal utility. Marshall even believed, as late as 1896, that, although the nineteenth century had "in great measure achieved *qualitative* analysis in economics," "quantitative analysis" remained to be achieved.[18] His interpretation, though insufficiently qualified, may be accepted, provided that it allows for the fact that the rate at which economics was undergoing quantification increased quite appreciably in the second half of the nineteenth century. It should be noted also that progress in quantification sometimes undermined what had earlier been considered progress in quantification; for example, the notion of utility was shown to be unnecessary, and the maximization of something called welfare, much discussed by Marshall and Pareto and others, was shown to be possible only under highly restricted conditions.

If we grant that economics remained primarily qualitative, though decreasingly so, up to the 1890's, we must account for the burgeoning of quantification that got under way in the 1890's and, even though slowed down by World War I, retained enough momentum to flourish once again thereafter. Many factors, of which we can do little more than take notice, contributed to this burgeoning. Most important, perhaps, is the fact that by the 1890's, many of the methodological differences which had distinguished the several schools of economics had been sufficiently composed, and many of the concepts in use had been sufficiently clarified, to make quantification easy. Quantitative techniques had improved and were continuing to improve rapidly. The number of persons familiar with such techniques, or capable of adapting mathematical and statistical devices and operations to economics, had greatly increased. The number of periodicals which gave considerable space to technical economics, and occasionally to papers wherein mathematics was used, had greatly increased between 1850 and 1900. Finally, and of great importance, is the fact that in and shortly after the 1890's there came to the fore a number of technically proficient and mathematically competent economists who were extremely enthusiastic about the role that mathematics and advanced statistics could play in the development of economic theory and in its empirical applica-

[18] See A. C. Pigou, ed., *Memorials Of Alfred Marshall* (London, 1925), p. 301.

tion. Mention may be made, for example, of Edgeworth, Cassel, Wicksell, and Pareto and his disciples, of Irving Fisher, H. L. Moore, and W. S. Persons; they may have been more restrained in their enthusiasm than Quetelet had been, and yet they served (much as did Keynes's young disciples in the 1930's) to extend the application of quantitative methods and to win adherents to their use; they triggered off the quantification-favoring potential that had been built up during the nineteenth century.

Although statistics may be said to have passed through an age of enthusiasm in 1830-1850, when statistical journals and societies were being established, this enthusiasm did not really infect economics, though it may have infected some statisticians who had come to look upon economics as a branch of statistics or of (an essentially Comtean) sociology. For nineteenth-century economists, armed with a fairly well articulated set of qualitative principles (whether in the classical, the historical, or other traditions), tended to view statistics as but a handmaiden to economics; and they also remained insufficiently committed to mathematical methods to develop much enthusiasm for this approach. In consequence, we may say, if we abstract from the unfavorable reception sometimes accorded Ricardo, that volatility did not characterize the adoption of quantitative methods by economists. Their adoption was slow but relatively steady, and the process remained so even after the 1850's when quantification began to progress more rapidly.[19] Economics did not, therefore, experience a retreat from a pronounced but merely temporary emphasis upon quantification.

THE SCHOOLS

Economists may be grouped into five schools, the classical, the Austrian, the historical, the Marxian, and the neo-classical, given that the essentially mathematical economists are not described as constituting a distinct school. Of these schools the neo-classical was quite favorable to the quantitative approaches, and the Austrian was relatively so; most of the mathematical economists (whose contributions were discussed earlier) may therefore be looked upon as having affinity with these two schools, or as being anticipators of them. On methodological grounds the classical school found the employment of some quantitative approaches to be of only limited use. The position of the historical and the Marxian schools is less easy to summarize; they did not, however, make much use of quantitative methods until the latter part of the nineteenth century. It may be said in general, therefore, that since the classical school exercised more influence than did any other during the first 60-70 years of the nineteenth century, the supersession of this school by an

[19] Ricardo's mode of exposition and analysis was comparatively abstract; it rested upon the use of many arithmetical models, and it seemingly disregarded constraints that might flow from institutional arrangements. It was therefore subjected to a great deal of criticism on methodological and empirical grounds by historical and other economists who were much less critical, however, of the sometimes more loosely phrased or more institutionally oriented views of Smith and J. S. Mill. Accordingly, if it be said that Ricardo's abstractly quantitative approach typified classical economics, it may also be said that subsequently classical economics did become less quantitative. It is questionable, however, whether Ricardo's approach may be said to typify that of the classical school, even though its members endorsed many of his propositions.

increasing powerful neo-classical school greatly facilitated the development and spread of quantitative approaches.

While some members of the classical school made use of statistical data, the four who concerned themselves explicitly with methodology (i.e., J. B. Say, N. Senior, J. S. Mill, and J. E. Cairnes) assigned little importance to the use of quantitative methods, though they sometimes found in quantitative materials confirmation of their deductions. Mill expressed a fairly representative view when he said that "the method *a priori* in political economy and in all other branches of moral science, is the only certain or scientific mode of investigation," and limited the role of inductive methods to one of verification and of assessment of disturbing circumstances. Even if one discovered what seemed to be an empirical law, one could not generalize it until the permanent connections underlying this law had been established.[20]

The Austrians centered their analysis upon the utility principle, finding therein both the connection between value and scarcity and a satisfactory explanation of economic behavior. Their system of analysis, though focused upon individual behavior tendencies arrived at introspectively, was translatable into mathematical but not into statistical terms. They did not accomplish much of a translation, however, restricting their efforts to the use of arithmetical models or of simple algebra; yet they may have anticipated problems today of concern to linear-programmers. Meanwhile, Jevons and Walras and others who shared some of the Austrian views did put them into mathematical terms and lay the ground work for further quantitative inquiry. Some of the more recent aprioristic successors of the Austrians have, however, so defined the scope of economics as virtually to rule out the use of quantitative methods.

While the later historical school made greater use of statistical matter than did the earlier historical school, its lack of emphasis upon theory of the neo-classical sort led it to neglect mathematical methods. Marx's approach resembled Ricardo's in that he deduced his conclusions from premises supposedly present in the capitalistic system but he used arithmetical and algebraic models to illustrate and expound his views, and sometimes found support for them in statistical data. Later Marxists made less use of quantitative matter, however, though the revisionists became such in part because of their interpretation of statistical trends. Revolutionary Marxists, such as Lenin, were interested primarily in the tactical or strategic usefulness of statistical matter.

The neo-classical school embraced most of the leading economists who wrote between the 1890's and the 1920's. They stressed the importance of theory, though they sometimes differed in respect of the degree of validity or applicability to be assigned particular principles. Many sought to translate economic principles into mathematical terms, or to use mathematics to render principles, or sets of principles, more precise and meaningful. Most of them sought, in varying degree, to make empirical application of these principles; they utilized statistics and/or mathematics when making such inquiries.

---

[20] Mill deals with social science methodology in his *System of Logic,* Bk. VI; it went through a number of editions. Mill was not an "apriorist" as was Senior or as are modern praxeologists, for he conceived his deductive approach to include induction and verification when necessary.

In light of this brief review of the approaches of the several schools, it is evident that the attitude of these schools to the use of quantitative methods depended largely upon their notions of the scope of economics, upon their views respecting the questions to which economics could and/or should seek answers, and upon their philosophical conceptions of the underlying socio-economic universe and of the "laws" or movements (mechanical, organic, dialectical-materialistic, etc.) to which this universe was subject through time.

SUCCESS OR FAILURE

The introduction of quantitative methods into economics did not result in striking failures or in striking discoveries. Non-availability or inadequacy of data limited the use of quantitative methods as, in some instances (e.g., the application of Walras's approach), did the non-existence of suitable computing equipment. At the same time the use of mathematical or statistical methods clarified intervariable relationships, distinguished substitution-affecting and demand-conditioning determinants (i.e., price and income changes), and introduced empirical content into propositions or functions that theretofore had been highly general and hence empty. Undoubtedly the gradualness with which quantitative methods were introduced, together with the complexity of social science data and its non-amenability to crucial experimentation, accounts for the fact that the augmentation of economic knowledge through use of quantitative methods was unmarked by striking successes or failures.[21] It contributed greatly to the fund of empirical economic knowledge, however.

TRANSFORMATION OR PRECISION-PRODUCTION

Did quantification transform economics, or did it merely render economics more exact? It would appear, from what has been said in the preceding section, that quantification merely rendered economics more exact, and this inference may even be supported by the fact that quantification made possible such findings as Edgeworth's that imposition of a tax might actually reduce the prices charged for transport service. In fact, Edgeworth himself seems to have held the view that the contribution of mathematics to economics consisted largely in a sharpening of existing modes of inquiry and in the eradication of sophistry; and yet, a mathematical predecessor, Walras, had held that mathematics was essential to showing how price equilibrium came about, thus maintaining a view which received some confirmation when economists began to allow for discontinuities and the possibility of an excess of some factor.[22] Edgeworth's interpretation is open to question, however; it rests on too short a temporal view. The accumulation of small changes over a long period of time—of changes inspired in varying measure by the increasing use of quantitative approaches—has transformed economics. Economics may deal with growth problems as did the classical school, or with imputational and alloca-

---

[21] This matter is touched upon further in the next section.

[22] See Edgeworth, *Papers Relating To Political Economy* (London, 1925), I, pp. 170-171; II, pp. 273-312; and L. Walras, *Elements of Pure Economics* (translated by W. Jaffe) (London, 1954), p. 43. Cf. also T. J. Koopmans, *Three Essays on the State of Economic Science* (New York, 1957), pp. 172-183, 197 ff. Cournot would probably have endorsed Walras's view.

tive problems, as did the Austrian school, and it may even emphasize the strategic importance of similar elements. Yet, when economics is viewed closely, it is found to differ remarkably from what it was 100-150 years ago. And this difference has been greatly accentuated in recent years by the introduction of essentially new quantitative approaches, such as game theory, activity analysis, linear programming techniques, and input-output models. One may say with certainty, therefore, that the use of quantitative approaches has made for a great increase in precision, at the theoretical level, and for a considerable increase in precision even at the empirical level, despite the difficulties that beset the study of empirical economic data. One can probably also say with validity that economics itself has been gradually transformed by the progressive quantification which that science has undergone, even though much of the data with which it deals still remains subjective in character.

SO FAR, AND NO FARTHER?

Every branch of economics has felt the impact of quantification. This is true in part because influences flowing from the body of economic theory, which is markedly quantitative or quantifiable and which is greatly depended upon even by branch-specialists, are felt in every branch of economics. It is true in part also because empirical studies oriented to any branch of economics almost inevitably assume a quantitative form. No branch, therefore, can elude quantification, even though it may be granted that some fields are more amenable to quantification than are others.

Economists have always focused their inquiries upon the economizing[23] responses of individuals, groups, or associations, to the fact that original resources, intermediate products, and final services are scarce and hence price-commanding. Today these responses are examined from two principal points of view. First, the economically oriented behavior of single- and multi-person decision makers—i.e., of consumers, individual proprietorships, households, corporate bodies, national and sub-national governments, and (possibly) meta-states—is subjected to analysis, with the object in view of discovering its underlying rationale and pattern in time and in socio-economic space. Second, the interrelations of members of selected groups of decision-making units, or of all such units considered as a whole, is subjected to analysis, with the object in view of discovering the nature and the behavior patterns of the systems and sub-systems which such units form in socio-economic space. Although the responses examined from one or the other of these two points of view may be looked upon as essentially endogenous to the economic system, this system may not be looked upon as completely closed. For decision-making units frequently find it necessary to adjust to changes that have originated in the society of social systems of which the economic system is but one, or that have been generated in the non-economic sector by the impact of earlier changes in the economic sector.

---

[23] Decision-makers economize when "they try to make the 'most,' as they conceive of the 'most,' of whatever resources they have." They would not, of course, be economizing if they rested their choice upon the outcome of lot-drawings. See R. N. McKean, *Efficiency In Government Through Systems Analysis* (New York, 1958), pp. 3-4.

Economizing responses may thus be studied in timeless situations, or in situations in which the passage of time allows scope to changes which may eventuate in fundamental modifications of previously stable equilibria. Mathematical methods are admirably adapted to the study of interrelations and adjustments of the sort that are prominent in timeless situations. Statistical matter is essential, however, to the empirical study both of the impact of equilibrium-modifying changes and of the behavior of the decision-makers who are generating or responding to these changes. In both situations, in sum, great assistance is to be had from quantitative approaches.

CAVEAT

In what has gone before, I have not discussed dangers inherent, not in the use as such of mathematical and statistical procedures, but in their uncritical use. Every methodological orientation gives rise, even as does every distinct approach to economic analysis generally (e.g., Marshall's, Keynes's), to a certain amount of bias: only certain questions are asked, only certain assumptions are taken explicitly into account, and so on. In so far as economic behavior is regular, uniform, and repetitive, and it becomes possible therefore to verify consequences, implications, etc., of hypothetical approaches and methodological orientations, the direct impact of bias may be minimized; its indirect impact potentially remains in that attention may continue to be diverted from questions which are of fundamental importance.

Human behavior, be it economic or otherwise, is extremely plastic and variable; it thus differs from the behavior of other primates, of lower forms of life, and of inorganic phenomena; it is subject to fewer constraints and therefore is, or may be, relatively unpredictable. The study of economic behavior remains amenable, nonetheless, to the use of quantitative methods; but these methods must be chosen with care, lest misleading results are gotten. For example, economists, acting upon the assumption that individuals are maximizing or minimizing some index in accordance with assumptions common to game theory and to various economic models, proceed as if unique equilibrium, optimum, etc., points exist, the specific locus of which depends upon the concrete circumstances present in the situation being envisaged. This emphasis upon uniqueness flows in part from the mathematical methods employed. In reality, however, the empirical existence of such points is to be doubted, even though the assumption of their existence may sometimes be useful on heuristic grounds. It seems to be methodologically more in keeping with economic reality, however, to assume that there exists an area within which interacting individuals or groups may settle into relatively stable and persisting patterns of interaction; in other words, there exists a set of solutions any one of which is essentially stable under current conditions. If this inference is valid, it becomes necessary to accommodate mathematical and other forms of quantitative analysis to the discovery of areas rather than of points of stability.[24] It becomes necessary more generally to accommodate

[24] The approach here but suggested has been variously developed by J. R. Commons in his *Institutional Economics* (New York, 1934); by C. I. Barnard, in *The Functions of* *The Executive* (Cambridge, 1938); by H. A. Simon, in *Models of Man* (New York, 1957); and occasionally in the *Journal of Conflict Resolution*.

the choice of quantitative methods to the nature of the empirical or social universe under consideration. Concern that economic analysts may fail to make such accommodations seems always to have underlain much of the criticism directed against particular uses of quantitative methods.

SECOND THOUGHTS

In the light of the papers presented at the conference, together with their discussion and thoughts provoked thereby, additional inferences may be drawn in respect to the quantification of economics.

(1) Factors endogenous to the several schools of economics long played a major part in their disposition to employ quantitative methods, in part because the theories and concepts relied upon governed both what was observed and how problems were posed.[25] At the same time the emergence and persistence of new (or newly observed) economic problems compelled a re-examination of the explanatory or manipulative adequacy of received theories and canons and brought about their modification far more rapidly than could either the chance occurrence of a "novel" approach, or the developmental processes "immanent" in the body of economic theory and organized economic knowledge.[26] Illustrative of this tendency in recent decades is the ascendancy of modern sampling, of mathematically formulated macro-economics, and of linear programming. (2) In general, as a science matures, it becomes more immune to endogenous events and conceptual changes, or, when these occur and are responded to, it responds to them selectively and, as a rule, at a quite abstract level. Accordingly, changes or improvements in the theoretical or conceptual structure of a science such as economics usually precede improvements in its quantification and use of measurement. Changes of this sort, moreover, may give rise to technological innovations (e.g., calculating machines, computers), or to their improvement and adaptation, and serve, as have tools developed outside a science (such as economics), to increase its empirical effectiveness and possibly even to stimulate its conceptual modification.

(3) In some fields of science less abstruse statements often precede more abstruse formulations of theory, the less abstruse serving to prepare the mind for the more abstruse. This sequence is not so prominent in economics, though an instance of it is had in the initial appearance of a less abstruse utility-theory which seems to have prepared the way for the later development and acceptance of a more abstruse utility-less theory of choice. (4) Crisis states of the sort sometimes occurring in physics and requiring the resolution of seeming contradictions have not emerged in economics any more than has the need or the opportunity to perform a crucial experiment. It has been necessary on occasion, however, to compose seeming contradictions flowing from differences in static and dynamic assumptions, such as that between static and

---

[25] Compare N. R. Hanson's account of microphysical thought in his *Patterns of Discovery* (Cambridge, 1958), pp. 18-19, 39-46; also Talcott Parsons, *The Structure of Social Action* (New York, 1937), pp. 41-42.

[26] On "immanent" developmental forces see *ibid.*, pp. 5, 725-726. Of course, within a given

conceptual framework, the accumulation of empirical knowledge renders obsolete an increasing number of underdeveloped empirical statements, most of which are likely to remain obsolete even after the given conceptual framework gives way to a more advanced one.

dynamic conceptions of the propensity to save or of the response of fertility to income-change. Composition of these seeming contradictions has usually entailed recognition of differences in the extent to which intervening and disregarded variables have been present. (5) The concept of innovation is applicable to the study of the history of a science. For, when a new discovery takes place in a field of science, uncommitted scientists flock to the area or branch most affected much as business men flock to areas in which an innovation is generating opportunities to profit. Today, of course, with communication so extensive and intensive, the implications and fruits of a scientific discovery are fully realized much more rapidly than in the past. (6) In economics and apparently in science generally, just as in the business world, there are at any time relatively active and relatively passive sectors; changes are initiated in the active sectors and are adapted to in the passive sectors. Detailed analysis might reveal if certain sectors of a science are more prone to initiatory change than are others and hence are describable as relatively dynamic.

Among the topics or areas of research of interest to those interested in the history of the quantification of social science, two warrant investigation. One has to do with the changes that have taken place in the conception, statistical or otherwise, that (say) economists have had of the universe with which their inquiries have been concerned. This conception has sometimes affected their notions of causality and of appropriate methodology; and its content has variously reflected the concepts physical and life scientists have had of their own universes of inquiry. The second has to do with the role quantification has played in military and related administrative practice. The relevant body of materials spans many centuries and also relates in part to the use of resources; its study might augment our understanding of the role of quantity in the past study of human affairs. In any such study, as in that of the role of quantity in economic affairs, attention needs to be given to the extent to which "chance," risk, and uncertainty were taken into account.

Notes on the History of Quantification in Sociology— Trends, Sources and Problems

By Paul F. Lazarsfeld[*]

INTRODUCTION

THE three major nouns in the title of this paper are necessarily vague. Quantification in the social sciences includes mere counting, the development of classificatory dimensions and the systematic use of "social symptoms" as well as mathematical models and an axiomatic theory of measurement. The notion of history is ambiguous because some of these techniques evolved several hundred years ago while others were developed within the last few decades. Finally, there is no precise line between sociology and other social sciences; with the economist, the sociologist shares family budgets, and with the psychologist he makes the study of attitudes a joint concern.

The task of sketching out the history of quantification in sociology is made more difficult by the fact that it rarely has been seriously attempted. Both the history and the philosophy of science have been concerned almost exclusively with the natural sciences. Their discoveries have been linked step by step with their antecedents; their relation to the political, social and religious events of the time has been spelled out; even their effect on belles lettres has been traced. The few comparable studies in the social sciences have usually been concerned with broad, semi-philosophical systems. There has been hardly any work on the history of techniques for social science investigation. In following some of these procedures back to their origins, it was often necessary to draw attention to historical situations or to men with whom the American reader is not likely to be familiar, and to report something about the broader political and ideological contexts in which the pioneers of sociological quantification worked.

The need for such details required a severe restriction in the scope of the paper. Actually, it deals with only three major episodes. They were selected because they carried the seeds of many subsequent developments and foreshadowed discussions which continue today. To give the three major sections of this paper a proper frame, a few words are needed about how a future history of quantification in sociology might look. It would begin with a preparatory phase lasting approximately from the middle of the 17th to the beginning

[*] Columbia University

of the 19th century. These first 150 years were dominated by the sheer difficulty of obtaining numerical information on social topics. Many historians
of statistics and demography have described this period, and I shall not try
to re-trace the ground which they have covered. I shall, instead, suggest points
at which sociological ideas entered into the work of some of the more famous
writers on society of the period. But my main attention will be focused on
the life, work and followers of one man—Hermann Conring. As I slowly
pieced together whatever information I could find about him, I became increasingly impressed with his importance. He saw the same problem faced by
his British contemporaries whom we remember today as the founders of political arithmetic. But his efforts took a very different turn. The first section
of my paper sketches his work, tries to explain it in the context of the times,
and traces its consequences.

A second period in this history begins with the work of the Belgian, Quetelet, and the Frenchman, LePlay. Both men started out as natural scientists, acquiring their interest in the social sciences during the period of social
unrest which culminated in the French-Belgian Revolution of 1830. Quetelet
was an astronomer who wished to uncover for the social world eternal laws
similar to those he dealt with in his main field of investigation. LePlay was a
mining engineer and metallurgist who believed that the minute attention to
concrete details which made him a success in his main occupation could also
provide the foundations for a true social science. The spirit in which these
two men worked and the role their ideas played in subsequent developments
are correspondingly different.

Quetelet concerned himself almost exclusively with the interpretation of
large-scale statistics which became available, at the beginning of the 19th
century, as a by-product of the rapidly expanded census activities undertaken
by various government agencies. He anticipated with varying degrees of
precision many basic concepts of quantification, and his writings led to sophisticated controversies which continued into the 20th century. It seemed to me
useful therefore to single out some of these ideas and to show how they were
slowly clarified. Section II thus will report the Quetelet story in reverse. My
implicit starting point will be some modern ideas on quantification, and I shall
trace these back to the writings of Quetelet, his opponents and his commentators.

It is more difficult to fit LePlay into my narrative because, in spite of his
many assertions, he never was nor really meant to be a detached scientist.
During his lifetime he created a number of ideological movements, and these
both attracted and distracted his followers. Those of his disciples who intended
primarily to develop his ideas on social research could never free themselves
entirely from the political position of the founding father. This was so in a
two-fold sense. They continued the organizational activities which LePlay
initiated, and had an interestingly ambivalent attitude toward the methods
which he had developed. They succeeded in making considerable improvements in these methods, but they experienced such achievements as impious
disloyalty to their great master. The history of the LePlay school following his
death is a curious example of what happens when a research tradition assumes

a sectarian form. So far as I know, this story has never been traced, and in Section III I shall give it somewhat more attention than strict adherence to the topic of quantification would require.

My paper thus concentrates on the development of some of the basic notions and broader ideas which introduced quantification into the study of social affairs. Any history of science must include at least three elements: the intrinsic intellectual nature of the ideas, their historical social context and the peculiarities of the men who made the major contributions. It will become obvious why I give most space to the intellectual element in Section II, the historical in Section I, and the biographical in Section III.

Throughout the paper, I have had to discuss repeatedly the historiography of the field itself. Because professional historians of science have paid so little attention to the social sciences, their history was often written by amateurs—specialists in social research who only occasionally looked into its past. As a result, quite a number of legends have been passed on from one to the next. While I am an amateur myself, I have for the major parts of this paper gone back to the original sources, including the commentators who previously have given them careful attention. At points where I felt that a further pursuit would exceed the time or the material available to me, I have brought specific unsolved questions to the attention of the reader. In a postscriptum to this paper, I shall indicate the topics I have not dealt with, my reasons for their exclusion and the places where one can find pertinent information.†

THE PREPARATORY PERIOD

The Political Arithmeticians

The idea that social topics could be subjected to quantitative analysis acquired prominence in the first part of the 17th century. There are conventional explanations for this emergence: the rational spirit of rising capitalism; the intellectual climate of the Baconian era; the desire to imitate the first major success of the natural sciences; the increasing size of different countries which necessitated a more impersonal and abstract basis for public administration. More specifically, one can point to concrete concerns: the rise of insurance systems which required a firmer numerical foundation, and the prevailing belief of the mercantilists that size of population was a crucial factor in the power and wealth of the state.[1]

Problems of demographic enumeration were the first topics to be discussed systematically. No reliable data were available, and no modern census machinery was in sight. Two obstacles are mentioned by the authors who have dealt with the work of this period: the unwillingness of the population to give information, because of their fear of increased taxes; and the tendency of governments, whenever statistical information was available, to treat it as highly classified, because of its possible military value.[2] Thus, the ingenuity

† In the bibliographical footnotes, foreign titles are given in their original form; in the main text these titles are usually translated and abbreviated so as to support the narrative.

[1] For an instructive survey and a new look see Trevor-Roper, "The General Crisis of the 17th Century" in *Past and Present*, 1959, *16*.

[2] Secrecy regarding statistical information collected by government agencies was maintained by some countries well into the 19th

of early scholars was directed mainly toward obtaining estimates of population size and age and sex distributions from meager and indirect evidence. Multiplying the number of chimneys by an assumed average family size or inferring the age structure of the population from registered information regarding age at the time of death were typical procedures in what was then called political arithmetic.

Today it is hard for us to imagine the lack of descriptive information available in the middle of the 17th century. The ravages of periodic outbreaks of the plague, for instance, made it impossible for anyone to know whether the population of England was increasing or decreasing. As a matter of fact, the first mortality tables, published in 1662 by Graunt, who is considered the originator of modern demography, were based partly on public listings of burials; they had acquired news value for the average citizen—somewhat comparable to the list of victims which nowadays is published after an airplane accident.

But soon the supply of facts increased, the analytical techniques were improved, and by about 1680 the art of "political arithmetic" was well established under English leadership. I have the impression that something like a community of *aficionados* developed: all over Western Europe, empirical data were traded for mathematical advice. Thus, for instance, in 1693, the English astronomer Halley published a paper on mortality based on registration figures of births and funerals in the city of Breslau. How had Halley obtained these figures? German historians discovered that Leibnitz was an intermediary. He had learned about the material through a friend, a clergyman in Breslau who, together with a local physician, was an ardent and capable amateur demographer. Leibnitz brought the data to the attention of the Royal Society, which asked Halley to express an opinion.[3]

A century later natural scientists still considered descriptive social statistics appropriate topics to be worked on. In 1791, Lavoisier, the chemist who was to be guillotined three years later, published a treatise for the National Assembly dealing with the population and economic condition of France; in this he expounded the idea that a revolutionary government had the opportunity and the duty to establish a central statistical bureau. At the beginning of the 19th century, the mathematicians, LaPlace and Fourier, dealt with population statistics; and, as we shall see, their work played an important role in Quetelet's life.[4]

I do not intend to pursue the development of political arithmetic in this paper. But I want to suggest that the sociological implications of some of these early writings be reexamined. To indicate the kind of analysis I have in mind,

---

century. The parallel to contemporary secrecy about atomic physics is obvious. Several revolutionary governments made it a point that statistical data should be made available to the public. I wonder whether the explicit mentioning of the decennial census in the United States Constitution had partly such ideological implications.

[3] This episode is interesting, incidentally, because it shows the efforts which even minor political arithmeticians made to put their work to practical use. The Breslau group wanted to counter the contention of astrologists that certain years in a man's life are especially dangerous. The pertinent historical papers are reviewed by Victor John, *Geschichte der Statistik* (Stuttgart: Ferdinand Enke, 1884).

[4] The facts mentioned up to this point can be found in any of the histories of statistics mentioned in the footnotes.

I shall briefly sketch out the work of two men. One of these is William Petty (1623-1687) who worked with Graunt and created the term "political arithmetic." After the Restoration, he decided to use his experience in Ireland to formulate a general theory of government based on concrete knowledge. He was convinced that to this end "one had to express oneself in terms of number, weight, and measure." He argued that Ireland was a good case study, not only because he knew it so well, but because it was a "political animal who is scarce twenty years old," and a place, therefore, where the relation between the social structure of the country and the chances of good government could be studied more closely. Thus originated his *Political Anatomy of Ireland* (1672).

A sensitive biography by E. Strauss[5] describes the political and social settings of Petty's work: for this reason alone it makes very worthwhile reading. Two chapters provide a more detailed guide through those parts of Petty's writings which are relevant to my paper. He anticipates ideas which only recently have been considered noteworthy intellectual discoveries. A few years ago, the Harvard economist Dusenberry argued that sociological factors must be taken into account in the economics of saving. He pointed out that whites save less than Negroes on the same income level, because white people have a broader range of social contacts and therefore must spend more money on conspicuous consumption. Compare this with the following passage from Petty:

> When England shall be thicker peopled, in the manner before described, *the very same people shall then spend more, than when they lived* more sordidly and inurbanely, and further asunder, and *more out of the sight, observation, and emulation of each other;* every man desiring to put on better apparel when he appears in company, than when he has no occasion to be seen.[6] (emphasis mine)

During the depression of the 1930's, a number of studies appearing in this country and abroad made it clear that, for psychological reasons, work relief is preferable to a straight dole. Petty also argued for unemployment benefits, and, while he phrases his beliefs in less humanitarian words than we would use today, the psychological foundations of his argument that even "boondoggling" is preferable to dole are certainly very modern:

> tis no matter if it be *employed to build a useless pyramid upon Salisbury Plain, bring the stones at Stonehenge to Tower Hill, or the like;* for at worst this would keep their minds to discipline and obedience, and their bodies to patience of more profitable labours when need shall require it.[7] (emphasis mine)

The second exhibit in my appeal for a sociological reconsideration of some of the early Political Arithmeticians is the German J. P. Suessmilch (1707-1767), who too first studied medicine. But he then turned to theology, and spent most of his adult life as a pastor, first with a Prussian regiment and later at the court of Frederick the Great. In 1741, a year after Frederick II ascended the throne, Suessmilch published his book on the "Divine Order as

---

[5] E. Strauss, *Sir William Petty* (Glencoe, Ill.: The Free Press, 1954).

[6] Strauss, *op. cit.,* p. 203.
[7] Strauss, *op. cit.,* p. 221.

proven by birth, death and fertility of the human species (Geschlecht)."[8] In his work, Suessmilch collected all the data published by his predecessors, and his book is considered the most complete compendium of the time. In addition, historians of statistics credit him with having been the first to focus attention on fertility (in addition to birth and death rates). But all of these reviews omit any reference to Suessmilch's broad-gauged interpretation of his findings. For instance, Westergaard[9] says at one point when describing Suessmilch's major work, "the succeeding chapters are uninteresting to the history of statistics insofar as Suessmilch here briefly presents arguments against polygamy, discusses proposals as to supporting married couples with numbers of children, as to hygienic matters, luxury, etc. After this long digression, the author resumes his statistical investigations."

Even a cursory look at this part of Suessmilch's text shows that much would be gained by a careful examination. For example, when he finds that the number of marriages has declined in a certain part of Prussia, he offers a variety of explanations: an increase in the number of students attending universities, of people called into military service, a shift to industrial work, increases in food prices, and so on. All in all, the *Goettliche Ordnung* is filled with social analysis. Suessmilch considers a growing population of crucial political importance; he therefore tries to uncover the political and social conditions which make for such growth, so that he can advise the king effectively.

It is true that Suessmilch frequently turns to theological arguments. He finds that slightly more boys than girls are born; he attributes this to the wisdom of the Creator, because young boys, who grow up under less sheltered conditions, have a somewhat higher mortality rate than do girls. At the time of marriage, the two sexes are in balance. At the time of widowhood, however, there are more women than men; but widowers have a greater chance of remarrying repeatedly (he created the term "successive polygamy"); in other words, even in the later phases of life, the sex ratio is functionally useful. Altogether, one could probably find surprising parallels between modern functionalism and Suessmilch's efforts.[10]

Having done no special research myself on the political arithmeticians, I feel somewhat hesitant about making one more suggestion before I leave the

[8] Suessmilch had become interested in demography through reading the work of William Derham, an English cleric, whose book, "Psycho-Theology, or a Demonstration of the Being and Attributes of God from His Works of Creation," had already gone through several editions by the beginning of the 18th century.

[9] Harald Westergaard, *Contributions to the History of Statistics* (London: P. S. King & Son, Ltd., 1932).

[10] It has often been noted that, in spite of the fact that Suessmilch's was the first serious discussion of the relation between standard of living and population growth, he had no direct intellectual effects or followers. Malthus, whose work did not begin until fifty years later (and who, incidentally, used many of Suessmilch's computations), received all the acclaim. In a later context, I shall try to explain this neglect of the Prussian pastor by his academic contemporaries. I have found only one English summary of Suessmilch's work which goes beyond the conventional histories of statistics, a dissertation by F. S. Crumm, "The Statistical Work of Suessmilch," in *Quart. Publ. Amer. Statist. Ass.*, 1901. It is a rather dry, but very specific and therefore useful, guide through Suessmilch's main writings. In the Festschrift for Toennies' 80th birthday, one contribution by a Georg Jahn is entitled, "Suessmilch and the Social Sciences of the 18th Century." It is very disappointing. The author gives a brief description of Suessmilch's work and expresses the hope that sociologists will one day pay more attention to it. Jahn's own contributions are some remarks on how Suessmilch fitted in with the rational theology of his period.

topic. Given the fact that political arithmetic, especially in its early phases, was equivalent to obtaining a quantitative foundation for broad social problems, it is surprising that it seems to have had so little relation with another stream in English intellectual history—the Scottish moral philosophers. Some of them, like Adam Ferguson, are cited as the precursors of modern empiricism, mainly because they wanted to substitute concrete anthropological observations for mere speculation about the origins of society.[11] But they were also much concerned with human nature. And, for these concerns, they could have derived much information from the work of the political arithmeticians, which was well developed by the middle of the 18th century. Yet, I have not been able to find a study of the points at which these two traditions merged, and, if they did not, an explanation of what accounts for this separation.

The Story of the Two Roots

In 1886, August Meitzen, a professor at the University of Berlin, published a book on statistics.[12] The first part of the volume dealt with the history of the field. It contains no detailed analysis of specific writings, nor does it pretend to be a history of ideas. Meitzen's main aims were to record the times and circumstances under which the early statistical organizations were founded, to list and describe the early publications of statistical data, and to provide brief sketches of the major writers who made notable contributions. The book apparently seemed important at the time, for in 1891 the American Academy of Political and Social Science published an English translation in two supplements to their regular series. (The second part contains sound advice on the collection, tabulation, and interpretation of demographic and social data, which might explain why the translation seemed desirable.)

In describing the main historical trends, Meitzen put forth the idea that the statistics of his time developed from two different roots. One was represented by the political arithmeticians whom I have just described. He correctly places their origins in the middle of the 17th century. The other root was an intensive interest in characteristic features of the state, from which the term "statistics" was derived. This brand of statistics considered anything which seemed noteworthy about a country, and was in no way restricted to the topics now covered by the term. As a matter of fact, numerical data played only a small role in this tradition.

Sometime toward the end of the 18th century, Meitzen writes, the English root of political arithmetic and the German root of university statistics (as it came to be called) became involved in a controversy about which of the two was more scientific and more useful. The battle was won, in Germany as well as elsewhere, by the political arithmeticians. From the beginning of the 19th century onwards, they also monopolized the title of statisticians. Whatever was left of the former activities of university statisticians was thereafter considered a part of political science.

[11] Herta Jogland, *Ursprünge und Grundlagen der Soziologie bei Adam Ferguson* (Berlin, Duncker & Humblot, 1959). The author informs me that the first use of statistical data she could trace with a moral philosopher is in a book by a George Combe, *Moral Philosophy or the Duties of Man* (New York: 1841).

[12] August Meitzen, *History, Theory, and Technique of Statistics* (Phila.: Am. Academy of Political and Social Science, 1891).

Meitzen designated a Göttingen professor, Gottfried Achenwall (1719-1772), as the founder of the German non-quantitative root. In 1749, Achenwall had published a book which included in its title the phrase, "The Science of Today's Main European Realms and Republics." He is, says Meitzen, *"therefore called the father of statistical science."* This paternity has been accepted by many contemporary writers. Thus, George Lundberg follows Meitzen's example.[13] While his sympathies, of course, are on the side of the victorious party, he acknowledges that Achenwall's book "gained such general recognition when it was translated into all languages that Achenwall was long hailed as the father of statistical science." George Sarton[14] and Nathan Glazer[15] write in the same vein.

There is something strange in this story, however. What happened in Germany during the ninety years between Graunt and Achenwall? Why did the political arithmeticians have so little influence in the German universities? How could the Göttingen professor create a "second root" so quickly that, within a few decades, it acquired equal standing with the English tradition to the point that, as we shall see, the final battle was fought in all the countries of Western Europe?

Part of the answer was given in another book which actually appeared two years before Meitzen's but which did not come to the attention of American social scientists for a long time. In 1884, Victor John, docent at the University of Bern in Switzerland, also published a history of statistics, but of a very different kind. He properly calls his work a source book,[16] and it is indeed a volume of remarkable scholarship in which he either summarizes or quotes sources that today are quite inaccessible.[17] He had noticed the queer hiatus between 1660 and 1750, left unexplained by traditional stereotypes. He was able to fill in this gap by focusing attention on the work of Hermann Conring (1606-1682). Conring was one of the great polyhistors of his time, holding three professorships at the Brunswick University of Helmstaedt: first in philosophy, then in medicine, and finally in politics. In 1660, at practically the same time that Graunt and Petty started their work, he began a series of systematic lectures under the title, "Notitia Rerum Publicarum." These lectures were first published as notes taken by his students, but later appeared, at the beginning of the 18th century, as part of a multi-volume collection of Conring's writings and correspondence. He had a large number of important students, some of whom went into public service and some of whom taught at other German universities. Many compendia of his system were in use throughout the Empire. And as John proves convincingly, the book which Achenwall published in 1749 was essentially the first systematic presentation in the *German* language of the Conring tradition which until then was available

[13] George A. Lundberg, "Statistics in Modern Social Thought," *Contemporary Social Theory,* Barnes and Becker (eds.), (New York: D. Appleton-Century, 1940).

[14] George Sarton, "Preface to Vol. XXIII of *Isis* (Quetelet)," *Isis,* 1935, 65: 6-24.

[15] Nathan Glazer, "The Rise of Social Research in Europe" in Daniel Lerner (ed.) *The Human Meaning of the Social Sciences* (New York: Meridian Books, 1959).

[16] Victor John, *op. cit.*

[17] John's work grew out of Knapp's broad interest in the history of statistics, to which I shall return in the section on Quetelet. Meitzen himself, who started the original confusion, corrected himself later. He wrote the entry on Conring in the influential German Encyclopedia of the Social Sciences.

almost exclusively in Latin. John demonstrates that all of Achenwall's basic ideas had been explicitly developed by Conring. As a matter of fact, Achenwall always conceded this: he was a pupil once removed of Conring's, and wrote his dissertation about him, still in Latin, incidentally.

Thus, John clarifies at least one point. There was no hiatus. The English root of political arithmetic and the German root of university statistics developed at the same time. But this fact only raises a number of new and more interesting questions. For one, why did the two countries develop such different answers to what was essentially the same intellectual challenge? Compare the programmatic statements of the two authors:

Petty	*Conring*
Sir Francis Bacon, in his "Advancement of Learning," has made a judicious parallel in many particulars, between the *Body Natural and Body Politic, and between the arts of preserving both in health and strength:* and as its anatomy is the best foundation of one, so also of the other: and that to practice upon the politic, *without knowing the symmetry, fabric, and proportion of it, is as casual as the practice of old women and empirics.* (Emphasis supplied)[18]	Just as it is impossible for the doctor to give advice for the *recovery or preservation of health when he does not have some salient knowledge of the body,* so it is also impossible for anyone who does not have *knowledge and awareness of the facts of public life to cure it* either in its totality or in some of its parts.[19] (Emphasis supplied)

Here were two men, equally concerned with problems of government, both trained in medicine and intermittently acting and thinking as physicians, both bent on finding empirical foundations for their ideas. And yet they took two completely different roads. The Englishman, citizen of an empire, looked for causal relations between quantitative variables. The German, subject of one of 300 small principalities and, as we shall see, involved in the petty policies of many of them, tried to derive systematically the best set of categories by which a state could be characterized. As I sketch out a tentative explanation of this difference, a collateral problem will arise. Once the German tradition was established, why was it so impermeable and, in the end, even so hostile to the quantitative tradition of the political arithmeticians? This second question is highlighted by the fact that 100 years later Suessmilch, writing in German at the same time as Achenwall, made no dent on the work of the German professors. And, finally, what was it in the European intellectual scene which kept Conring from having any international influence as a statistician when, at the time of the great battle 150 years later, German university statistics and English political arithmetic were pretenders of equal strength and prestige throughout Western Europe?[20]

[18] Strauss, *op. cit.,* p. 196.

[19] John, *op. cit.,* p. 58, here translated from the Latin quotation.

[20] Anyone who wishes to trace the theory of Conring in English studies will encounter difficulties. Both Frank Hankins and Westergaard agree with John's views that Conring is to be considered the founder of the German tradition, yet both men devote a mere paragraph to Conring and several pages to Achenwall. They might have had difficulties with John's review which always quotes Conring in Latin, and without translation, a tradition incidentally which continues in the more recent

Hermann Conring and German Universitätsstatistik

It is difficult to visualize intellectual life in Germany in the decades following the Thirty Years' War. The educated layman knows the connection between Locke and the Glorious Revolution; he is aware of the brilliance of the French theater when Louis XIV established his hegemony in Europe through a series of wars. But who remembers that at about the same time (1683) the imperial city of Vienna was besieged by the Turks and saved in the nick of time by a Polish army—except, perhaps, if he has heard that this brought coffee to Europe and thus greatly affected the intellectual life of London?

The physical devastation of large parts of Germany at the time of the Westphalian Peace (1648) and the drastic decline in the population would lead one to expect a complete blackout of the mind. And yet, recovery had to come; and indeed, it did come, but it gave German intellectual activities a peculiar complexion. First of all, there was abject poverty. It is true that both Petty and Conring were involved in shady financial transactions, but the differing social contexts affected the scale of their misdeeds. Petty dealt in huge fortunes, while Conring's correspondence resounds with begging and waiting for a few gold pieces promised to him for some political service. In the two-score German universities, professors remained largely unpaid and the life of the students was at an all-time low. No middle class existed, no intellectual center, no national aristocracy which might have supported the work of artists and scientists. Whatever help there was had to come from the three hundred princes who ruled their ruined little countries with absolute power.

These princes were, by and large, all concerned with the same problems. One was to maintain their independence against the Emperor whose power had been greatly weakened by the great war. At the same time, there was enough national feeling to make a possible invasion by France a common concern, especially in the western part of the realm. The relation between Catholics and Protestants, although formally settled by the peace treaty, was still very much in flux. And finally, the jealousies and battles for prestige between the various courts kept everyone on the move. This competition is especially relevant for my narrative. As one could expect in as many as three hundred principalities, there was a typical distribution of ability and culture among the rulers; for the better kinds, the advancement of knowledge and the improvement of government was a serious concern or at least an important competitive tool. It may sound somewhat strange to compare this situation with what happened in the Italian city states during the Renaissance. There was, of course, little money and probably less taste to build palaces, to paint murals, or to collect sculptures. But people were cheap. Therefore, if a man acquired some intellectual renown, several courts might bid for his services. The natural habitat for an intellectual was still the university corporation; so a relatively large number of small universities were created (and disappeared) according to the whims of some of the more enlightened rulers.

---

publications. The original writings of Conring were not available to me. But the German sources give many and often overlapping quotations; thus frequent internal checks were possible.

But again, what was expected from the learned doctors was colored by the peculiar situation. All in all, the critical German problem of the time was civic reconstruction. Problems of law and of administration had high priority. The competition between the principalities pressed in the same direction: the struggle over a little piece of territory; the question of which prince should have which function in imperial administration; questions of marriage and succession among ruling houses were discussed and settled in the light of precedent, and by the exegesis of historical records. International law started a few miles from everyone's house or place of business. No wonder then that it was a spirit of systematically cataloguing what existed, rather than the making of new discoveries that made for academic prestige. This, in turn, prolonged the life of the Scholastic and Aristotelian traditions which had dominated the medieval universities and by then had withered away in most other parts of Western Europe. In the second half of the 17th century, when English and French intellectuals wrote and taught in their own language, the form of communication among German academicians was still exclusively Latin, even in the numerous "position papers" they were asked to publish by the princes whom they served.

The life and work of Hermann Corning must be examined against this background. He was born in 1606 in Friesland, son of a Protestant pastor. His gifts were soon recognized and he was taken into the house of a professor at the University of Helmstaedt. This town belonged at the time to the Duchy of Brunswick which in turn was part of the general sphere of influence of the Hanoverian Duchy.[21] In 1625, Conring went to the University of Leyden, probably because his family still had many connections with the Netherlands from which they had originally come. (Four years before, Grotius, who was also a student at Leyden, had fled his native country because he had been involved on the liberal side of religious and political controversy.) The best source on Conring's study period in Holland is Moeller.[22] Conring stayed in Leyden for six years and was greatly attracted by the breadth of its intellectual life. He tried very hard to get a Dutch professorship, but did not succeed. So in 1631, he returned to Helmstaedt as professor of natural philosophy and remained there for the rest of his life.

From what we know about him today, we can conclude that he would undoubtedly have become a European figure like Grotius who was twenty years his elder and Leibnitz who was forty years his junior, if like them, he had spent part of his mature life outside Germany. I have no space here to document in detail what is known about Conring as a person. Instead, I shall briefly compare him with these two men with whom we are so much more familiar. Conring never met Grotius, but he came back to Helmstaedt imbued with his ideas. Whenever it was not too dangerous for him, he stood up for religious tolerance and if possible, for reunification of all Christian churches. In many respects the two men seem to have been similar, as may be seen, for

<hr>

[21] It should be remembered that not long after the death of Conring in 1681, Hannover and Brandenburg were competing for top prestige in Germany. When the Brandenburg Elector acquired the title of Prussian King by a legal trick, the Hannoverian tried to balance this success by accepting somewhat reluctantly, the crown of England.

[22] Ernst V. Moeller, *Hermann Conring* (Hannover: Ernst Geibel, 1915).

example, from a character sketch of Grotius by Huizinga.[23] Huizinga described how Grotius was "permeated in every fiber with the essence of antiquity": that in his writings on public affairs he mixed contemporary cases and "examples from antiquity in order to give advice to his own day"; that his knowledge in all spheres of learning was so great that "the capacity and the alertness of the humanist memory has become almost inconceivable." Practically the same terms are used of Conring by his contemporaries and by the historians who tried to reconstruct his image from his very extensive correspondence. The only difference is one of morality. All authorities on Conring agree on his veniality and servility, although some point out that this was characteristic of German academicians of the time.

Leibnitz and Conring had repeated personal contact. A brief summary of how this came about will bring the description of Conring's life one step further. From early in his Helmstaedt career, Conring lectured on politics although officially he was made professor of this subject only in 1650. One of his students was the young Baron J. C. Boineburg (1622-1672) who defended the dissertation he had written under Conring in 1643. A few years later, after having changed his religion, Boineburg entered the service of the Archbishop Elector of Mainz, who was one of the leading rulers of Germany in the period after the Westphalian Peace; and Boineburg became possibly the most prominent German statesman of the time. The crucial problem of the principalities in the Rhine area was how to contain the power of Louis XIV. The Mainz Elector changed his position, being first in favor of appeasement and then in favor of organizing defensive alliances with Protestant countries. Boineburg remained an appeaser throughout his political career which brought him repeatedly into conflict with his own prince, but at the same time made him an important bridge between Germany and the West. Whenever he had to make a political decision, he turned to his old teacher for advice. Many times he asked Conring to write pamphlets on current issues to support a specific position. Boineburg was also very much concerned with the possibility of reunifying the Christian churches which, incidentally, was also Grotius' main interest towards the end of his life (1645). At one time, Boineburg suggested an exchange of statements by relatively conciliatory representatives of the Catholic and Protestant positions. Again, he called upon Conring who wrote a number of monographs from the Protestant point of view; the whole affair came to nothing. These "expert opinions," always based on extensive historical and legal research, are one of the sources of knowledge about Conring. An instructive and well organized inventory can be found in Felberg.[24]

At the same time that Boineburg turned to his teacher either for advice or for backing of his various political schemes, he was on the outlook for other intellectuals he could use for similar purposes. His attention was drawn to a young Saxonian who, at the age of 24, had written a treatise on "A New Method of Teaching Jurisprudence" (Methodus Nova), a work in which he wanted to apply to legal studies and research the same ideas which Bacon had

[23] Johann Huizinga, *Men and Ideas* (New York: Meridian Books, 1959).
[24] Paul Felberg, *Hermann Conrings Anteil am Politischen Leben Seiner Zeit* (Trier: Paulinus-Druckerei, 1931).

sketched in his Novum Organum for the natural sciences. Boineburg prevailed upon Leibnitz to enter the service of the Elector of Mainz; he accepted, and remained in this position for ten years—from 1666 to 1676. Boineburg wanted to be sure of his judgment and sent Leibnitz' drafts to Conring.[25] The latter was not overly impressed, but Boineburg retained Leibnitz nonetheless. As a result, Leibnitz and Conring came into continuous contact with each other. Both were Protestants, and the one was directly, the other indirectly, attached to a Catholic court. Boineburg called on Conring for informal or formal expression of expert opinion. Leibnitz he used more as a personal representative. For four years, beginning in 1672, Leibnitz was Boineburg's representative in Paris, a stay which was interrupted only by a brief visit to London. This was the period in which Leibnitz made contacts with French and British academicians and laid the foundations for his international fame. The only return Conring got out of it was a small French pension for which he was expected to contribute to the fame of Louis XIV in his public writings.

Leibnitz never completely escaped Conring's shadow. When he moved to Hannover in 1676 to become court librarian, a position he held until the end of his life (1716), his administrative superior was a man who again had been a student of Conring.[26] Between Conring and Leibnitz an atmosphere of mutual respect and ambivalence prevailed. The former was probably jealous of the rising fame of this new, and last, German polyhistor. He may also have had the feeling that he had been born a few decades too early. When he was thirty, Germany was still in the middle of the great war, and the main problem of a German professor was to keep out of the hands of various occupying armies and to clothe and feed his family. When Leibnitz was thirty, the agent of a German statesman could make trips all over Europe and take active part in public affairs. By then, Conring was old; and while he was famous, his participation in the recovery period was restricted to the written word.

Conring's isolation during a crucial intellectual period may also explain a final disagreement between Conring and Leibnitz. By the middle of the 1670's, Leibnitz was already deeply involved in mathematical studies and his reputation in this field, however controversial, was at least as great as his reputation as a social scientist. Conring thoroughly disapproved of all such mathematical ideas and advised Leibnitz not to waste his time on them.[27] This blind spot in Conring cannot, however, completely be attributed to Conring's age. All in all, he seems to have had only a limited understanding of mathematical thinking. A careful and systematic compilation of everything which Conring wrote on population problems[28] shows that he had a static view of the problems

---

[25] It is possible to trace all this in some detail in Guhrauer's biography of Leibnitz. (G. C. Guhrauer, *Gottfried Wilhelm Freiherr V. Leibnitz* [Breslau: Ferdinand Hirt's Verlag, 1846].) This two-volume book puts great emphasis on Leibnitz' personal contacts and either quotes directly from correspondence or gives at least references as to where further information can be found. It is, of course, written with Leibnitz as the central figure and therefore the many allusions to Conring are often brief. It should be worthwhile to follow up Guhrauer's references and to piece the picture together with Conring in mind. Among the monographs on Conring, I have not found one with this emphasis.

[26] Guhrauer, *op. cit.*, p. 212.

[27] Guhrauer, *op. cit.*, pp. 213f.

[28] Reinold Zehrfeld, "Hermann Conring's Staatenkunde" in *Sozialwissenschaftliche Forschungen*, 1925, 5: 79ff.

involved. While interested in studying size and social structure of populations in relation to public policy, he had no conception of or interest in birth and death rates or any of the other dynamic ideas so characteristic of contemporary British political arithmeticians.[29] Whether further research could explain these blind spots, I cannot tell. One rather obvious root is Conring's continuous concern with Aristotle's writings. They were the topic of his dissertation; later, he published many commentaries on and new editions of Aristotle's political texts; his own work, which created the tradition of German university statistics, was deeply influenced by Aristotelian ideas. I feel it was necessary to sketch this general background before I could turn to this part of Conring's efforts.

Conring wants to bring order into the available knowledge about various countries. His purpose is explicitly threefold: he looks for a system which should make facts easier to remember, easier to teach, and easier to be used by men in the government. To this end it is necessary to have categories of description which are not accidental, but are deduced, step by step, from basic principles. His "model," as we would say today, is *the state as an acting unit*. The dominant categories are the four Aristotelian causae. His system is consequently organized under four aspects.

The state as an acting body has a goal or *causa finalis*. The second aspect is a *causa materialis* under which Conring subsumes the knowledge of people and of economic goods. The *causa formalis* is the constitution and the laws of a country. The *causa efficiens* is its concrete administration and the activities of its elite. Under each of these main categories, Conring systematically makes further subdivisions. The causa efficiens, for example, describes the concrete ways by which the state is governed. They are either principales or instrumentales. The former are the statesmen themselves; the latter are again subdivided into animatae (staff) and inanimatae. At the point where he has arrived at a "causa efficiens instrumentalis inanimata," his main example is money. And under this rubric he then develops elaborate monetary ideas which, I gather, were quite advanced for his time.

One should notice, behind this forbidding terminology, a number of very modern topics. Thus, contemporary social theory is much concerned with the goals (causa finalis) and subgoals of organizations, their possible conflict and the duty of the "peak coordinator" to attempt their integration. The distinction between causa formalis and efficiens corresponds almost textually to the distinction between formal and informal relations, which is fundamental for all modern organizational analysis. The many examples which Conring attaches to his definition can be gleaned from Zehrfeld.[30] And Conring does not stop at a merely descriptive presentation of his categories. He often adds what we would call today speculative "cross-tabulations." For example, con-

---

[29] As far as I know, political arithmetic is about the only topic of contemporary knowledge on which Leibnitz himself did not write. It is therefore well possible that Conring did not even know of the work of his English contemporaries. He was, however, informed on English developments in at least one other field: among his medical writings, I found mention of a treatise on Harvey's discovery of the circulation of blood (in addition to texts on skorbut, fractured skulls and iatrochemistry).

[30] Zehrfeld, *op. cit.*, pp. 15ff.

sider his conjoining the causa formalis and the causa materialis: in a democracy, all people should be studied; in an aristocracy, knowledge of the elite is more relevant.

These ideas are first developed as a general system and then applied consistently to one country after another. Stress is laid on interstate comparisons. Conring's richest material pertains to Spain, which he still considered the leading European power. It would not be too difficult to reconstruct from his very extensive comments an "Anatomy of Spain." By comparing it with Petty's work on Ireland, one should get a better picture of the difference in style of thinking which distinguishes these two authors. Conring himself, incidentally, was very explicit about his method. He classifies the type of sources available to him and gives detailed criteria as to how to judge their reliability; he tries to separate his own work from that of the historian, the geographer, the lawyer, etc.; and again in the frame of Aristotelian logic, he discusses elaborately the kind of inferences which can be drawn from descriptive facts of rules of conduct for the responsible statesman.[31]

The first publication of Conring's on the "notitia rerum publicarum" were unauthorized notes by one of his students; the original manuscripts were published only after Conring's death. Soon, his students began to give the same course at other universities. Various compendia appeared, usually under a title such as "Collegium Political-statisticum." (It is controversial when and how the term "statistics" was introduced for this tradition.) By the beginning of the 18th century, the Conring system was taught all over Germany.[32] It had the advantage of being eminently teachable even by minor men, and gave an academic frame of reference to the training of civil servants, which remained a common problem to all the little German states up to the end of their existence in the Napoleonic era. Conring's political activities helped in the diffusion of his main idea. He spent some time in about ten other German principalities in his capacity at temporary advisor; it can be taken for granted and could probably be proven from a perusal of his correspondence that on such occasions he established academic contacts.[33]

In any case, when Achenwall was a student at various German universities in the years around 1740, he met a well-established tradition. He began to collect statistical information in the Conring sense and when in 1748 he received a call to Göttingen, he was prepared to make it the base of his main course. As a matter of fact, his inaugural lecture was a defense of the whole system against representatives of related disciplines who feared the competi-

[31] Zehrfeld, *op. cit.*, pp. 46ff.

[32] One day the history of universities should be rewritten from a social scientist's point of view. Stephen D'Irsay (*Histoire des Universités* [Paris: Auguste Picard, 1933]) is altogether too superficial, although his footnotes on sources are very valuable. Paulsen's "History of Academic Instruction in Germany" is a fine piece of analytical writing and contains much information on the period after the Thirty Years' War (Friedrich Paulsen, *Geschichte des Gelehrten Unterrichts* [Leipzig: Veit & Comp., 1919]). His main interest, however, is with the ups and downs of the classical studies and he pays less attention to the men and institutions relevant to my narrative.

[33] Several princes gave him the title of "Personal Physician and States Counselor" which shows how the many facets of his reputation were fused. I do not discuss here the similar positions he held for a while in Denmark and in Sweden. There is evidence that in 1651 he hoped to move to Sweden permanently; but again nothing came of this effort to escape the small town atmosphere of Germany.

tion with their own prerogatives. I have already mentioned that Achenwall's writing in German helped to focus attention upon his work. But the image of a "Göttingen school of statistics," which got abroad rather quickly, was much strengthened by an institutional factor.

The Göttingen School

The University of Göttingen opened in 1737. To it, historians of higher education trace back some of the main ideas of 19th century German university life. Professors should do original research, not only transmit available knowledge; sons of upper-class families, who traditionally were educated in private schools, should be attracted; and they should not only listen and recite, but be active in their studies. (The prestige of Göttingen was greatly enhanced by the creation of a library which was considered the outstanding one in Europe.) It is not surprising that this university became the center for the development of statistics understood as knowledge of the state. It was interesting to young men who came from a more literate background; it gave opportunity to do research in terms of the accumulation of more and more information about more and more countries; the material was useful for future civil servants.[34] In addition, however, it provided for several generations of professors a methodological continuity; and nothing is more conducive to institutional fame and stability.[35]

From Achenwall on, we are in often described territory. He and his successors refined Conring's categorical system, raised new methodological questions (e.g., what is *relevant* for a necessary and sufficient description of a society), and added a great deal of substantive material. The main figures in the Göttingen tradition are Schloezer, Achenwall's successor, who in 1804 created the slogan that statistics is history at a given point in time while history is statistics in flux; and Nieman, who, in 1807, published the most elaborate classificatory system which he, incidentally called a "theory."[36] By then the confrontation with the political arithmeticians was in full swing. It developed by a somewhat roundabout route. Among the offshoots of the Göttingen group were men who were especially concerned with the *presentation* of comparative information on countries. This led to the idea of two-dimensional schemata: on the horizontal dimension, the countries to be compared and on the vertical dimension, the categories of comparison. Originally the entries in those "matrices" were verbal descriptions or references to sources. But this schematization was naturally conducive to the use of figures wherever they were available, if for no other reason than that they took less space. This in turn favored topics which lent themselves to numerical presentation (more and more such information became available due to the increasing number of

---

[34] Achenwall presided over a weekly seminar where transient explorers and diplomats reported on their experiences abroad; it was the task of the student to subsume this information under the proper categories of "the System."

[35] Denifle, in his book on the origin of medieval universities (*Die Entstehung der Mittelalterlichen Universität* [Berlin, 1885]) raises the question as to why the University of Paris remained intact after the death of Abelard, while preceding foundations disappeared after the death of the charismatic master. He thinks that it is the *methodological* idea of the disputation, the finding of truth by a staged dialectic controversy, which provides the explanation.

[36] John, *op. cit.*, p. 98 f.

government agencies collecting census materials). The guardians of the Göttingen tradition were afraid that this would give a "materialistic" flavor to the comparative study of states and deflect from the educational, social, and spiritual significance of their teaching. They invented the derogatory term, "table statisticians" which today would be considered a pleonasm, but was very apt in the context of the time. A distinction was made between "refined and distinguished" in contradistinction to "vulgar" statistics. John gives a number of quotations from the *Göttinger gelehrte Anzeigen* to indicate the vehemence of feelings at the beginning of the 19th century. The vulgar statisticians have depraved the great art to "brainless busy work." "These stupid fellows disseminate the insane idea that one can understand the power of a state if one just knows its size, its population, its national income, and the number of dumb beasts grazing around." "The machinations of those criminal politician-statisticians in trying to tell everything by figures . . . is despicable and ridiculous beyond words."[37] The only thing missing here is the apt expression of quantophrenia which Sorokin has recently created in a similar mood.[38]

In spite of John's very detailed documentation of this fight,[39] I do not feel satisfied that it has yet been clarified. Thus, for example, it should not be forgotten that the period of the Napoleonic wars led to a temporary collapse of Göttingen and the meteoric rise of the University of Berlin after its foundation in 1810. It is also likely that the helplessness of the German states in the face of the Napoleonic onslaught discredited the claim of the Conring tradition that it provided the factual foundation for successful statecraft. And the beginning of a broader German nationalism probably made the academic world more receptive to the kind of general causal relations which the British political arithmeticians looked for under similar political circumstances one hundred fifty years earlier. There is here still a piece of history which deserves much more careful investigation than is available in the literature so far.[40]

But the story sketched in the preceding pages helps to explain why German academia was for so long a period impervious to the political arithmeticians. What Conring started served the most immediate needs of his country. It could not afford the intellectual investment which in England led to a better rate of growth in general knowledge; one can be concrete in surmising that Conring, even if he had thought of them, could not have afforded the computations with which Graunt started. Later the system served well the educational needs of the many little German universities, staffed by mediocre people. When Achenwall gave it additional prestige in Göttingen, something like vested interest began to play a role. Schloezer worked for a while in Berlin and knew of Suessmilch—yet why should a professor at the leading university pay attention to a military pastor?[41] But their king, Frederick the Great, did.

[37] John, *op. cit.*, pp. 129f.
[38] Pitirim Sorokin, *Fads and Foibles in Modern Sociology* (Chicago: Henry Regnery, 1956).
[39] John, *op. cit.*, pp. 128-139.
[40] One might record the victory of the table statisticians with an ironical smile. Today, they themselves are beginning to be looked upon as mere social bookkeepers. Many a mathematically trained statistician would not deal with the problems the political arithmeticians inaugurated; he would reserve the term "statistics" to an abstract theory of inference.
[41] Actually Schloezer promised in one of his books to one day present Suessmilch's ideas, but "never got around to it."

Upon Suessmilch's advice he ordered a number of statistical surveys and therewith contributed to the downfall of the university tradition.

Meantime, the Germans had acquired an international audience. Things had greatly changed since Conring's time. In 1774, twenty-five years after Achenwall's first publication, Goethe published Werther. When Schloezer's book came out, Fichte's philosophy was well developed and the whole romantic school was in full flourish. I have no knowledge of an early contact between the Weimar-Jena humanists and Göttingen which was the center of the German social sciences in the broadest sense. (At the creation of the University of Berlin in 1810, the convergence is well documented.) But as the rest of Europe paid very serious attention to the German humanistic flowering, it should not be too surprising that even the more specialized efforts of the university statisticians were considered abroad as a major intellectual development which deserved as much attention as the contemporary work of the political arithmeticians in England. The fact that by now the former are practically forgotten while the latter are considered the foundation of the modern notion of statistics should not keep us from realizing that the intellectual balance might have looked very different at the end of the 18th century. It would not be too difficult to trace how influences from these two centers radiated to other countries and where and how they overlapped. From a cursory inspection, I have the impression that early Italian writers were especially influenced by the Germans, while in 18th century France combinations began to emerge.

The question can be raised why I consider the development of classificatory systems a legitimate part of the history of quantification in the social sciences. I want to postpone my answer until I have described another effect of this kind by the LePlay school. First, I turn to the writer who marks the beginning of what one should consider modern efforts at sociological quantification. I agree with John's judgment that a major turning point came about when Quetelet's first publication appeared. "He is the focal point, at which all the rays of the first great period of statistical history converge, to be redirected through moral statistics and similar developments into many new fields."[42] While this simile too will need some correction, it is certainly a deserved tribute to the man who is the central figure of my next section.

QUETELET AND HIS "STATISTIQUE MORALE"

Life and Writings

Quetelet was born in 1796 in the Belgian city of Ghent. He grew up in modest circumstances, but his abilities were recognized early. He originally wanted to become a painter and sculptor, and for a while he was an apprentice in a painter's studio. He also had strong literary interests: he published poetry at an early age and had a play performed in a local theatre. In order to make a living, he took a job at the age of eighteen as a teacher of mathematics in a lycée. When he was about twenty, he came under the influence of a mathematician at the University of Ghent who prevailed upon him to extend his mathematical studies. In 1819 Quetelet received his doctorate. His thesis, on

[42] John, *op. cit.*, p. 9.

a problem in analytical geometry, was considered a major contribution. However, he retained his humanistic interests, and up to 1823, when he was twenty-seven years old, he continued to publish essays on literary criticism and to translate Greek poetry into French. Many of his friends at this time were writers and philosophers.

Quetelet's thesis brought him to the attention of the Ministry of Education and in 1819 he was called to Brussels to teach mathematics at one of the several institutions of higher learning in the capital of the Belgian part of the Dutch kingdom.[43] Part of his teaching involved what we would today call adult education, and this seems to have fitted in well with his literary inclinations; repeatedly thereafter he wrote popular monographs on a variety of scientific topics. I am stressing Quetelet's many-sided and humanistic background, because the quality of his later work cannot be understood without knowledge of it.

Quite soon after coming to Brussels, Quetelet became deeply involved in a plan the origins of which are unknown: he wanted to start an astronomical observatory. For almost a decade until the plan became a fact, it had priority among all his activities. It also brought about the main turn in his intellectual life, although this occurred in an unexpected way. In 1823 he was sent to Paris to study astronomical activities and to find out what kinds of instruments would be needed for the Brussels observatory. While in Paris he became acquainted with the great French mathematicians whose headquarters were at the Ecole Polytechnique. He was especially impressed by Fourier and LaPlace and by their work on probability of which he evidently had known nothing before. Both of these men, as was mentioned earlier, had analyzed statistical social data. This combination of abstract mathematics and social reality obviously provided the ideal convergence of the two lines along which Quetelet's mind had developed. He quickly realized that a whole new field of activities, embracing all of his interests, could be opened up. In later reminiscences he said that after he had become acquainted with the statistical ideas of his French masters, he immediately thought of applying them to the measurement of the human body, a topic he had become curious about when he was a painter and sculptor. With his return from Paris in 1824 at the age of twenty-eight, the basic direction of his intellectual career was essentially set.[44] Soon the Dutch government gave him an opportunity to do something about it.

In 1826 Quetelet was asked to help the work of the Royal Statistics Com-

[43] The University of Brussels was not created until a decade later.

[44] In connection with his work for the observatory, he made a number of other trips, including one to Germany in 1829 when he stayed in Weimar for a week and had several meetings with Goethe, then 80 years old. Goethe was quite fascinated by his young visitor. While Quetelet meant to stay only a few hours, Goethe kept him for a week and remained with him in correspondence for the remaining years of his life. There exist several contemporary reports on this encounter and Quetelet himself wrote at the age of 70, a reminiscence. The material has been collected by Victor John "Quetelet bei Goethe," *Festgabe für Johannes Conrad*, H. Paesche, ed. (Jena: Gustav Fischer, 1898). Goethe discussed with Quetelet repeatedly his favorite notion of "types." John surmises that this might have given Quetelet the idea for his terminology of the "Homme Moyen." Some of John's material has been briefly summarized in a contribution by Auguste Collard to *Isis* ("Goethe et Quetelet," *Isis*, 1933, 1934, *20*).

mission, and he participated in the preparation of plans for a Belgian population census. His first publications covered quantitative information about Belgium which could be used for practical purposes including mortality tables with special reference to insurance problems. In 1827 he analyzed crime statistics but still with an eye to improving the administration of justice. In 1828 he edited a general statistical handbook on Belgium which included a great deal of comparative material obtained from contacts he had formed during his stays in England and France. The unrest leading to the Belgian insurrection in 1830 intensified Quetelet's interest in social topics.[45]

Quetelet's two basic memoranda appeared in 1831. By then he had decided that from the general pool of statistical data, he wanted to carve out a special sector dealing with human beings. He first published a memorandum entitled "The Growth of Man" which utilized a large number of measurements of people's size. A few months later he published statistics on crime under the title "Criminal Tendencies at Different Ages." While the emphasis in these publications is on what we today would call the life cycle, both of them included many multi-variate tabulations, such as differences in the age-specific crime rates for men and women separately, for various countries, and for different social groups.[46] In 1832 a third publication, giving developmental data on weight, made its appearance. By this time the idea of a social physics had formed in his mind, and in 1835 he combined his earlier memoranda into one entitled "On Man and the Development of his Faculties," with the subtitle, "Physique Sociale." With this publication all of Quetelet's basic ideas were available to a broader public.

Quetelet's literary background and the fact that his humanist friends remained an important reference group for him help to explain the manner in which he published his works. When he had new data or had developed a new technique, he first published brief notes about them, usually in the reports of the Belgian Royal Society, and sometimes in French or English journals. Once such notes had appeared, he would elaborate the same material into longer articles and give his data social and philosophical interpretations. He finally combined these articles into books which he hoped would have a general appeal. He obviously felt very strongly that empirical findings should be interpreted as much as possible and made interesting to readers with broad social and humanistic concerns.

The statistical data which he published in the period just reviewed were

---

[45] Two years before Quetelet's birth, Belgium was still one of the provinces under the domination of the Austrians. During the Napoleonic Wars, it became a part of France, and after the settlement of 1815 it was made a part of the Netherland Kingdom which combined Belgium and the old Dutch provinces to serve as a buffer state against possible future aggression on the part of the French. The French Revolution of 1830 spread into this new kingdom, however, and led to the separation of Belgium and Holland. Since that time, Belgium has existed in the form in which we know it today. The unrest leading to the Belgian insurrection in 1830 intensified Quetelet's interest in social affairs. So far as I can tell, Quetelet was never active in politics in the narrow sense, and this may account for the fact that his emphasis was always on social science in general, not on the role of the government which was of such great concern to the Political Arithmeticians.

[46] Quetelet talks often about the "social system" and its "equilibrium." What he means is the fact that the social strata contribute each their own rates, which are constant over time but different from each other.

always averages and rates related to age and other demographic characteristics. Around 1840, however, he became interested in the *distribution* of these characteristics. It occurred to him that the distribution of the heights and weights of human beings, when put in graphic form, looked very much like the distribution of errors of observations which had been studied since the turn of the century. This led him to the conviction that the distribution of physical characteristics could be looked at as if they were binomial and normal distributions. They were currently discussed in terms of two models. One was the idea of trying to hit the bull's eye of a target with a rifle. Measuring the distance radially from the center, one would find that most of the hits were near the center and the less frequent the greater their distance from the center. This could be represented mathematically by assuming that a very large number of incidental causes, such as movements of the air, involuntary movements of the triggering finger, and so on, affected the tendency of the marksman to hit the center of the target. To obtain the proper derivation through the application of probabilistic mathematics, one had to assume that these incidental factors were independent of each other.

The other model used the time-honored urn of balls. Suppose that in such an urn one has, say, one hundred balls, thirty of them black and seventy of them white. By drawing many samples of ten balls from this urn (always replacing the balls after each draw), one would find that most of the samples contained three black balls. The frequency of samples with very few or very many black balls would decline the more the number of black balls deviated from the "true number" in the urn, here three out of ten. The distribution of black balls in many samples could again be computed mathematically.

It was Quetelet's idea that the distribution of people's size originated in the same way. Nature, like the marksman, kept trying to hit a perfect size, but a large number of accidental and independent causes made for deviations in the same way that the rifle shots deviated from the bull's eye. Or using the urn scheme: the "true size" corresponding to the number of black balls in the urn was due to basic biological factors. People were samples in which varying numbers of black balls were drawn. This was just another way to account through probability theory for the actual distribution of size which Quetelet saw in his data.

In his earlier publications Quetelet had been primarily interested in the fact that the *averages* of physical characteristics and the *rates* of crime and marriage showed a surprisingly stable relation over time and between countries with age and other demographic variables. It was these relations which he had pointed to as the "laws" of the social world. By now, however, he was concerned with the distributions about the averages. He was convinced that if he could make enough observations, his distributions would always have the normal or binomial form. The notion of "law" was now extended: the distributions themselves and their mathematical derivations, as well as their constancy over time and place, became laws.

In the middle of 1840 Quetelet published a number of articles along these lines. One dealt with "probability as applied to moral and political sciences," another with the "social system and the laws which govern it." He now developed in addition another terminological distinction. Originally he had talked about "physique sociale" when he had dealt with people rather than with general statistical information about commerce, armament, and so on. He now distinguished within this area between physical and other characteristics of men and women. The quantitative study of non-physical characteristics was called "statistique morale." The same data and the same ideas were again used and re-used in a large variety of publications, including popular treatises on probability theory itself.[47]

In 1855 Quetelet suffered a stroke from which he recovered only slowly. After a while he resumed work, but never again developed any new ideas. His publications continued, however, and in them he reported new data and reiterated his basic propositions. In 1869 he published the two volumes on which his international fame is based, entitled Physique Sociale or an Essay on the Development of Man's Faculties,[48] thus reversing the order of the title used in 1835. The work was introduced by a translation of an article of the English astronomer Herschel who, writing in the *Edinburgh Review* in 1850, had drawn the attention of the English public to Quetelet's applications of probability theory to the social data. The first volume, divided into two parts, dealt in the main with population statistics, such as birth, death, fertility, and so on, and with the application of these statistics to public administration and medicine. The first part of the second volume dealt with physical characteristics such as size and weight, and added some data on physiological investigations. It is the second part of this volume, Book 4, which contained the material relevant to the social sciences. Intellectual abilities and insanity were treated in the first chapter. A second chapter deals with the development of "moral qualities." The emphasis was on crime statistics, but data on suicide and on all sorts of behavioral manifestations such as drunkenness, duels, were also included. These two chapters will serve as the basis for our specific discussion of Quetelet.[49]

Anyone who draws his information from this book, generally considered the standard source for Quetelet's writings, should be warned that it is a very confusing compilation. Large parts of it are verbatim reprints of previous publications including the most important ones from the early 1830's. Sometimes footnotes are added to enlarge on an idea; in other places, Quetelet adds chapters containing more recent data and offers an interpretation which overlaps almost word for word with interpretations of similar data in other chapters. Furthermore, because his thinking on the social and philosophical implications of his work varied over the thirty years of his productive career, some statements on quite basic ideas contradict others made in a different part of the "Physique Sociale." Even in his lifetime the confusing nature of Quetelet's prodigious literary output had created concern. The German economist G.

---

[47] While his early publications on geometrical problems are considered important mathematical contributions, Quetelet did not do any original work in probability theory. He only extended its applications to social phenomena.

[48] Adolphe Quetelet, *Physique Sociale,* Vol. I, C. Muquardt (Bruxelles, 1869).

[49] A short book 5 is an extension of book 4. But its introductory pages give a good picture of Quetelet's ideas on the relation of his work with literature and art; he develops a notion which today we would label "national character."

F. Knapp published in 1871 an analytical catalogue of Quetelet's publications in order to trace where various parts of his texts appeared for the first time and where he subsequently repeated them more or less verbatim in other publications. Knapp also wrote extensively on Quetelet's substantive ideas and created great interest in him among his own students and contemporaries.[50] A very helpful book on Quetelet was published in 1912 by a Belgian, Joseph Lottin.[51] This is an outstanding example of intrinsic analysis. Organized by topics, it combines and confronts extensive quotations in order to bring out what Quetelet most likely intended to convey. Lottin's book probably contains all available biographical material on Quetelet. It provides a well-organized chronology of his publications and, most valuable of all, it lists almost all the German, English and French literature on the various debates which started during Quetelet's lifetime and continued well beyond his death.[52] English-speaking readers will find Frank Hankins' dissertation[53] the best source of information about Quetelet. This author was well aware that there is no English equivalent for the French term "statistique morale" or the German "Moralstatistik." He decided to use the phrase "moral statistics," and I shall follow his example.

Throughout his life Quetelet was active in many enterprises, such as the organization of international statistical congresses, the improvement of census work in his own and in other countries, and so on. Because of the specialized focus of my paper, I shall not give attention to these aspects of Quetelet's life and works, but rather try to elucidate some of his ideas on quantification.

The Distribution of Non-Physical Human Characteristics

I mentioned previously Quetelet's work on the distribution of size and weight in large-scale human populations. He was convinced that similar distribution curves could be found for intellectual and "moral" characteristics if appropriate measures were used. He made explicit his belief that such measure-

[50] Knapp became famous mainly because of his monetary theory. The article about him in The Encyclopedia of the Social Sciences is informative, but the appended bibliography does not include any of his numerous publications on Quetelet's moral statistics, nor his editions of statistical classics. (A series of pertinent papers by G. F. Knapp appeared in the 1871 volumes of Bruno Hildebrand, *Jahrbücher für Nationalökonomie und Statistik* (Jena: Friedrich Mauke).

[51] *Quetelet, Statisticien et Sociologue* (Louvain: Bibl. de L'Inst. Sup. de Philosophie, 1912).

[52] Lottin's book also contains valuable material on Quetelet's relation to his contemporaries. Comte, as is well known, complained that Quetelet had stolen the term "social physics" from him, and that he had therefore had to invent the word, sociology, to identify his approach. In his review (*op. cit.*, pp. 357-368), Lottin argues that the Belgian probably did not know of the Frenchman's terminological

invention. And he adds interesting comments on the very different images of the social sciences held by the two men: Comte was trying to derive from history broad developmental trends which could be projected into the future, while Quetelet was bent on finding precise regularities which would help to explain the contemporary social scene. Quetelet rarely engaged in controversy. The most serious one was with the Frenchman, Guerry, who invented the term, "moral statistics," and who was analyzing crime statistics at the same time that Quetelet was. Lottin provides a detailed analysis of the relevant drafts and publications (*op. cit.*, pp. 128-138). The question of priority is a subtle one, because, although their interest in crime statistics developed independently, they were informed of each other's work through a common friend. According to Lottin, Quetelet wins in a photo finish.

[53] *Adolphe Quetelet as Statistician* (New York: Columbia Univ. Press, 1908).

ments were possible in principle, and that the lack of data was due only to technical difficulties. Much of his general interpretive writing on moral statistics hinges on the kind of quantitative data he used as substitutes for the variables he felt would be really desirable. Debates about Quetelet's work usually focus on his idea of an "average man" or his shifting pseudo-psychological comments on his data. A careful reading would show, however, that his underlying theory of measurement, partly brilliant and partly a confused foreshadowing of later developments, gives the clue to much of his work.*

On pp. 148 ff. Quetelet makes a statement not on his findings themselves nor their interpretation, but on the *formal* nature of the variables which can be used to *"measure the qualities of people which can only be assessed by their effects."* The passage which follows is a somewhat condensed summary of his presentation which I will reanalyze in the light of contemporary thinking about measurement in the social sciences.

One can use numbers without absurdity in the following cases:

(1) When the effects can be assessed by a *direct* measure which shows their *degree of energy:* effects, for instance, which can be seen by strength, by speed, or by work efforts made on material of the same kind.[54]

(2) When the *qualities* are such that their *effects* are about the *same,* and are *related to the frequency of these effects,* as, for instance, the fertility of women, drunkenness, etc. If two men placed in the same circumstances got drunk, the one once per week and the other twice, then one could say that their propensity to drunkenness has a 1:2 ratio.[55]

(3) Finally, one can use numbers if the causes are such that one has to take into account the *frequency of their effects as well as their energy* ... this is especially true when it comes to moral and intellectual qualities such as courage, prudence, imagination, and so on.[56]

   When the effects vary as to their energy but appear in approximately the same proportions, the matter is greatly simplified. One can then disregard the element of energy, and work only with frequencies. Thus, if one wants to compare the propensity to theft of 25 year old and 45 year old men, one could, without too much error, just consider the frequency of thefts committed at these ages. Variations in the degree of serious-

---

* All page numbers without an additional reference are from the second volume of Quetelet's *Physique Sociale*. Direct quotations from the original are my translations; the underscoring of sentences is done to emphasize points in the present discussion and does not appear in the original.

[54] Here Quetelet inserts an elaborate footnote that the measurement of memory might be of the same type if records were made of the length of time different people remembered a text they had learned. He emphasizes that such measures can be used to study variations by age, just as one can study developmental differences in eyesight or acuity of hearing.

[55] The most frequently quoted example is the measurement of courage by counting the number of courageous deeds. It is followed by the suggestion of a courage-poll (p. 147) : "Assume now that society, *in a more perfect state,* keeps track of and evaluates all acts of courage and virtue, *just as one does today in regard to crime;* would not this make it possible to measure the relative propensity to courage and virtue in different age groups?"

[56] Quetelet had previously mentioned (p. 143) that in order to measure the productivity of writers one would have both to count the number of works and weigh each item according to its literary merits; having elaborated on this and similar examples at some length, he obviously felt that he could deal with the general idea briefly. He therefore proceeded immediately to the question of feasible approximations.

ness of these infractions can be assumed to be about the same in both age groups.

I think that *all the qualities of people which can only be assessed by their effects can be classified in the three categories which I have just established;* I believe also that the reader will feel that the temporary impossibility of using numbers in such assessments is due to the *unavailability of data rather than to shortcomings in the methodological idea.*

For the moment, let us disregard the references to cause and effect, a topic to which I shall return presently. The three types of variables described here are then quite familiar. The first is a continuous variable which we would exemplify today in the "moral" area by the amount of time an individual watches television, the distance a child walks on an errand without being distracted by something which makes him forget his original goal, and so on. Whether a variable is continuous or not is a question of empirical fact, which has nothing to do with the substantive content of the subject matter to which it is applied.

The same is true for the second of Quetelet's types. These we would call discontinuous variables (or rather, variates, if we wanted to be very precise). Examples would be the number of times per year that an individual buys a weekly magazine, the number of times he goes to the movies, and so on. The natural sciences also deal with such discontinuous variables and do so for a broad range of phenomena, whether it be the number of meteorites in a certain sector of the sky or the number of atoms per section of a bombarded screen.

Finally the third, or mixed, type is well known today. A price index combines price changes of a variety of products; a scholastic aptitude test counts the number of mistakes made, and might give different weights to different items. To simplify matters, we shall forget about the mixed type for the time being, and just distinguish between continuous and discontinuous variables.

Why were these distinctions important to Quetelet? The answer is simple. The type of discontinuous variables which Quetelet had in mind plays an important role in the social sciences. But the observations needed to establish them usually require a considerable amount of time. They have nevertheless one great advantage: if we only wish to compare subgroups in a population, we can often *substitute a one-time observation of many people* for *repeated observations of one person.* This is especially true if we are only concerned with averages, which in this case take the form of rates. Suppose we want to know whether men or women are more faithful readers of a particular weekly magazine. The logically correct procedure would be to select a sample of both sexes, find out from each person the number of weeks in a year he had bought the magazine, and then compute the average. This would be the number of weeks per year the average person of both sexes performed this act. Dividing this average by the number of weeks in a year gives us the probability that the average man (or woman) will buy the magazine. Instead of proceeding in this way, under many conditions we can approach the problem differently. We can interview a sample of men and women *just once* and ask them whether they have bought the magazine *this week.* The proportion of positive replies will be the same as the probability obtained through the more precise procedures.

It is this substitution of observations over people for observations over time which is one of Quetelet's central ideas. And as long as one wishes only to compare averages, this is the standard procedure in social research today. But when it comes to measuring *distributions* of these discontinuous variables, we are of course in a very different situation. In these cases we would need the full variable over time for each person and therefore observations over time. In many of the major writings of Quetelet and his commentators, the existence of such distributions is implied. A digression on two of these commentators will be enlightening at this point.

Lottin states repeatedly that Quetelet never wanted to make measurements of such discontinuous variables on *single* individuals. This is one of the few points on which Lottin is wrong. As the preceding quotation shows, and as can be corroborated in many other citations, Quetelet considered such measurements desirable and, in principle, feasible. One would misunderstand much of his writing if one overlooked this point, for Quetelet was convinced that, if such measurements were available, they would show distribution curves just like the ones he published for size and weight.[57] He gave these hypothetical distributions exactly the same interpretation that he gave his biological data, substituting society for nature. Society aims at a certain average which it obtains in a majority of cases but from which it deviates up and down according to the laws of probability. Today we deal with many empirical distributions of the sort which Quetelet had more or less clearly in mind. These include scores on intelligence tests, frequencies of sociometric choices addressed to each of a group of individuals, the number of times an individual did not vote in a series of elections, and so on. Within the range of precision which Quetelet thought of, the distributions of such measures do indeed look like distributions of physical characteristics.

Yet there is an important difference between the first two types of measurements in Quetelet's list; this leads to an interesting episode in the criticism of Quetelet. Durkheim's disciple Halbwachs wrote a monograph on Quetelet in 1912.[58] He was not clear about the important difference between looking at averages of discontinuous non-physical variables and studying their distribution, just as Quetelet himself was never really explicit about this distinction. But one can deduce from Halbwachs' text that he had these distributions in mind when he launched his main attack on Quetelet. The distribution of physical characteristics, he argued, might be accounted for in the same way as are shots or astronomical observations, namely as the effect of a large number of minor *independent* factors which make for deviations from the average. But clearly this could not be true for data in the area of moral statistics, because here the interdependence of social action becomes crucial. Halbwachs stated and restated the notion that individuals influence each other, that the various sectors of society are dependent upon each other, that contemporary society is affected by past ideas and experiences. From such con-

---

[57] It is true that Quetelet repeatedly says that he does not deal with individual measures. This occurs, however, only when he wants to argue for the validity of his rates. As can be seen from our main quotation and from many other passages, he always insisted that, in principle, quantitative information on individuals could and should be obtained.

[58] Maurice Halbwachs, *La Theorie de l'-Homme Moyen* (Paris: Felix Alcan, 1912).

siderations he developed an argument against Quetelet's basic idea of probabilistic analysis which rests on a serious misunderstanding. Because of the
dominant position of the Durkheim School in French and in modern sociology,
it is worthwhile to consider this point in some detail. We are confronted here
with the following situation. An early author, Quetelet, has a correct idea
which he develops, however, only within certain limits. A subsequent author,
Halbwachs, instead of adding what was missing, misjudges the partial contribution which his predecessor had made. As a result, instead of steady pro-
gression, we find temporary discontinuity in intellectual developments. Only
many decades later when the idea of stochastic processes developed was the
trend resumed. And it is fairly safe to say that the modern version was created by men who knew nothing of Quetelet's work.

Typical of Halbwachs' arguments are the following:

> All these circumstances *preclude the idea that the laws of chance play a role
> in the social sciences.* Here the combination of causes (represented by indi-
> viduals) are connected with and dependent upon each other, because, as one
> of them comes about, similar ones are reinforced and tend to occur more often;
> therefore, we are not in the same situation here as we are in games of chance,
> where the players as well as the dice are not supposed to acquire habits, to
> imitate each other, or to have a tendency to repeat themselves. (*op. cit.,* p. 146)

> Society and the moral acts of its members are probably, of all phenomena,
> the area in which it is least possible to consider an individual and his acts in
> isolation from the behavior of all others; this would mean leaving out what is
> really essential. *This means, at the same time, that this is an area in which
> the calculus of probabilities is least applicable.* (*op. cit.,* p. 174)

The crucial sentences are those I have underscored. Halbwachs sets up an
antithesis between social interaction and the application of probability mathematics. This has been proved to be completely wrong in more recent applications of mathematical models in the social sciences. Let us consider an example. Suppose that we are observers at a ball attended by men and women
who do not know each other and suppose moreover that more women than
men are present. As the music starts, each man chooses a partner at random
by drawing a woman's name out of a hat, and this is repeated for ten dances.
At the end of the ten dances, we can classify the women according to the
number of times they had partners. We will find a normal (more exactly, a
binomial) distribution: the women will have had some average number of
dances, the lucky ones who exceed this average being balanced by the number who were more or less out of luck. This would indeed be a situation
corresponding to an error curve of the kind Quetelet had in mind.

Now let us change the situation slightly. At the time of the first dance each
woman has the same probability of being chosen by chance. But suppose that
the men watch the situation and believe that the women chosen the first time
are the more desirable partners; a first choice thus increases their chances of
being selected a second time. One might assume, to translate this situation
into probability terms, that at the second dance the names of the women chosen
the first time are put into the proverbial hat twice. Then even if the partners
for the second dance are again chosen at random (by drawing slips from the

hat), obviously the women who were chosen the first time will be more likely to be chosen again. Suppose that we allow this process to repeat itself for ten dances, and, after the tenth dance, we make a statistical count of how often each woman was chosen. The number of women with very many and with very few partners will now be clearly larger than in the previous "model," although the average number of "successes" will be the same.[59]

Here then is a situation in which, contrary to Halbwachs' opinion, social interaction is taken into account and probability considerations are still applicable. In the same way there is no difficulty in developing so-called stochastic processes in which probabilities of individual choices at time $(t + 1)$ depend upon the total probability distribution at time (t). Modern mathematical sociology has proven the Durkheim School wrong and Quetelet right. It is true, however, that Quetelet himself was unaware of the fact that his sociological thinking exceeded the specific mathematical model upon which he drew. In his discursive writings, Quetelet often talks about social interaction and the effects of the past. As far as I am aware, however, he never went beyond the classical normal distribution which, indeed, makes no provision for these more complex processes.

Let us return now to the way Quetelet worded his distinction between the three types of measurement. He talked of "qualities which can only be assessed by their effects." Today authors would talk interchangeably of hypothetical constructs, disposition concepts, underlying characteristics, or mathematical latent structures. But his three types of measurements classify manifest, observable data, not the underlying qualities themselves. Quetelet thought that certain things, such as size and weight, were human qualities that could be measured directly. Other qualities, such as a tendency to suicide or marriage or, most of all, to crime, could be measured only indirectly. Now here he obviously confused two completely different problems. Certain variables are quite conventional: an individual's height, the prices of commodities, or the amount of income. As one turns to the new area of social investigation, other variables have to be developed: the number of times a man gets drunk or the amount of money a person contributes to charity (another example which Quetelet himself gives). These variables may somehow sound different, but as far as the required observations go, all are on the same level of reality. A difference arises only *if one wants to make different uses of such information.* One might be interested in the size of people; then that is all there is to it. Or one might be interested in the charitable tendencies of people; then the amount of money they give to organized charity is an *indicator*, perhaps only one of several that might be used. This fact of course, is equally true for physical characteristics. Suppose one were interested in a child's "propensity to physical growth." Then actual size would be a reasonable indicator,

---

[59] Early work on these more complicated distributions was carried out by the German economist and mathematician, Wilhelm Lexis. He was a charter member of the Verein fur Sozialpolitik in 1872, and taught at Strassburg where, somewhat later, Knapp formed a center for work on Quetelet and the history of statistics in general. Lexis had broad interests, co-edited the German Encyclopedia of the Social Sciences, and wrote himself on moral statistics. Whether the Lexis "distribution with contagion" was developed with reference to Quetelet, I do not know, but the question suggests a good topic for further research.

although physical anthropologists could certainly give us many others. The relation of propensities (or tendencies or however else one wants to translate Quetelet's favorite term, "penchant") to manifest data is always the same, regardless of subject matter. It is true that in the social sciences the inferential use of manifest data is more frequent than in the natural sciences. But medicine is an interesting borderline case: diagnosticians use manifest physiological data to make inferences regarding unobservable physiological propensities. It is this general problem and its partial misconception which we now have to trace in Quetelet's writings and the subsequent literature they inspired.

Propensities and Their Measurement

The matter is best explained in connection with Quetelet's writings on criminal tendencies ("penchant au crime") which fill the largest part of Book 4 of his "Physique Sociale" (pp. 249-363). What he had before him were crime rates carefully computed for a large number of subsets in the population. However, he was not satisfied with what we today would call descriptive correlations. He wanted to fit his findings into a much broader picture. In order to do so, he considered his rates as measures ("échelles") of underlying tendencies. From his point of view, this had two advantages. He could talk about his findings in more dramatic language, and he could speculate on interpretations which seemed to him of great human interest. If murder was more frequent among younger than among older people, that gave occasion to write about the violent nature of youth. The higher crime rate among men allowed him to speculate about the restrained nature of the female personality.

Quetelet constantly refined his arguments. Often he stresses the comparative uses of his data. It is true, he would say, that crimes are committed more often than criminals are caught. But, as police vigilance is a rather constant phenomenon, this plays no role if we just want to *compare* the criminal tendencies of various age or other population groups. It is true that the same criminal tendency can lead to manifest crime under one set of conditions and not under another. So we measure only the "penchant apparent" and not the "penchant réel." But for comparative purposes, either serves equally well. On p. 343, he demonstrates this interchangeability by analyzing the age distributions of indictments, convictions, and acquittals.

At other points, Quetelet met a more general statistical difficulty. He looked at crime rates as probabilities. In order to compute this probability for a specific group, he had to know both the absolute size of the group and the number of crimes committed by its members. But often he only had data on the criminals themselves, without the corresponding population figures. Thus, for instance, he could distinguish his criminals according to whether they were illiterate, could read and write a little, or had a considerable amount of education (L'Influence des Lumières). But no educational statistics were available for the country as a whole. Again, relative rates were the solution. He gives a table cross-classifying French crime reports by sex and level of education (and, incidentally, for two different years). And then follows a typical interpretation (p. 297): "I think that one could explain these findings by saying that in uneducated strata, the habits of women are similar to those of men; in more educated strata, women have a more retiring style of life and consequently have less opportunity to commit a crime, all other things being equal."

But none of this touches on the central issue: What is implied when one makes inferences from a committed crime to a criminal tendency? Does Quetelet do more than substitute for the observed crime rate the *word* criminal tendency? It is not difficult to gather his own position. For him, the crime is an *effect* of the tendency which he thinks of as a *cause*. Today, we would talk of a propensity and its indicator rather than of a cause and its effect. This may be only a difference in linguistic fashions; I will follow the modern usage without attaching any importance to the difference.[60]

Quetelet assumes a *deterministic* relation between the hypothetical construct and its manifestations. This obviously derives from his training as a natural scientist. In the natural sciences, for example, the acceleration of an object is related to a force in a deterministic way. But in the social sciences, indicators or symptoms have a *probabilistic* relation to the underlying propensity. It is curious that Quetelet never hit on this idea in view of the fact that he was so imbued with probabilistic thinking in other contexts. Much of what I quoted before should have led him to this notion. Crimes are not always detected; whether or not they are committed depends on opportunity—all this would be best formulated by saying that the individual criminal tendency should be measured by the probability of committing a crime. This would have clearly raised the question how such probabilities assigned to individuals could be ascertained.

But Quetelet overlooks this question because of another idea which he repeats many times in his writings. He continually stresses that the only assumption he introduces—we would call it an axiom today—is that "the effects are proportional to the causes." To put this in modern terminology again, he assumes a *linear* relationship between the latent continuum he tries to measure and the probability of the manifest indicator he can observe. Even in the deterministic world of classical physics, this is undoubtedly wrong: the angle by which the needle of an instrument deviates is by no means always linearly related to the strength of an electric current which is to be measured. Measurement theory, as developed in modern social science, has made it quite obvious that such linearity does not prevail. The matter is important enough to justify two examples.

Suppose we want to develop a conventional test to measure conformity towards social regulations. One item in the test might be the question, "Are there situations in which white lies are justified?" The probability of a positive answer will be great all along the intended continuum: only at the extreme, let us say, right end, where people have very strict feelings about always doing the right thing, will this probability be small. A graph relating these probabilities to the underlying axis—authors call it variously a traceline or an operating characteristic—will look convex upwards. Take then the ques-

---

[60] In Book 3, Quetelet discusses in great detail the measurement of human strength with the help of dynamometers. These sections give leads to the imagery by which he was probably guided, when he tried to explain his ideas on indicators of moral qualities.

tion, "Are people entitled to break rules if it is clearly to their advantage?" The probability of a positive reply will be high only at the extreme left where people have quite loose moral standards; it will then rapidly decrease and remain low along the rest of the continuum. The corresponding graph will look concave upward. In other words, the relation between the effect (the answer to the question) and the cause (the underlying attitudes) can take various forms.[61] The situation becomes even more interesting when we look for an example which comes closest to Quetelet's use of rates. He takes it for granted that a high aggregate rate of criminality indicates a high average criminal tendency in a given population. He would certainly also take it for granted that a high proportion of male births expresses a high average tendency to have male children mediated "obviously" by the tendency of families to go on having children until at least one of them is a boy. But Leo Goodman has recently shown that the relation can be the reverse (personal communication). If all families pursue this practice, the couples who biologically are likely to have more girls would produce more children. The "effect," the rate of male births, would go in the opposite direction than the "cause," the penchant to have male children. Quetelet thus makes a much over-simplified assumption on the relation between a tendency and its manifestation.

The matter becomes even more complex if more than one indicator is at stake. On page 224 Quetelet talks about the possibility of measuring foresight (prévoyance) especially in its economic implications. He argues that the propensity to foresight existing in a certain country can be measured and he gives a series of examples on what data could be used: the amount of savings people have, the amount of insurance they purchase, how often they use pawn shops (because they do not properly balance their income and their necessary expenses in advance), the frequency of gambling, the number of bankruptcies; even visits to nightclubs are suggested as measures.[62] At this point, where Quetelet is only speculating, he sees that the "cause" he wants to measure, lack of foresight, can have a variety of effects or indicators, and that the inference as to the underlying tendency would be the safer the more of these indicators were used. But how would they be combined? Quetelet is dimly aware of this problem and this is obviously why he introduces his third type of variable as described in the main quotation above. He would probably correctly say that crude measurements of "lack of foresight" would be an additive counting of all these instances just listed. But he does not see the implication this has for the criminal tendencies in which he is interested.

Measuring the productivity of writers or the lack of foresight of householders is an *intrinsic procedure*. A measurement has to be constructed either

[61] Readers unfamiliar with recent developments in theory of socio-psychological measurement might find useful Paul F. Lazarsfeld, "Latent Structure Analysis," *Psychology: A Study of a Science*, Sigmund Koch (ed.), (New York: McGraw-Hill, 1959), pp. 477-491.

[62] This idea has come up all through the period covered by my paper. Thus Petty made this suggestion as "the measure of vice and sin in the nation": "the quantity spent on inebriating liquors, the number of unmarried persons between fifteen and fifty-five years old, the number of corporal sufferings and persons imprisoned for crimes" (Strauss, *op. cit.*, 196). And 250 years later, William James exemplified the pragmatists' notion of a "prudent" man: "that means that he takes out insurance, hedges in betting, looks before he leaps." Lazarsfeld, *op. cit.*, p. 480.

by a mathematical model or by some cruder kind of reasoning; but there is no *outside* criterion by which it could be validated. No single one of the eligible indicators is a priori more relevant than any of the others.[63] The same idea would have to be accepted for the measurement of criminal tendencies. Starting out with a conceptual analysis, one would have to look for indicators of aggression, contempt for law, and so on. One *might* include the actual performance of a criminal act as one of the indicators. But this would spoil the main use to which such a measure could be put. What we would like to know is the *empirical* relation between the criminal tendencies, measured independently, and the frequency of criminal acts in various populations and under various social circumstances. Actually Quetelet at one point adopts (page 250) a conceptual distinction which really implies what has just been said here. He states that the criminal act is the resultant of three factors: the *general* criminal *tendency,* the *skill* to perform a certain *class* of crimes, and the *opportunity* to go ahead and do it on a *specific* occasion. But Quetelet never proceeds from this formal distinction to a clear awareness that therefore *independent measures of propensities have to be developed.* He thought that in his comparative rates he had partialled out skill, opportunity (and chance of detection) and that they measured therefore dispositions, tendencies only. Subsequent research has shown that these assumptions are wrong. It is necessary to develop measures of criminal tendencies independent of the criminal act itself—provided that the notion of "penchant" is to be maintained.

But should it be maintained at all? This was the question raised by the German philosopher and mathematician, M. W. Drobisch, one of the first who brought Quetelet to the attention of his German colleagues by a review published in 1849. In 1867 he wrote a monograph,[64] the first part of which brings the review of Quetelet's work up to date and focuses on the question, whether criminal tendencies could be imputed to all people or should be considered restricted to criminals only. He argues strongly for the latter position: "the regularities demonstrated by moral statisticians have bearing only on certain classes of arbitrary human action and refer always to small proportions of a country's people who are especially disposed to these actions." (Translated from p. 52.) Such a statement is trivial if it means that the crime rate pertains to criminals only. But if it implies something about criminal dispositions then it has to be tested empirically. An independent instrument of measurement to support Drobisch would have to show a *bimodal* distribution of these tendencies; on the contrary if the tendencies of criminals —whatever their origin—are only extreme forms of everyone's experiences, then the distribution should be unimodal. As long as only *rates,* or to put it more generally, the *averages* of propensity distributions, are known, the issue cannot be decided. A uni-modal and bi-modal distribution might well have the same average. It is surprising how many prominent writers participated in a "discussion bizantine" as Lottin calls it in a review of the pertinent literature (*op. cit.,* pp. 550ff).[65]

---

[63] In the parlance of modern measurement theory, this is called construct-validity.

[64] Moritz Wilhelm Drobisch, *Die moralische Statistik und die menschliche Willens-* *freiheit* (Leipzig: Leopold Voss, 1867).

[65] Drobisch himself deserves a more detailed study. His exposition of Quetelet is extensive and clear. He was a logician interested in all

Halbwachs drew another conclusion from Quetelet's analysis without noticing that he here accepted probabilistic thinking which he disapproved of so strongly in other contexts. Combining his functionalism with Quetelet's idea of normally distributed criminal tendencies (and elaborating on a remark made by Durkheim in his Rules of Sociological Method), he makes the following statement:

> In order to supress all crimes, it would be necessary to instil in all people a deep collective aversion against the qualities leading to such acts, such as ruthless ingenuity, a spirit of intrigue and manipulation. But this maybe is not desirable; in fact, *as society permits the regular occurrence of a stable proportion of crimes, it undoubtedly feels that it would do more harm than good if this number were further reduced.* (*op. cit.,* p. 151, emphasis supplied.)

In quantitative terms, what Halbwachs says is this: One cannot just cut off the extreme tail of a distribution of attitudes or traits: if one wants to curtail certain *excessive* degrees of vitality, one would have to move the *whole* distribution of the relevant propensities towards a lower level of intensity. While substantively Halbwachs' take-off from Quetelet seems less realistic than the one Drobisch made, it certainly is logically more in the spirit of what Quetelet was driving at.

It took a hundred years after Quetelet before his effort to quantify penchants was taken up again in Thurstone's well-known paper, "Attitudes Can Be Measured."[66] I am confident that Thurstone did not know about Quetelet; even Allport, who traces the conceptual antecedents of the notion of attitude measurement, finds the first seeds in Spencer.[67] I have the impression that this discontinuity is greater in the social than in the natural sciences. But I have no evidence on this; nor do I have a good explanation, even if I should be right.[68]

After Quetelet

From time to time Quetelet published speculations on the philosophical implications of his work. Did the apparent constancy of crime, marriage, suicide and other rates over time imply that human beings have no free will? He never could make up his mind, but he certainly engendered a large literature on the topic. The debate led to the formation of a "German School"

---

sorts of statistical applications. I have not had access to a paper of his which seems to be one of the first examples of content-analysis: "Statistischer Versuch über die Formen des Lateinischen Hexameters," published by the Saxonian Scientific Society in 1865.

[66] L. L. Thurstone, "Attitudes Can Be Measured," in *J. Sociology,* 1928.

[67] Gordon W. Allport, "Attitudes" *Handbook of Social Psychology,* Murchison, Carl (ed.), (Worcester, Mass.: Clark University Press, 1935).

[68] Stephan remarks on the same discontinuity in his field: "The foregoing examples suggest that *modern sampling procedure might have developed at least a century sooner than* it did if it had received more attention from the scientists of the day. Only the officials of statistical bureaus ... were preoccupied with ... the important problems of trade, finance, industry, agriculture, public health, etc., for which statistical data were needed. Hence they favored complete censuses or the closest approach to them that was feasible." See footnote 112. Quetelet himself is a good example for Stephan's argument. At one point he says that midwives would be a bad source for anyone who wanted to establish the sex ratio at birth; their observations are based on small numbers. He does not argue for a *representative* sample but for a *complete* enumeration.

of moral statisticians which fought a rather imaginary "French School" with undertones quite explicitly related to the Franco-Prussian War of 1870. One gets a good idea of this rather curious discussion from a survey paper by Knapp *(op. cit.)* who also refers to the main literature up to 1871. The topic would deserve a new review in the light of modern ideas on the role of mathematical models as mediating between statistical findings and theories on human behavior; in the confines of my present paper I cannot do more than draw attention to the matter.[69]

Moral statistics as a topic of empirical research expanded rapidly during the 19th century. Also, more and more areas of social life were made the object of enumerations: literacy, the circulation of newspapers, voting, and so on. Correspondingly, new substantive fields of statistics were created parallel to or as subdivisions of moral statistics: thus came into being educational statistics, political statistics, social statistics, and so on. The Germans were particularly apt in thinking of appropriate classifications. The most comprehensive effort is undoubtedly the voluminous textbook by George V. Mayer. Meantime, sociology as a discipline had penetrated the universities and its relation to the data collected by descriptive statisticians became a topic of discussion. Quite a literature on "Sociology and Statistics" emerged written by representatives of both disciplines; in a way it can be considered the beginning of the modern debate on the role of quantification among sociologists. An especially perceptive contribution, containing also interesting historical material was a short monograph by the Austrian, Franz Zizek.[70] The most creative effort to give structure to the ever-increasing mass of data was made by the Italian, Alfredo Niceforo. From the end of the 19th century on, he had been interested in what he called "the measurement of life."[71] He finally exemplified his main ideas in a small book on the measurement of civilization and progress, published in French.[72]

The title is characteristic: instead of just classifying available data, Niceforo starts out with the problem of how one would characterize quantitatively a civilization in "space and time." In Chapter 2, he defines what he means by civilizations, and in Chapter 3, he proposes what today would be called the dimensions of this concept. For each dimension he then proposes a number of crucial (signalétiques) indicators. In his first chapter there is an especially clear discussion of this three-level relation between concepts, dimensions and indicators. He calls his whole effort "social symptomatology," and the logical clarity of his ideas is remarkable. Niceforo incidentally is the earliest sociolo-

---

[69] Since the appearance of Buckle's 'History of English Civilization" (1861), writers mention a Quetelet-Buckle position. A study of Buckle's book shows that he makes only some very inferential references to Quetelet, never seriously uses his material, nor adds any new statistical data. But Buckle mentions Quetelet very early in his long book, and there uses him as a witness for his own social determinism. It is curious that such a completely external coupling has led to a continuously repeated but substantively quite unjustified stereotype which I was able to trace even in books appearing in 1960.

[70] *Soziologie und Statistik* (Leipzig: Verlag von Duncker & Humblot, 1912).

[71] Alfredo Niceforo, *Les Indices Numeriques de la Civilization et du Progrès* (Paris: Ernest Flammarion, 1921) and Alfredo Niceforo, *La Misura Della Vita* (Turin: Fratelli Bocca, 1919).

[72] *Les Indices numeriques de la Civilization et du Progres* (Paris: Ernest Flammarion, 1921).

gist I found who used correlation coefficients explicitly, and who competently demonstrated their place in such a study.[73]

One cannot talk today about a Quetelet school; his thinking, his way of analyzing data have become an integral part of empirical social research.[74] In one respect, however, he did not transcend the intellectual climate in which he worked. While he repeatedly mentioned the idea that special data could be collected to form the empirical basis of a new concept, he never set a concrete example; he only reinterpreted material collected by the social bookkeeping procedures of contemporary society. The tradition of starting with an idea and collecting observations under its guidance must be credited to the man to whom our last section is devoted.

LEPLAY AND HIS "METHODE D'OBSERVATION"

LePlay's Life and Writings

LePlay was born in 1806, and thus was ten years younger than Quetelet. He grew up in a small Norman fishing village, and received his early education at various regional schools. In 1824, at the age of eighteen, he moved to Paris where he soon thereafter graduated as a mining engineer. In his early jobs, he had to inspect mines and pass judgment on the possible commercial values of mineralogical deposits. In 1829, he made a trip through Germany in the company of a friend from his student times with whom he had hotly debated social issues over the years. They stayed for a while with the family of a miner and wrote down detailed observations on its way of life. This became the first of several hundred family monographs which formed the body of LePlay's empirical social research.

In 1830, during the July Revolution, LePlay was hospitalized because of an accident in a laboratory experiment. The turbulent events of the day reinforced his decision to devote himself systematically to the study of social conditions. For eighteen years, he was equally active in both of his chosen fields. He became a professor of metallurgy, head of the official committee on mining statistics, but at the same time, continued his travels, collecting his family monographs and pondering their use for the sake of social reform. In 1848, the second revolution occurred in his lifetime. He decided to give up his regular profession and to devote himself completely to the cause of social reform as he understood it. In 1855, he published a selected number of his monographs under the title of "The European Workers." A year later, he founded an international society for social economics which organized the

[73] Recently Raymond Cattell has used correlation analysis to develop dimensions relevant for the description of regions and countries. He is obviously not aware of Niceforo's work, another example of the discontinuities referred to previously. Niceforo gives in the last two chapters of a historical review of early quantifications of cultural phenomena. As one who has done work of this kind, I was embarrassed to find how many techniques considered contemporary inventions have been used many decades ago.

[74] It would be worthwhile to follow more in detail the ways in which Quetelet's ideas penetrated into specific subject areas. An interesting example, accidentally noticed, is the close personal contact between him and Florence Nightingale, described in E. W. Kopf, "Florence Nightingale as a Statistician," *Journal of the American Statistical Association,* December 1916.

collection of family monographs all over the world, and published them under the title, "The Workers of Two Worlds" in a series which continued until after the First World War.

After 1848, LePlay's source of income came partly from the Academy of Science, and partly from public offices which were entrusted to him by Napoleon III. Most conspicious were his activities as French representative for a series of international exhibitions. The reports on these exhibitions stress his organizational ability and describe him as a master of classificatory devices which facilitated the exhibition of products and the orientation of visitors among the vast variety of activities going on at these international affairs. In 1864, he was appointed Senator by Napoleon III. By that time, he was a well-known public figure, and had published a large number of books and pamphlets on current affairs.

In 1871, the Paris Commune was the third upheaval which LePlay witnessed at close range. From then on, he devoted himself completely to the setting up of various reform organizations, supervised the writing and distribution of numerous pamphlets, and finally founded a periodical, "La Réforme Sociale." His travels brought him repeatedly to England, which he admired because of its social stability; among his many publications is one on the British Constitution. Beginning in 1877, he published the six volumes which form the basis for our subsequent discussion. The book is known as the second edition of "The European Workers."[75] The first volume was newly written and presents in 650 pages an autobiography, a detailed account of the methods he used in his social investigation, and numerous prescriptions about how the results should be used for public policy. The other five volumes reprint the family monographs as they were presented in the first publication of 1855, including the earlier introductions. In addition each volume contains a newly written appendix which comments on the changes which had taken place between 1855 and 1877 in the regions he had studied. The family monographs themselves contain a great many policy considerations which are either summarized or extended in the new appendices. The cases are classified according to what LePlay considers their degree of social disorganization. In the second volume he starts with families from Eastern Europe, where he sees the highest degree of social stability; he then moves to the Scandinavian and English countries, where he still finds a considerable amount of stability (Volume III); Volumes IV and V then divide the Western continent into two groups of increasing difficulties; the sixth volume is devoted to family monographs mainly collected in the Mediterranean region, and they all are examples of disintegration.

In scrutinizing the literature about LePlay, I have found that many authors refer to the first volume only; it is indeed an impressive document. But as to his research techniques it tells what LePlay thought he did, not his actual procedure; this can be gathered only from a reading of the monographs themselves. I shall, when I discuss his methodology, also draw on Volumes II to VI. It is necessary to describe the rigid external form in which the fifty-eight family monographs are presented. At the center of each, as Sections

[75] Frederic LePlay, *Les Ouvriers euro   peens,* Vol. I (Alfred Mamé et Fils, 1879).

14, 15 and 16, one finds the famous budget, divided by accounts of incomes, expenses and supplementary details. The budget is preceded by thirteen sections which again are divided into four groups under the following headings:

A. Description of the locality, the occupational organization, and of the family itself (Sections 1 - 5)

B. Sources of subsistence (Sections 6 - 8)

C. Style of life (Sections 9 - 11)

D. History of the family (13)

Each of the first eleven sections is about a page long and consists in the main of vivid descriptive detail, the purpose of which is to help interpret the main budget account. Beginning with Section 17, each monograph is followed by about four to eight additional sections headed by the general title: "Various Elements of the Social Structure (Constitution Sociale)." The impact of the monographs derives mainly from these miscellaneous sections which range in length from two to ten pages. Some of them are based on direct personal observations to which I shall come back presently. Others are summaries of what today we would call organizational and institutional arrangements: descriptions of the steps by which a young worker in a certain region advances from apprenticeship to the status of master; classification of the kind of contracts which existed between workers and entrepreneurs; detailed information on the economic and technical aspects of the industry in which the family worked; wherever possible, LePlay draws attention to the inheritance laws or customs to which he attaches great theoretical importance. The sources of these descriptions are sometimes personal interviews with informants who know the area, and sometimes quotations from books. Another group of these accessory paragraphs consists of interesting but uncorroborated statements on what we would today call empirical correlations. He classifies workers into certain categories and claims that they vary according to the rate of illegitimate births; he divides the population of an area according to their ethnic characteristics and states that they also vary according to their colonizing ability—the topic of emigration is of great interest to him. Still another type of comment deals with one of the central topics of all his writings: What is it in the personal habits of a family or the conditions of their work which facilitates or inhibits their rise in the social scale?

The purpose of these sections of the family monographs is quite easily discernible. LePlay is not concerned with the families for their own sake. He is convinced that his case studies are the best means of understanding the working of the whole social system. He therefore wants to link the individual facts he has established up to Section 16 with whatever information he can gather about broader social structures. His contemporaries understandably admired him equally for his naturalist approach to the individual family and for his ability to abstract, during a relatively short trip, an enormous amount of information from crucially located informants and from literature only locally available. Even now, readers will be captivated by the vividness of his descriptions and the plausibility with which he argued connections between phenomena observed on very different societal levels. It is no wonder, then, that it took quite a while, as we shall see, before anyone asked whether his stories were correct and his interpretations sound. I am confident that much of his contemporary fame was due to the fact that he never just reported something the way a traveler would tell about a "cute" observation. Everything was part of a description of the functioning or malfunctioning of a coherent social system.[76]

LePlay tried to make each volume of "The European Workers" self-contained. As a result there is much repetition in explaining the purpose of his work and emphasizing the conclusions he wants drawn. Here is a brief summary of his main position.*

1. LePlay was convinced that he was creating an objective social science similar to the kind of mineralogy so familiar to him.

> In order to find the secrets of the governments which provide mankind with happiness based on peace, I have applied to the observation of human societies *rules analogous* to those which had directed my own mind in the *study of minerals and plants. I construct a scientific mechanism.* (Vol. I, first page of the Foreword)

He stated repeatedly that "the conclusions of 'The European Workers' are logically derived." (Vol. I, pp. 432, 436)

2. He did not see any contradiction between his claim to objectivity and the many statements that his personal history made him discover so many "truths" (les verités) overlooked by other students.

> My first impressions, which I mention here because they are so vivid, *devel-*

[76] Another element which accounts for the persuasiveness of the whole work is the skill with which he uses classificatory devices. I have already indicated the way each monograph in the six volumes of "The European Workers" is explicitly organized. In turn, the various introductions and appendices contain a great many cross references. In the first volume, which has a very complex organization, LePlay repeatedly stops to explain to the reader at what point he finds himself at the moment and where the following sections are supposed to lead him. This classificatory urge has obvious relations to his work as a metallurgist and reminds one also of his contributions to the international expositions mentioned above. It is undoubtedly also related to his grave doubts about whether writing books is an appropriate means of communication. In a long passage (Volume 1, p. 549), he explains that he has created so many reform organizations because his main reliance is on personal influence. At the same time, he knows that printed empirical descriptions are very important; so he continuously looks for ways of overcoming the obstacle of reader inertia. Charac-

teristically, each volume contains an alphabetic glossary explaining his main terms as well as pointing out where his factual material can be located in the volume.

I have not drawn upon the long series of monographs in "The Workers of the Two Worlds." Having read a fair sample of them, I agree with the judgment of several French writers that they are inferior. While LePlay was, for the first years, the general Secretary of the International Society which organized the collection, he seemed to have had relatively little contact with most of the individual contributions. It is incidentally worth translating the full title of the international collection: "Studies on the work, the domestic life and the moral conditions of the workers of various countries and the relations which connect them with other classes."

* If in the following pages references are given only by volume and page, they refer to *Les Ouvriers europeens;* the quotations are my translations from the second edition; I had no access to the first one; the underscoring is mine.

oped over the salutary influence of religion, national catastrophe and poverty. (Vol. I, p. 400)

He always disliked Paris. It is easy to explain why some people disagree with him.

> They were educated in urban agglomerations, and in educational institutions where in France all forms of error are accumulated; *they have acquired preconceived ideas,* the sinister influence of which I have just explained. (Similar references—Vol. I, pp. 41, 432, Vol. VI, p. 32)

Both statements are in the tradition of good sociology of knowledge. It is just not clear why the environment in which LePlay grew up led to truth while the upbringing of his adversaries bred error.

3. LePlay was quite explicit about the use he wanted made of his monographs. In his opinion, they bring out, by comparative analysis, the conditions under which people are happy or unhappy. This knowledge was to be conveyed to the elite of a country (les classes dirigeantes). They, in turn, were supposed to take the necessary measures so that favorable conditions prevailed. This is the main sense in which he uses the term "reform." The word he often uses to describe the groups responsible for the well-being of a society is "patronage." Patron is the French word for the small entrepreneur who still has quite close contact with his workers; he uses the term also to include the resident landlord. Occasionally, however, he personalizes this social function of a specific group:

> I clearly understood that the greatest interest of my fellow citizens is to *escape the errors which push them to disaster;* and I have even clearly seen that for someone who is in a favorable situation and has the qualities necessary for our times, it would have been easy to lead our people (race) back on the road to salvation. *I have not stopped looking for such a saviour.*

I cite this quotation, not only because of its characteristic wording, but because it appears in a chapter (Vol. I, Chap. 13) which for more than forty pages details his relations with various public figures of the July Monarchy and the Second Empire. His reports are undoubtedly biased; but an historian acquainted with the period will find in these pages important leads to study the relation between public policy and the beginning of social research in that period.

4. The large majority of the working people should contribute to the stability of society by conducting their family life according to two major principles: observance of the Decalogue and strengthening of paternal authority. These two terms are repeated well over a hundred times through the six volumes of "The European Workers." They are reiterated in the introductions and appendices to each volume; they are likely to appear in any of the sections of the cases themselves; and they form almost the theme song of the first volume. The word, "Decalogue," is not used in any metaphorical sense; LePlay is convinced that the Ten Commandments do indeed contain the essence of social wisdom.

5. Actually LePlay is concerned with the life of people at a relatively early period of industrialization in Western Europe. But he describes it in exclusively moral terms. People have vices and are corrupt; evil prevails in all strata of society; the population is degraded and offers no resistance to the "invasion du mal"; the "pratique du bien" disappeared; we live in an "époque d'erreur et de discord"; only the "reform" which is derived from LePlay's Methode d'Observation can bring help. Even the most descriptive parts of his monographs are so permeated by this terminology that it is quite pointless to pick out specific page references. The reader cannot glance at any three pages without meeting this vocabulary; in addition, each volume registers them in the glossary.

6. None of these evils is explained in terms of social and economic dynamics or as due to changes in technology. They are the result of "false teachings" and "fundamental errors" which have been disseminated. There are essentially two sources of these social heresies which have infected all strata of society. One is the writings of Rousseau, and especially his idea that man is born good; the child is a "dangerous barbarian" and it is the main task of a strict paternal regime to teach him order, obedience and submission to authority. The second source of all false ideas is Thomas Jefferson with his insistence on equal rights. He speaks of Jefferson's "deplorable presidency" (Vol. III, p. 426; for other examples of attacks on Jefferson, see, for instance, Vol. I, p. 626, Vol. VI, p. 28 and p. 546; I am sure that I have by no means caught all of them.) LePlay considered the United States the most vicious social system of all he knew, and predicted for it an early and complete disintegration. This was his position in the 1855 edition of "The European Workers" and it is reiterated with even more emphasis in the second edition (1877).[77]

7. According to LePlay, the success of his reforms will depend on the outcome of an "eternal battle between the good and the evil": the good is defined by the "hommes de tradition"; they stand for the "éternelles verités." The enemy are the "hommes de nouveauté." Most of them are intellectuals—the "lettrés." One repeatedly finds the opposition of "les lettrés" versus "les sages," the men who are usually old and without formal education, but imbued with the wisdom of the past. In Chapter 4 of the first volume, LePlay deals with the contributions which various occupational groups make to the welfare of society; it is no surprise to find that the liberal professions have a bad record, indeed. They come about as part of a necessary division of labor. "But earlier or later (they) misuse their authority; they oppress those whom they should protect, and they become dissemination points of corruption." (Vol. I, p. 131) A reference to the glossaries will round out the picture. Under the heading, "écoles," LePlay stresses that professors do harm if they do not consider themselves supplementary agents of parental authority; otherwise, they diffuse "bad principles." The next entry is *Economie Politique,* and it is *defined* as a "regrettable influence exercised by one such principle upon the mutual understanding of employees and workers."

[77] He refers at one point to de Tocqueville's "Democracy in America" as the "most evil book ever written by a man of good will." (Vol. 1, p. 193).

8. LePlay can in no way be seen as a defender of vested interests. He continually stresses the moral duties of the "patronage." He considers Adam Smith a sinister influence (Vol. I, p. 124) because he encourages the entrepreneur to be guided only by his economic interests. He feels that the absentee landowner neglects his moral duties. He is against the repression of free speech; but he argues characteristically that, if there were no free speech, the authorities would be deprived of sources of information which would help them to exercise their functions better.[78] He approves strongly of the incipient British factory legislation, but again, mostly because it sets limits to the freedom of the individual manufacturer. (Vol. III, p. 432ff.)

We are thus faced with a very strange phenomenon. Here is a natural scientist successful as a man of affairs and organizer of great public enterprises. He wants to develop an objective social science, to be based, as we shall see, on quantitative evidence. But the purposes to which he wants to put this knowledge are seen in a system of ideas which is not only conservative in terms of a Burke tradition but which, in modern usage can only be described as "fascistic." Much of the later history of the school which he created (and I shall talk only about those of his followers who continued his empirical investigations) can be understood only if all this is kept in mind.

The Purging of the Saint

From the middle of the 19th century, LePlay attracted waves of men who wanted to learn his research techniques. They shared his political and religious convictions. But in addition, they always looked at the social science which they wanted to practice as a kind of revelation which they were called upon to develop and pass on to subsequent generations. During LePlay's life, they were his apostles, grouped around the organization and the magazine, "Réforme Sociale." In 1896, four years after his death, those who considered themselves scientists as much as reformers started a new journal called "La Science Sociale" which appeared in monthly issues up to 1915. Its approximately 40,000 pages deserve intensive study because of their strange intertwining of a charismatic tradition and empirical research. There does not exist careful analysis of the LePlay tradition similar to Lottin's work on Quetelet. This may be due partly to the fact that LePlay described so extensively his own life and the development of his ideas as he saw it; existing accounts are essentially summaries of what LePlay had written himself. But also the mere labor of going through the thirty years of "Science Sociale" may have appeared too staggering. Nevertheless, I hope that such an effort will be made one day; it would contribute much to the main topic of this paper. The following pages try to indicate its possible value.

The journal, "Science Sociale," was subtitled "according to the Method of LePlay." The articles most interesting in the present context were the elaborations on the method and the periodic reviews of the organized efforts to apply LePlay's ideas to the empirical study of concrete situations.[79] A second group of contributions are new family monographs in the LePlay

[78] Frederic LePlay, *Collection des Grands Economistes,* Louis Baudin (ed.), (Paris: Dalloz, 1947).

[79] The methodological emphasis of the group is quite remarkable and a continuous progress towards increased explication and improve-

tradition. A third kind of paper reanalyzed earlier writings: thus, for instance, we find an interesting series of papers on Montesquieu and the kind of evidence he adduced in the "Esprit des Lois"; another scrutinized Necker's writings on public opinion. A fourth group of efforts were devoted to the social interpretation of literary products: What was the social context of the Iliad? What was Balzac's image of the French middle class? The fifth type of essay deals with the historical record of whole cultures like the Assyrian or the ancient Chinese. Finally, there are discussions of contemporary problems, such as the early difficulties in the colonization of Algeria, the reform of the French educational system, the question of anti-semitism, etc.

All these contributions presume that the LePlay school had developed a method by which social subject matters could be treated in an objective and definitive way. Many of these articles contain valuable factual information or lucid insights into other people's writings; all of them reflect a considerable amount of righteousness and self-assurance. The whole style of writing is quite reminiscent of contemporary Christian Science literature. Instead of talking about the Science Sociale, they just refer to it as "La Science"; Le Methode d'Observation becomes "La Methode." And yet, if one scrutinizes the articles carefully, a very significant change in tone becomes noticeable. To make the drama of this play more understandable, some of its actors must first be introduced.

The editor of the journal, up to his death in 1907, was Edmond Demolins. Almost forty years younger than LePlay, he was an historian trained in a provincial Jesuit college, who came to Paris in 1873. He soon fell under the spell of LePlay and began to give public lectures on his methods. During the early years of "Science Sociale," he wrote periodic reviews on the progress of the movement. He was clearly the public relations agent for LePlay; some of the foreigners, who later on disseminated the ideas of the group in their own countries, never met LePlay and refer to Demolins as their main source of inspiration. He was always engaged in a diversity of activities. In the early 1890's, he created an anti-socialist league and tried for a while to use the journal as its communication center.[80]

---

ment of methods can be traced in "Science Sociale" almost from year to year. Nathan Glazer's opinion that LePlay's method was not further developed is obviously based on the fact that he did not have access to the journal (See footnote 15). Special issues summarizing new methodological developments or reassessing the state of affairs will be found in many volumes; see especially November 1912 and October 1913 of "Science Sociale."

[80] At the turn of the century, Demolins created a school for young boys, Ecole des Roches. The school was located in the open country and the students organized their own work and life. Great emphasis was put on observations of nature as well as on field studies in the local communities and farm regions. The school still exists today. At the time, there was a similar movement in Germany, initiated by Lietz; this later on was im-

portant in the history of the German youth movement. Demolins organized exchange visits with other institutions and there is interesting correspondence between him and W. R. Harper, the first president of the University of Chicago. Demolins' own publications, after he became a LePlay convert, were a combination of his early historical interests and LePlay's insistence on contemporary field studies. In recent bibliographical reviews, Demolins is usually classified as a geographical sociologist. The best source on him is the detailed biography which appeared in "Science Sociale" at the time of his death. The journal also published from time to time reports on the activities of the Ecole des Roches. Demolins incidentally published also a variety of more popular pamphlets on the research of the LePlay group which I have not examined.

While Demolins was the activist of the group, the man who was increasingly considered the intellectual heir of LePlay is Henri de Tourville (1843-1903). He was an abbé who lived most of his life in seclusion, trying to make LePlay's work more systematic. His great contribution was a classificatory system which was always reverently called the "Nomenclature" with a capital "N." During the first two years of the journal, de Tourville wrote a series of articles entitled "Is Social Science a Science?" His answer was, of course, affirmative. But he made the point that the genius of LePlay could be utilized by his disciples only if his system was made more explicit. His starting point was the way in which the family monographs were reported. He pointed out that while the first thirteen paragraphs were fairly systematic, the richest insights of LePlay are found in the supplementary paragraphs for which the founder had never provided a systematic guide, thus leaving future workers somewhat up in the air. De Tourville wanted to work out a system of categories which would give a place to every relevant observation LePlay made. I shall come back to this idea presently.

The next major figure in the sequence is Paul de Rousier. His contribution lay in further clarification of the core of LePlay's family monographs—the budget. In issues of "Science Sociale" appearing around 1890, he suggested certain improvements to which we also shall return later. At about the same time, de Rousier also made several trips to the United States, which were to become very important in the further history of the school. His main move at the time was to show that LePlay had been too harsh on the Americans. Here were all these rich people like the Carnegies and the Goulds who had just the sense of responsibility which, according to LePlay, was the duty of the elites. The same men on whom we today look back as economic robber barons Rousier described in "Science Sociale" as the true modern aristocrats. The youngest among the more prominent men in this sequence is Paul Bureau; he joined the group a few years after LePlay's death. By introducing explicitly psychological elements, he was the first to bring about a major change in the Nomenclature. His new category was what he called "representation de la vie" which he proposed as the translation of the German word "Weltanschauung."[81] Bureau was considerably influenced by Gabriel Tarde and, later, wrote an interesting account of the way in which his ideas developed.[82]

Beginning in the late 1890's, a tone of aggression enters into the writings of the group; increasingly a strong ambivalence is apparent. LePlay is still compared with Newton and Galileo and any other great scientific hero who comes to mind. But, in fact, he is being purged. Beginning in 1904, the subtitle of the journal is no longer "according to the method of LePlay" but "Selon la Methode d'Observation." The new series starts with a review of the present state of "La Methode Sociale." The achievements of the last twenty years are no longer described as explications and clarifications of LePlay's own ideas, but as important discoveries made by the younger men. The master left grave

---

[81] Paul Bureau, *Introduction à la Méthode sociologique* (Paris: Blond & Gay, 1923).

[82] Bureau finally broke with the later Le-Playistes, accusing them of materialism. He quotes as a witness the French economist, Charles Gide, to the effect that "in reality the new school has not preserved much from the method of their master" (*op. cit.,* p. 116f).

gaps in his monographs; his use of the budget implies a series of errors; his family monographs are monotonous; his family types are badly defined; de Tourville's work is "more scientific and more interesting" (de Rousier). Le-Play made intuitive observations but does not tell on what he based his conclusions; his analysis was oversimplified and incomplete; he was badly deceived and made grievous errors (Demolins). LePlay's family types were quite wrong; he based his classification on the way property was transmitted, but the correct principle of classification would be the kind of educational tradition a family has; his stem-family covers a variety of quite different phenomena. He was especially wrong in his anti-Americanism. Not only are the people in the United States not decadent, their spirit of individualistic enterprise is the best bulwark against the spread of socialism (Pinot). This is the mood in which "La Science Sociale" is written until 1915.[83]

We are thus faced with the following situation. Here is a school created by a charismatic personality who makes an important innovation in social methodology and intertwines it with very strong and activitistic ideological beliefs. One group of his disciples share his beliefs and want at the same time to make methodological progress. Under normal circumstances, a scientific innovator is respected by his students, and it is taken for granted that his successors make continuous advances beyond the teacher. In a charismatic context, this leads to a tension between the scientific and the sectarian element in the tradition. This would be a matter of only secondary interest if it were not for the fact that rather suddenly, the LePlayistes disappeared from the French sociological scene. At least as far as one can see from a distance, the school which was so extensive and articulate up to the First World War has been completely replaced by the Durkheim tradition to which they paid only casual and rare attention in the "Science Sociale." In various reviews of French sociology which Frenchmen have recently written the LePlayistes are not even mentioned.[84] Do we face here a political phenomenon? Did the few relevant university posts all go to the Durkheim group at a time when the French government had an anti-clerical tendency? Did the descriptive fervor of the Le-Playistes exhaust its potentialities, and make it less attractive than the conceptualizing of the Durkheim School to a younger generation? Do we face here the difficulty a charismatic movement has: in spite of their ambivalence to the founder, did the LePlayistes form too much of a sect to be acceptable to the regular academic bureaucracy?

[83] This is the last volume available in Harvard's Widener Library and I suppose that the First World War brought the publication to an end. Unfortunately, a few earlier volumes are missing, among these, the volume of 1903 which precedes the change of name and the review issue I have just described. I do not know, therefore, whether a special explanation was ever given for the change. The volume of 1904 has an imprint "19th year, second period"; I pass over some other technical changes which the editors made. The type of content remains otherwise quite unchanged and Demolins remains editor. The later history can be picked up in the retrospective pages of Bureau (*op. cit.,* Introduction and pages 115 ff.).

[84] This is strictly true only for Levi-Strauss' contributions to "Twentieth Century Sociology" (New York, Philosophical Library, 1945). Stoetzel mentions LePlay several times in passing when he stresses the empirical tradition of French sociologists in his contribution to "Modern Sociological Theory" (New York: Dryden Press, 1957). He also refers to Bureau and so, incidentally, does Merton in his review of French sociology ("Social Forces," 1934). As far as I can see, Bouglé in his "Bilan de la Sociologie Française Contemporaine" (Paris: Alcan, 1935) never mentions the LePlayistes.

I cannot tell. Certainly the methodological ideas of the school were interesting and susceptible of further development as I shall discuss presently. But first, I must trace briefly the effect which LePlay had abroad, especially in England and in the United States and here, strangely enough, the theme of the purge can be continued. While we find outspoken and clamorous admirers of his in the two Anglo-Saxon countries, they changed his ideas even more than did his French disciples, each in his own way and perhaps without knowing it.

Ramifications Abroad

In 1878, a young Scotch biologist by chance visited a lecture of Demolins. He was deeply impressed, spent the remainder of his Paris study trip in contact with Demolins—he seems never to have met LePlay personally—and in his later writings always described himself as a LePlayiste.[85] There are several biographies of Patrick Geddes, the Edinburgh professor of botany who, in 1902, joined with Branford in creating the Sociological Society in London. All stress Geddes' magnetic personality, his great schemes and his tremendous energy; but they offer little information on his intellectual development. I must therefore depend upon Geddes' own story in "The Coming Polity" which has a special chapter on "LePlay and his method" and many references as to how LePlay's French background can save the social sciences from the evils of "Prussianism" (the book was written during the first World War).[86] I come reluctantly to the conclusion that Geddes never really read LePlay's monographs. In vague terms, he speaks of him as a regionalist and praises him for his fine maps (pp. 183 ff.); Geddes, himself, was famous for his graphical presentation of social facts, but LePlay never published a map, except one indicating the geographical location of the families he studied. Geddes thinks of LePlay as a kind of rural sociologist, and seems unaware of the master's political views which certainly were not congenial to his own position. He and his students[87] kept hammering upon a presumed central formula of LePlay—(place-work-folk)—which does not play any role in his monographs and which can at best be read into some chapter headings in the first volume of the second edition of the "European Workers." Geddes kept in touch with Demolins—he had him as lecturer in summer schools organized by the "Outlook Tower," the famous Edinburgh building, where his farflung activities as city planner were centralized. I guess that the charismatic atmosphere engendered by LePlay appealed greatly to Geddes who himself had the same effect on his disciples. Branford, one of them, was a wealthy businessman who in 1920 donated a house for the work of the British Sociological Society, and called it "LePlay House." Yet from available literature I cannot trace any concrete influence of LePlay's actual research upon the city surveys of the Geddes school. Perhaps British colleagues can provide further clarification.[88]

[85] Victor Branford and Patrick Geddes, *The Making of the Future, The Coming Polity* (London: Williams and Norgate, 1917).

[86] Philip Boardman, *Patric Geddes, Maker of the Future* (Chapel Hill: Univ. of North Carolina Press, 1944).

[87] S. Branford and A. Farquharson, *An Introduction to Regional Surveys* (Westminster: The LePlay House Press, 1924).

[88] The matter is not clarified by a first scrutiny of the "Sociological Review," the journal created by Branford. As a matter of fact, a curious episode emerges. One of Geddes' followers was the geographer, Herbertson, whose

Another British social scientist presents a more puzzling problem. Charles Booth, the organizer of the great survey of "Life and Labour of the People in London" (the enterprise started around 1880), did in two respects work quite reminiscent of LePlay. He was an avid and skillful observer of family lives, an ability which is well documented by the examples in a biography written anonymously by his wife;[89] and he did at certain points of his work, study budgets. Strangely enough, however, I have in all the writings on Booth not been able to find any evidence that he was even aware of LePlay. The latter is neither mentioned in the chapter of Beatrice Webb's *Autobiography* devoted to her collaboration with Booth nor does he play a role in a recent biography by Simey and Simey.[90] They point out that very little is known about the origin of his ideas; this might be an explanation for this gap in the evidence. But one should also keep in mind that there are vast differences in the basic approach of the two men in spite of the external similarity of their procedure. Booth's thinking was centered around the problem of poverty and he tried to measure it as precisely as possible. LePlay was guided by a vague notion of corruption and never had the idea that some systematic classification of families could ensue from it. Booth is much nearer than LePlay to modern procedures of translating a concept into a well defined system of indices. The difference in technique has a consequence which might exemplify the interplay of ideology and methodology. Both men were started on their inquiries by discussions with friends who were of a radical political persuasion; LePlay and Booth believed that the consequences of industrialization did not require the remedies advocated by their interlocutors. Booth, as a result of his own studies became convinced that he was wrong; LePlay never changed his belief in his own righteousness. The difference is of course mainly due to the general attitudes of the two men. But actually Booth's procedure permitted a check on the amount of existing poverty, while LePlay's observations could neither settle how much "evil" there was, nor to what it was due.

---

wife Dorothy wrote a biography of LePlay around 1900. It was essentially a compilation of statements taken from the first volume of "The European Workers." She sent the manuscript to Branford, who did not know what to do with it. When LePlay House was created, people became curious about the man after whom it was named. Branford remembered the manuscript of Mrs. Herbertson (she had died meantime), edited and published the first four chapters, which summarized the external data of LePlay's life, in "The Sociological Review." He never published the rest. I am satisfied that the reason is as follows: When he came to edit further chapters, Branford noticed that they mainly contained a summary of some of LePlay's outmoded anthropological ideas (Chapters 5 and 6); lengthy descriptions of the categories used in his budget accounts (Chapters 7-9); LePlay's judgment on what various occupational groups contribute to society, seen from his point of view and based on the situation of fifty years earlier (Chapters 11 and 12); and repetitions of LePlay's statement on his own political mission. It was like taking all the ashes from LePlay's altar and leaving the fire behind. Branford obviously found the manuscript too embarrassing. The present editor of the Review published the whole manuscript in 1950 as a special issue. His short foreword contains a number of interesting historical remarks; he has a slightly different explanation of why Branford discontinued publication. He mentions incidentally that latter-day LePlay-istes were active in the Vichy Government during the Second World War. (For addition to this footnote, see p. 5, Section III)

[89] Charles Booth, *A Memoir* (London: Macmillan & Co., 1918).

[90] T. S. Simey and M. B. Simey, *Charles Booth, Social Scientist* (London: Oxford Univ. Press, 1960).

I shall show presently that LePlay and Booth make very different uses of their budget data. Whether their qualitative monographic work is similar or not I cannot tell. The answer would have to come from a very detailed comparison of some of their cases. This has not been done yet but would certainly be worth the effort. The Simeys point out that Booth is badly neglected by contemporary sociologists, and I very much agree with them. When however, they call him "the founding father of the empirical tradition in the social sciences,"[91] they certainly do a great injustice to LePlay.

In the United States, in 1897, the *Journal of Sociology* published a set of instructions for the collection of family monographs.[92] But already, a few years earlier, American social scientists seemed to have become interested in the LePlay school. At the time of one of his visits to the United States, de Rousier was asked to describe its activities; his report was published by the American Academy of Political and Social Sciences.[93] This publication is interesting because it already foreshadows the subsequent ambivalent criticism of the LePlay disciples. To have overlooked this point is the only objection I would raise against the best available English-language presentation of LePlay's own work and that of his followers. Sorokin in his book on contemporary sociological theories devotes more space to them than to Durkheim and Weber taken together.[94] He is mainly concerned with substantive ideas and not with methodological matters; a review of his analysis therefore does not fall within the scope of this paper. Two of his students however made themselves the American exponents of LePlay's family studies and their enterprise requires a more detailed discussion.

In 1935, Zimmerman and Frampton published a book on "Family and Society."[95] The last part of it consists of a 240-page long condensation of the first volume of "The European Workers." The original translation was made by Samuel Dupertuis, and the American version carries the introductory note that the condensation was done "without destroying a single idea." A comparison with the original text shows, however, that somewhere along the line a strenuous effort was made to attenuate LePlay's position so as to make it palatable to an American academic audience. All attacks on America are omitted, the word "Decalogue" never appears—in its place are terms like "moral law," "mores," "universal moral code," etc.; sometimes the phrase "Decalogue and paternal authority" is presented only by the second term. One should also know that LePlay's careful editorial structure, so characteristic of him, is destroyed; in the American version, a major chapter of LePlay's original occasionally begins in the middle of a paragraph. What most emphatically has been eliminated are LePlay's major obsessions without which he cannot be understood at all. Because the Dupertuis version provides American readers with their only access to the French author, I give one example in

[91] *Op. cit.,* p. 190.

[92] Frederic LePlay, "Instruction in the Observation of Social Facts According to the LePlay Method of Monographs on Families," trans. by Chas. A. Ellwood, *The American Journal of Sociology,* 1896-1897, 2.

[93] Paul de Rousier, "La Science sociale,"

in *Ann. Amer. Acad. Polit. Soc. Sci.,* Jan., 1894.

[94] Pitirim Sorokin, *Contemporary Sociological Theories* (New York: Harper & Bros., 1928).

[95] Carl Zimmerman, *Family and Society* (New York: van Nostrand, 1935).

some detail. Here is a passage from p. 453 in Zimmerman-Frampton, corresponding to about pp. 167-169 in LePlay, Vol. I.

> The sophists of England and Germany inspired by the eloquence of Rousseau, have tried to meet the situation. They conclude that social disorders come especially from the constraints prescribed by the mores (!) and exercised by the family heads, and by the civil, religious and political hierarchies which increase the strength of paternal authority. They seek to abolish these constraints by overthrowing the rulers, if necessary.

Now this statement reads as if it belonged to a distinguished conservative tradition à la Burke (whom LePlay indeed quotes in a footnote). But in the original text the first sentence is preceded by a lengthy passage beginning with: "Around 1750, thinking began to be misled in the literary academies and in the Parisian salons, where the intellectuals, the aristocrats and the financiers met together." The imagery of a conspiracy, the notion that social changes are fostered by "people in the backroom" can never be found in the American version, although it is so characteristic for LePlay; as a matter of fact, a few lines later, the French author repeats that these people "began to pervert the minds of their contemporaries with their sophistries." The first sentence of the Dupertuis translation is correct but he omits about ten lines coming before the second sentence. These Rousseauian opinions are described as "absolutely false" and "contrary to the opinion of all thoughtful men (sages) and to the evidence available daily to the mothers of babies and their nurses." This anti-intellectual element in LePlay's text is avoided throughout the Dupertuis translation. And in the same ten omitted lines, we find still another of LePlay's favorite themes: "Logic applied to Rousseau's fundamental error (leads) to conclusions from which, as a fatal consequence, derives the ruin of any society adopting it." The idea that there are fundamental errors and verities from which logical inferences lead to wrong or correct views about society is the counter-part of LePlay's drive toward empirical observations: a reader cannot really assess the latter if he does not at the same time become aware of LePlay's pseudo-logic which permeates all his arguments. Even the last sentence in our quotation has in its original form an additional implication. The original says: (the sophists think) "that these constraints and hierarchies should be abolished; and if the rulers hesitate to accomplish this task, they should be overthrown." LePlay imputes even to the revolutionaries that they first would try to make the rulers change their evil ways and then only, if this does not work, would they be overthrown.[96]

The French disciples of LePlay were much concerned with the methodology of his work. They were exasperated by the fact that his monographs made fascinating reading while his procedures were loose and often manifestly faulty. The whole history of the "Science Sociale" group can be understood as an effort to capture his spirit and to make it transmittable to others. His Anglo-Saxon admirers probably hardly knew his actual studies which to my knowl-

---

[96] Let me add that in the eighty pages where the authors of "Family and Society" comment on the importance of what they call "LePlay's Theories" none of the actual family monographs is mentioned.

edge are even now accessible only in French. They were fascinated by his programmatic writings and transmitted them in varying degrees of vagueness and distortion.

The first check by an outsider was published in 1913 by Alfred Reuss.[97] His important monograph deals with "LePlay's significance for the development of methods in the social sciences." However, it is not so much concerned with his procedures as with the reliability of his observations and the relation between his data and his conclusions. The most startling part is Reuss' reanalysis of one of the family descriptions that LePlay had made (Volume IV, Case 6). Reuss went back to the German village in which two children of an observed family still lived, and he made use of a great deal of available documentation on local social conditions. He provides a fifty-page translation of the original case study and then confronts it with the material which he himself collected. The discrepancies are of various kinds. Thus, the budget figures make it appear that the man's only recreation was drinking, while actually he was active in a number of civic organizations, interests which are nowhere mentioned by LePlay, which do not show up in the budget, but which in the light of local political habits, explain the large amount of money spent in pubs. (Germans use the term "Bierbank Politiker" to describe a local worthy of this kind.) LePlay's more general considerations made him overlook facts which happened not to fit in with his preconceived notions. Thus, he was greatly concerned with the negative effects of the French inheritance laws which led to the progressive splitting up of farms. In the area on which Reuss checked, LePlay had remarked how the family life of the oldest son had benefitted from his being able to keep his parents' farm intact; but LePlay neglected the bad effects that this had had on the lives of the younger children about whom, according to Reuss, there was ample evidence. As one would expect, the worst misperception occurred on what we today would call labor relations. Reuss documents from contemporary newspapers the occurrence of repeated local riots because of low wages, exploitation by company stores and unsanitary working conditions. Nothing of this is mentioned by LePlay. Reuss's monograph still deserves careful reading; in our context, pages 85-89 on "the rise of figures by LePlay" are specially worthwhile.[98]

One final example combines the charismatic role of LePlay and what happens when "outsiders" enter the scene. In 1886, ten years after Geddes, a young French Canadian spent a few months in Paris and fell under the spell of Demolins. Upon leaving France, he pledged that he would devote his life to the study of Canada in LePlay's spirit. Leon Gerin, who became a distinguished civil servant, collected monographs which were published in "Science Sociale." He also revisited families which had been first reported in "Workers

[97] Alfons Reuss, *Frederic LePlay in Seiner Bedeutung für die Entwicklung der Sozialwissenschaftlichen Methode* (Jena: Gustav Fischer, 1913).

[98] In 1950, Eliot and Hillman, *et al., Norway's Families* (Philadelphia: Univ. of Pennsylvania Press, 1960) studied a Norwegian family to compare it with case 2 in Vol. III of LePlay. Their interest was in analyzing change, not to check on the case LePlay had collected more than 100 years earlier. But from historical records they feel that LePlay painted too rosy a picture of Northern Europe, which is the subject of Volume III. The authors mention in passing that they could not trace the existence of the 1845 family.

of Two Worlds"; he never doubted their authenticity. The official obituary speaks of him as the founder of Canadian sociology. At the age of seventy-five, he published a selection of his cases, several of them introduced by devoted memories of his initiation by Demolins. Since Gerin's death, however, younger Canadian sociologists have cast grave doubts on the LePlay-Gerin approach. The discussion deals less with research methodology than with controversial interpretations of Canadian social history; I therefore mention it only in passing.[99]

LePlay's monographs captivate the reader by his insights, his reckless generalizations, his stream of alleged evidence, his superb style, the clear structure of his writings, and, even if one disagrees with it, the consistency of his philosophical position. Outsiders have sided with or against him mainly on emotional grounds, since, except for Reuss, none of them has analyzed his empirical work; and Reuss wrote at a time when methodological thinking on social research was still in its infancy. The following pages are intended to give an outline of the direction in which a systematic study of LePlay's monographs holds promise.

Quantification and Diagnostics in LePlay's Monographs

Le Play is probably best remembered as the man who introduced the family budget into the tool chest of the empirical social scientist. He is quite outspoken about its central methodological role. One finds many remarks like the following:

> Every action which contributes to the existence of a working family leads more or less directly to an item of income or expense...(Vol. I, p. 225)

> There is nothing in the existence of a worker, no sentiment and no action worth mentioning which would not leave a marked clear trace in the budget. (Vol. I, p. 237)

He repeatedly compares budgetary analysis with the work of the mineralogist which he knew so well.

> The surest way an outside observer has to know the spiritual and material life of people is *very similar to the procedure which a chemist uses to understand the nature of minerals.* The mineral is known when the analysis has isolated all the elements which enter into its composition, and when one has verified that the weight of all these elements adds up exactly to that of the mineral under analysis. A similar *numerical verification is always available to the student who analyzes systematically the social unit represented by the family.* (Vol. I, p. 224)

LePlay wrote in great detail about the best way to classify and compute the budget items he obtained in periodic talks with his respondent. In this sense,

[99] Philippe Garigue, *Etudes sur le Canada Francais* (Montreal: Universite de Montreal, 1958) and Leon Gerin, *Le Type Economique et Social des Canadiens* (Montreal: l'A.C.-F., 1938). I am indebted to Professor Sigmund Diamond, who, in the course of his own research on French Canada noticed the great role of the LePlay tradition among French Canadian sociologists. Some information on Gerin can be found in the 1951 proceedings of the Royal Society of Canada.

he can indeed be considered the fountainhead of an important quantitative technique. But his analysis of the data was quite peculiar and it took others to develop the whole range of possibilities.

In principle, there are three major ways to use budget data; these may be tagged as the analytical, the synthetic and the diagnostic procedure. By *analytical* is meant the study of specific expenses, either in relationship to each other, or to the total income of the family, or to some of its general characteristics, such as occupation, age of children, etc. Already, during LePlay's lifetime, the interest of some of his contemporaries shifted towards the search for such generalizations. In 1857, the German economist, Ernst Engel, published his famous law stating that the proportion of income spent on food increases as the total income of a family decreases. His data were taken in part from LePlay's monographs.[100] Since then, this kind of generalization has been the main objective of an ever-increasing number of budget studies. They represent early forms of multivariate analysis; on the same income level, for example, white collar families spend more on rent than manual workers. I know of no evidence that LePlay was aware of this use of his material. There is very little doubt that he would not have thought well of it. He, as well as his students, found statistical generalization quite pointless.[101]

In the *synthetic* mood of budget analysis one combines all the information to form what in principle are types, although often the information is finally translated into uniform money terms. The best example for our narrative is the way Booth, in his first social survey of life and labor of the people in London, tried to establish his poverty line. For a large number of items of food, clothing, shelter, etc., he listed the minimum supply which, by expert opinion, was needed for the sustenance of a family of given size. If its income did not permit it to supply itself with these items, it was classified as poor. To find the extent and distribution of poverty was the main purpose of this enterprise, as was mentioned before.[102]

What then did LePlay himself do with the pages of budgetary information covered in Sections 14-16 of each monograph? In his methodological introduction, he gives the following example:

> Often a single figure says much more than a long discourse. Thus, for instance, one cannot doubt the degradation of a Paris worker after one has learned from the study of his budget that each year he spends 12% of his income to get drunk, while he does not devote a cent for the moral education of his five children of ages 4-14. (Vol. I, p. 226)

In other words, he selects specific items and uses them for what is best called

---

[100] Engel, himself a mining engineer by training, wanted to combine the LePlay and the Quetelet traditions. He created the term "Quet" for the basic unit in a consumption calculus.

[101] Bureau quotes an extensive diatribe by LePlay against statistics (footnote 82, p. 228) without giving the source. In an issue of "Science Sociale" (Nov. 1912) Descamp compares LePlay's methods with other procedures in social research and again argues against the kind of evidence which today we would call correlation analysis; one of his negative examples is Durkheim's "Suicide."

[102] The Booth survey was repeated later by some of his former assistants. In Vol. III of "The New Survey of London Life and Labour" (London, Orchard House, 1932) one can find a sophisticated discussion of the way Booth tried to translate the notion of poverty into a classificatory instrument. See especially pages 8 ff., 70-77, 97-106.

diagnostic purposes. Space does not permit us to discuss the logical foundations of this kind of social symptomatology. I can list only a few examples here. LePlay uses specific budget items as indicators of broader sentiments or social configurations. A French tinsmith pays high dues to a labor union, which shows how aggressive he feels against upper class people; the family of a London cutlery worker spends much money on food, which allows one to infer that they will have little chance to advance on the social ladder; a German worker's income derives partly from gardening, which accounts for the moral stability still prevailing in his type of family. Most of these observations refer to moral issues: too much money for drink, not enough for religious practices and education, too much for "useless recreations." One has to keep in mind that these budget items are mentioned as part of general observations and discussions which go far beyond the quantitative evidence. One can get the full impact of LePlay's monographs without ever looking at the dreary pages of balance sheets for earnings, occasional incomes, fringe benefits and expenses.[103]

The later LePlayistes increasingly abandoned the budget; as a matter of fact, they became highly critical of it. The nature of this criticism in itself deserves some attention because it signals an interesting trend in the whole history of quantification. When de Rousier in the first issue of the new series of "La Science Sociale" listed all of LePlay's shortcomings, he quoted many examples of the kind which were exemplified above by the summary of Reuss' reanalysis. He thought that LePlay was just following the "habit he had acquired during his professional studies (as a mineralogist)." According to him, LePlay was "seduced by this desire for numerical verification and as a result, left aside the phenomena *which cannot be expressed in numbers and therefore elude such verification*" (emphasis supplied). But if one looks at some of de Rousier's examples, one notices that today they would in no way be considered unquantifiable. Thus, for instance, he says that many families do not spend money, but time, on the education of their children. He obviously did not consider the possibility of a time budget, which today has become quite conventional. He says that expenses for devotional candles are not an appropriate measure of religious devotion, but he does not consider the possibility that records of church attendance or family prayer might at least enlarge the scope of quantitative measurement. In other cases, statistical records of the kind of personal contacts a family has would cover well de Rousier's examples of phenomena which supposedly are accessible only to qualitative comments. LePlay, incidentally, often reports what the members of his families talk about with each other. Even quantified inventories of conversations, although still rare, have cropped up in recent empirical studies.

We face here an episode in the history of quantification which has many parallels. LePlay proposes budget items as a social measure. After a while, the instrument proves deficient and so time budgets or sociometric records are

---

[103] On the other hand, they now form important documents for the economic historian. LePlay repeatedly stressed the relevance of his work for the future historian, who, due to him, would have better information about social conditions during his lifetime than for any other period.

proposed. They cover more ground but after a while, they too, appear to leave out some significant parts of social reality. Bureau, for instance, reproaches the LePlayistes for being materialistic because they fail to consider what today we would call attitudes. Now attitudes are being measured and the objection is that this is an atomistic approach and that it does not take into account "climates of opinion" or "collective norms." These periodic waves of optimism and pessimism are one of the topics which the history of the LePlay school suggests for further investigation.[104]

I now return to another aspect of LePlay's diagnostic procedure. Anyone who has done field work or who has reported to sociologically-minded friends about a personal trip hopes to find incidental observations which throw light on a complex social situation. Professors at the Sorbonne do not list their telephone numbers in the directory; how well does that indicate their exalted status and their social distance from students? In some American towns, families do not lock their doors when they leave the house; to what extent is this an indicator of mutual trust? Anthropologists developed great skill in such observations because of the language barrier between them and the people they visited. In contemporary society, students like Riesman and Margaret Mead have come to symbolize the art of making such incisive diagnostic observations. The logic of the procedure is by no means yet clarified and I will not try to discuss it here.[105] But LePlay's monographs certainly contain pertinent examples. To show the religious indifference of a London cutlery worker, he mentions that the man did not even know how to find a minister when a

[104] In Gabriel Tarde we find a typical remark (condensed translation from his "Lois de l'Imitation" p. 227): "Statistical data are only poor substitutes (for what we really want to know). Only a psychological statistic, reporting on changes in the specific beliefs of individual people—if this were at all possible —would provide the deeper reasons for the ordinary statistical figures." Just as Tarde considers attitude measurements impossible so does Zizek feel about the measurement of occupational prestige, which today has become a research routine. He says (*Soziologie*, p. 25, condensed translation): "In the study of social stratification statistics deal with tangible occupational characteristics, while for the sociologist other aspects, like e.g. social prestige might be of importance. The sociologist will therefore often combine statistical data with non-quantitative information." Toennies (Ferdinand Toennies, *et al., Sektion Soziographie, Siebenter Deutscher Soziologentag* Tübingen: Mohr, 1931]) the great believer in "Sociography" always added that "of course" many things cannot be quantified; but he was diplomatically vague as to where the limits were.

[105] A systematic collection of such global indicators from a variety of community studies has been made by Patricia Kendall (*Qualitative Indicators in Field Work* [mimeo], New

York: Bureau of Applied Social Research, Col. Univ.). The technique is, of course, well known to the historian who often must depend on the interpretation of a single letter or the report on a ceremonial event. Rosenberg has analyzed such procedures in the writings of a number of historians and recreated the transition from the medieval mind to the spirit of the Renaissance. (George Rosenberg, "Without Polls or Surveys," Ph.D. dissertation, 1960, Columbia Univ.)

Among several Geddes biographies the one by Boardman (Philip Boardman, *Patrick Geddes, Maker of the Future* [Chapel Hill: Univ. of North Carolina Press, 1944]) is relatively the most sober one. Even there Geddes' initiation to LePlay through a lecture by Desmolins is described in the following way (p. 42): "In a flash Geddes saw that in LePlay's travels and his actual observation of society, there lay a method of study which both satisfied him as a scientist and inspired him, as one who often puzzled over mankind's ways and institutions, to follow this lead."

In tracing the charismatic nature of the LePlayist world, one will have to keep the age of the actors in mind. LePlay started his role as a "prophet" at the age of fifty. His most immediate French apostles were thirty to fifty years younger than he was.

family member who was ill requested religious consolation. (Vol. III, Case 6) The high status of women in a nomadic family of the Urals is demonstrated by a description of how the wife interfered when LePlay interviewed the husband. (Vol. II, Case 1). The social alienation of a tinsmith in French Savoy is exhibited by the fact that he and his wife collect mischievous gossip about dignitaries of the town. (Vol. III, Case 4). An impoverished family who won a special prize spend most of the money buying new clothes which shows that they hope to regain their former social status. (Vol. VI, Case 7) Living with the family of a Viennese carpenter, (Vol. VI, Case 1) LePlay tries to teach the wife an economic lesson: he lends her money so that she can buy sugar wholesale. The experiment fails because the children keep begging for more and it is easier for the mother to refuse when she can point to an empty cupboard. For LePlay this is a sign that the family will never become an economic success, but at least he appreciates the tender heart of the mother.

What one might call the global indicator game is something which binds together whole generations of would-be LePlayistes. Lewis Mumford wrote a short essay on Patrick Geddes and Victor Branford, both of whom he knew in connection with his interest in city planning.[106] He makes the usual undocumented and stereotyped references to LePlay's influence on the two men, but he certainly catches the spirit of the affinity when he characterizes a typical stroll with Branford:

> He would gleefully point out some sinister exhibition of the social process, as in the combination of a bank with a meeting hall in the Methodist Center in Westminster, or the juxtaposition of the bust of Cecil Rhodes with the new examination buildings in Oxford, which sorted out the brains of an imperial bureaucracy. (p. 684)

It would clarify the nature of LePlay's work and the logic of this diagnostic procedure if one were to collect and analyze systematically all pertinent examples in LePlay's monographs. I have the impression, however, that they are not very numerous. LePlay gives much more space to observations which go beyond the individual family and link it to broader sociological statements. Or, to put it more precisely, he soon leaves the specific family and focusses his attention on broader contexts. Thus, in the case of the London cutlery worker, he tells us that the poorer workers in his neighborhood go to church in the evening, while the middle-class people go in the morning; the preacher is aware of this stratification, and custom tailors his sermons accordingly. The social ressentiment of the Savoy tinsmith leads to an instructive digression on the spreading power of the labor unions in this area. One of the most interesting examples can be found in paragraphs 18 and 19 of Case 7 in Volume 6. LePlay obviously selected this family because it got a prize for having produced a large number of children and bringing them up decently under very restricted economic conditions. In four pages, LePlay makes ten statements as to the factors which account for high fertility. Formulated as hypotheses,

[106] Lewis Mumford, "Patrick Geddes, Victor Branford, and Applied Sociology in England: The Social Survey, Regionalism, and Urban Planning," *An Introduction to the History of Sociology,* Harry Elmer Barnes (ed.), (Chicago: Univ. of Chicago Press, 1948).

they would do honor to any modern textbook, and most of them would be controversial even today after a century of empirical research has piled up. LePlay is of course convinced that his opinion is the only one conceivable.

The French disciples of LePlay were very much concerned about the loose connection between the family monographs themselves and the broader social observations which were considered LePlay's most important contributions. This explains the dominant role which de Tourville's "Nomenclature" played in the pages of the "Science Sociale." De Tourville wanted to provide a system of categories which would give a place to every relevant observation and at the same time permit a reorganization of the original work of LePlay. He was also confident that his system would facilitate comparative analysis. The Nomenclature consisted of twenty-five major categories, which approach the families under study, so to say, from two sides. The first nine corresponded approximately to the first thirteen paragraphs of the original monographs: the geographical setting and the type of work done by the family members (a and b), its sources of income, properties, expenses and savings (c - f), the obligations and rights of the family members, the style of life and its history (g - i).

The remaining categories tried to see the family in ever-broadening circles of its social context: the technical, commercial and cultural conditions of the industry in which they worked (j - l); the religious practices, the neighborhood relations and the professional and communal organizations in which the family was embedded (m - q), the broader characteristics of the country in which the family lived, the city, the province and the laws of the whole state inasmuch as they had bearing on the life of the family (r - u); finally, the broad history of the country, its national composition, and its relation (especially emigration or immigration) with other countries (v - z). For a long while, de Tourville's Nomenclature was considered the perfect key to all social analysis. The general argument went about as follows: it guaranteed, so to say, the basic elements needed to describe any social system. After they have been provided, the task of the analyst is fairly easy. He has to find how these elements are related to each other in a specific case and how they vary from one to the next.

Here again is another major wave of categorization, so characteristic of the history of the social sciences. The reader will undoubtedly have anticipated the parallel with Conring and the school of German university statistics. Their aim was certainly the same as the one of the LePlay group, although we can take it for granted that the latter did not know of this earlier effort. It is not too difficult to pinpoint the major difference between the two approaches. The starting point for the Conring school was the state and the administrative tasks of the statesman. In a cameralistic system, he took it for granted that the welfare of the state depended upon the activities of the rulers. Their activities, therefore, were the starting point for the relevant categories: increase of population, defense against potential enemies, improvement of agriculture, monetary policy and so on. Matters like the family would be derivative problems related, for instance, to the number of available conscripts; individual characteristics of diverse population groups would be worth knowing if the statesman wanted efficient compliance with his administrative measures. The LePlay group took the reverse view. The welfare of the country depended upon the morality, the industry and the submissiveness of the citizens at large and upon the sense of responsibility of the elite. These qualities were formed in the confines of the family. The system of categories, therefore, had to start out with a description of this primary group; it drew in the characteristics of the larger context only to the extent that this explained what happened at the social core. LePlay, so to say, saw society from within outward. Conring and his school looked at society as a large social system, the main characteristics of which they wanted to describe; they paid attention to the primary group only to the extent to which it would affect the actor on the big scene. Anyone who knows the literature of modern sociology is aware that the development of nomenclature is still an honorable pursuit. One might say that recent literature is trying to combine the Conring and the LePlay traditions.

POSTSCRIPTUM

What other major episode might have belonged in this introductory survey? I have not described in detail the coming of the British social survey; recently good summaries have become available, especially Abrams' introductory chapters to his book on social surveys[107] and McGregor's paper on the social background of the survey movement.[108] The development of quantification in Germany is a complex topic. Toennies, best known for his conceptual distinction between Gesellschaft and Gemeinschaft, was for years a vigorous promoter of an empirical "Sociography"; but twice, once before the First World War and again before the rise of Hitler, this development was cut short. Max Weber is the great symbol of broad-scale historical research. Only rarely is reference made to his periodic interest in quantitative research and the ambivalence of his efforts. Space limitations have forced me to reserve the German materials for a future publication.[109] The Italians have an empirical tradition of their own. Not knowing their language, I had to leave their side of the story to other students; Niceforo's books provide many leads to historical sources. Americans came later into the scene of course. Nothing is stranger than the idea often expressed by European colleagues that quantification is a U.S. export endangering their tradition. It is true that when this country took over the European empirical research techniques, it did so on a large scale. But the steps by which this came about are little known. Here is a vast area for further inquiry; I have not touched upon it in this paper, because the tracing of institutional and personal contacts, as well as analysis of the literature, would be required.

Some time at the end of the 19th century, quantification in sociology takes on its modern function: to translate ideas into empirical operations and to

[107] Mark Abrams, *Social Surveys and Social Action* (London: Wm. Heinemann, Ltd., 1951).

[108] O. R. McGregor, "Social Research and Social Policy in the Nineteenth Century," *The British Journal of Sociology*, 1957, 8.

[109] Paul F. Lazarsfeld and Anthony Oberschall, *History of Quantification in Germany*, (mimeo) (New York: Bureau of Applied Social Research, Col. Univ.).

look for regular relations between the variates so created.[110] Histories of specific techniques will be needed to clarify this general trend. Helen Walker has done it for correlation analysis[111] and Stephan for sampling.[112] The use of questionnaires has a long past which still waits for its recorder. Mathematical models of social behavior have a curious history. At the end of the 18th century, men like Condorcet worked on them very seriously. For a long while thereafter, the idea was monopolized by the economists. In very recent years, psychologists and sociologists have reentered the scene. The literature increases rapidly; but it is still an object for the book reviewer rather than the historian.

In any case, much work must be done, if we want to match the increasing quantity of sociological quantification by better quality of insight into its history.

[110] For a sketch of this whole trend, see Jahoda, Lazarsfeld and Zeisel, *Marienthal* (Allensbach, Demoskopie, 1961).

[111] *Studies in the History of Statistical Methods* (Baltimore, 1929).

[112] Frederic Stephan, "History of the Uses of Modern Sampling Procedures," *J. Amer. statist. Ass.,* March 1948.

Quantification in Biology

By R. W. Gerard*

THE conference on quantification in science lacked a paper specifically on biology and I was asked to supply that lack. Since I write after having read the other papers and after having participated in the discussion of them, this paper is necessarily rather different in approach. Because I lack the particular expertness of an historian but am much concerned with integrative efforts, the approach will be more summative. This is the more permissible since Shryock has admirably woven into his paper many biological, as well as medical, threads; and also because several important aspects of the development of quantification are so clearly common to all fields of science. Indeed, as one long concerned with the nervous system, I shall in part reverse the assigned title and consider the biology of quantification. The few primary or even secondary historical sources here used appear in some earlier articles, which I shall quote, as convenient.

The most salient point about quantification in science, and one happily touched on by all essayists, is that it must follow, not precede, adequate qualification. Measurement can be helpful only when the proper things have been found to measure. It derives from, feeds into, sharpens and clarifies, and discriminates between alternate qualitative descriptions and models; it cannot generate them.

The process has some circularity, of course, and the formal properties of an experimental situation can now and then point the direction of restructuring the model. As A. Rapoport says:[1]

> Occasionally, an important parameter [makes] itself known as some mathematically determined invariant. For example, the energy and the entropy changes in a system reveal themselves as "state variables" in the thermodynamic sense by being represented as certain line integrals independent of the path of integration. Here a mathematical invariance points to a physical "reality." Once this principle is recognized, one naturally hunts for other invariants, and a number have proved their conceptual usefulness, e.g., the Helmholtz work function, the enthalpy, etc.
>
> Now game theory has been hailed as a major break through in social science. . . . The value of game theory is conceptual, not predictive. It offers no usable models of behavior aside from normative ones which are of no practical significance except in the simplest cases, because no game beyond the trivially simple ones can be completely analyzed by a human mind, and game theory always assumes such analysis to have been carried out. But game theory does provide *concepts* with which to work. These concepts are the prod-

* Mental Health Research Institute, University of Michigan.
[1] A. Rapoport, "In search of quantifiable parameters of group performance." *First Conference in System Engineering* (New York: Wiley and Sons, 1960).

ucts of game theory. But they can be taken as the raw material of a behavioral theory to be developed in real contexts.

One might even maintain that a sufficiently penetrating mind could reach all its conclusions without the impedimenta of equations and calculations. The famous problem of the fly, that flew at 30 miles per hour from the nose of one horse to that of a second five miles away, and so back and forth until crushed, the horses running toward each other, respectively, at 5 and 10 miles an hour, can be solved in two ways. Mathematicians tend to set up and solve an infinite series; physicists and other naïve persons, more rapidly and simply, reason that the horses, approaching at 15 miles per hour, will require 20 minutes to cover 5 miles; during which time the fly, traveling 30 miles per hour, will cover 10 miles. The story has it that von Neumann, given the problem, answered at once; but, on questioning, admitted he had solved the series, none-the-less.

A similar example is the geometric problem of calculating a line length. On the horizontal radius of an upper right quadrant of an 8 cm. circle, erect a perpendicular to the radius at a point 6 cm. from the center of the circle. From the point at which this perpendicular meets the circumference draw a horizontal line to the vertical radius. How long is the diagonal between the two points on the radii? Since the other diagonal of this rectangle is a radius, no trigonometric functions need be calculated—but few people see this solution.

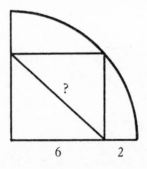

Kuhn has made this point most fully and emphasized that: "The road from scientific law to scientific measurement can rarely be traveled in the reverse direction." Indeed, he well argues that without a "law" no meaningful numbers can be wrested from nature and that, in a sense, theories are self-fulfilling prophesies.

Without such orientations the welter of phenomena would be overwhelming; with them, phenomena fall into a pattern, take on form and relative importance, and can be grappled. The major zigs in the zig-zag course of science result from shifts in such orientations. But, it bears repeating, these only furnish the basis for the detailed analysis which eventually reveals mechanisms. A mechanical pressure, due to osmotic swelling, due to metabolic products, due to a rich supply of oxygen, due to its surface position, leads to the folding of the outer embryonic layer which forms the neutral tube; the forming retina liberates a specified chemical which diffuses to the surface cells nearby, modifies the protein they form so that the molecules are parallel

threads rather than scattered balls, and leads to the production of a transparent lens: such are the answers one seeks to demonstrate by experiments
directed toward mechanisms. And only such answers enable one, in time, to
tinker intelligently with the works—by increasing osmotic pressure in other
known ways, by adding other chemicals to influence protein formation, by the
myriad tricks that man has learned from nature. Mechanism adds utility to
truth.[2]

Crombie emphasizes the appearance of adequate instruments and measurements only in response to a need—felt in many aspects of practical life, as
of precise weights for assay of metal alloys, but not in relation to academic
theorizing. Shryock, similarly, insists that only when the quantitative work
a man does is really significant does he think to measure. Spengler notes explicitly, as Boring implies, that qualitative models are needed before applying
quantitative analysis; and Lazarsfeld offers as his first postulate, "Any measurement is an intended ordering of objects within a frame of reference engendered by some conceptual imagery." Perhaps the point is best made by the
exchange between a modern Socrates and his follower: "How many birds are
there in a flock?" "I cannot say." "How many bees in a swarm?" "I am uncertain." "How many dwarfs with Snow White?" "That I know, Sir, seven."
"Ah, then you have firmer knowledge of fairies than of birds or bees?"

> Again, each important advance in form, in structured truth or beauty, is the
> result of a new closure, of a fresh set of axioms—a better set, resulting from
> the greater knowledge and understanding built with the aid of those dying.
> The forming mind of the young can use the new as comfortably as the old,
> but the formed mind of the teacher cannot readily run along the new-gauge
> tracks. The concepts of infinity, relativity, indeterminism in the physical realm,
> as evolution in the biological, were difficult for the established generation,
> simple for the oncoming one. Yet unless we forever question the basic im-
> aginative constructs of our predecessors we condemn ourselves to working
> at progressively more detailed and trivial levels, to filling in further digits
> past the decimal point.[3]
>
> It would be an error to consider technology as unimportant even in the
> most individual arts; where would they be without chisels or strings or paper,
> without printing and radio, without, for that matter, the tool of language it-
> self? As Shotwell has well put it, we "need a Sartor Resartus in the history
> of literature to show how naked and helplessly limited is thought except when
> provided with mechanism." (This, to anticipate, is equally true for supply-
> ing fresh ingredients to think about as for expressing the resultant thoughts.
> Technology enhances the sense organs of man and enriches his experience, no
> less than it gives power to his expression.)[4]

Quantification sharpens the image of things seen by the mind's eye, both
external phenomena and internal conceptions, but it is useless or worse until
the right things are in the field of viewpoint. What the mind looks at and how
it sees it, what pictures gain attention, is no longer a problem of philosophy
or even primarily of psychology. Today neurophysiology, aided by experi-

---

[2] See R. W. Gerard, "The scope of science,"   imagination," *Sci. Mon.,* 1946, *62:* 477-499.
Sci. Mon., 1947, *64:* 496-512.   [4] Gerard, "The scope of science," *loc. cit.*
    [3] R. W. Gerard, "The biological basis of

mental psychology, is offering clear evidence on the neural basis for meeting and structuring man's universe. There are, indeed, models of the world built into the patterned neurones of the brain by the past experience of each individual.

The evidence that nerve impulses which carry ordered sensory messages to the brain lead to related enduring material changes in the nervous system is now indisputable.[5] Triangles and circles can be seen only with practice in seeing them; and if such experience with patterned vision is denied an infant chimpanzee for some weeks, while the brain is developing, good vision is never acquired. The traces in the brain have been localized by operations and stimulation, the conditions of their formation have been examined, their chemical and physical bases are in active exploration, and their general nature is reasonably well understood. Certain neuron groups become functionally joined so that activity spreads through them in characteristic paths—as a flowing river both forms and is channeled by its bed. Smaller groups can be joined to form larger ones, and these still larger ones.

Thus are the simpler inputs or sensations able to be handled as elements of experience, and these grouped into larger and ever larger entities. Repeated patterns become units, as letters, which easily combine into greater words and phrases. On the motor side, equally, basic movements are learned, as typewriter key pressing or phoneme enunciation, and built into flowing writing or speech. As children develop reading blindness and are literally unable to distinguish letters (even when other pattern vision is not disturbed), so they develop speaking blind spots and rarely, after the teens, learn to speak a new tongue without an accent. And our conceptual pictures of the world are built entirely comparably, of primitive abstractions that combine in varied levels to give each individual's set or *weltanschauung*. Language and number are prime examples; but the logical and spatial and temporal orientation, the heuristic weightings and value judgments, the whole personality structure, are no less the products of the impress of his environment on the malleable brain of each individual. It is time to become specific.

Man depends overwhelmingly on vision for his cues to the world—two of the three million sensory nerve fibers that bring information to the nervous system are in the optic nerves.

> Man cannot see the world other than as it unfolds itself within the sensory projection areas of his brain. These determine his basic orientation to externality. In the very spatial arrangement of the areas of vision, skin, and muscle sense is embedded an unformulated geometry. The basic units of physical science are distilled from these areas: space (centimeters) from vision, touch, muscle sense, and the vestibular system (the balance organs located within the ear); substance (mass, grams) from smell, taste, touch, muscle sense, and secondarily, vision—a congenitally blind person, on achieving vision, feels objects "hitting" his eyes until he learns to project his experience

[5] Gerard, *Fixation of experience.* Symposium on Brain Mechanisms and Learning, ed. J. F. Delafresneye. (Oxford: Blackwell Scientific Publications, 1960). Also see Gerard, "The schizophrenia and psychopharmacology project." Amer. Psychiatric Assoc., Scientific Paper and Discussions, Divisional Meeting (Detroit, Mich., 23-31 Oct., 1959) 258-278, 1960.

into the third dimension, as we all project the sense of touch to the end of
a stick with which we explore the bottom of a pond—and perhaps, even, the
notion of force comes from touch and muscle sense, of matter more from taste
and smell; and time (seconds) most directly from hearing. At least, as evidence for this last, is the powerful reaction to heard rhythm, tapping to a tune,
and the fact that a sound track of words or music run backwards is completely
meaningless, whereas a reversed light track, though often ludicrous or impossible, is perfectly meaningful. Moreover, one's subjective judgment of time
certainly depends on a brain clock, which runs fast in fever according to a
precise mathematical function of the brain temperature. (In another, more
fanciful, sense one might think of time running through the cortex from behind forward. Sensations, from already past events, enter behind the Rolandic
fissure; motor impulses, which will set off future actions, leave from in front
of it.)

From space, mass, and time comes, in turn, the notion of entity—the basic
gestalt of all and the first flutter of imagination. In this sense, that entity is
given by the sensory organization of the nervous system, Kronecker's famous
mathematical dictum takes on a profounder meaning: "God made the integers,
man did all the rest." And, in supplying the substratum for thought, vision
in man is surely of overwhelming importance. Our thought words are almost
all of visual reference, although we do "apprehend" a meaning and refer to a
"tangible suggestion" or a "weighty problem," and we may say of something,
"it looks heavy or hard," but never that "it feels red." Brightman has written
the telling paragraph, quoted below, on the indications from language; and
Sherrington showed how the eye, the main distance receptor in the higher
vertebrates, has dominated the evolution of the cerebrum.

> A survey of language shows that many of the terms used by common
> men as well as by scientists and philosophers in expressing their funda-
> mental concepts are words which point only to visual experience, away
> from the invisible experience of free, purposive valuing. . . . Even theo-
> retic man has clung to the visual tradition, or as it has been called, 'The
> Spectator Theory of Knowledge.' A spectator is one who looks; theory
> means looking; knowledge is the only word here that originally allows
> a non-visual experience. Realism, of course, refers to the visible thing,
> the *res*. But even idealism is named from the root i δ, which means see.
> Intuition (*intueor*) is simply looking at what is seen; vision, that sup-
> posedly spiritual act, means only seeing (*video*). No matter how intel-
> lectual we try to become, we cling to *insight*. We seem to talk by sight
> and not by purpose in our etymology. If our insight reaches its highest
> level, it is synopsis, in which the optical is evident (as vision is evident
> in the very word 'evident'). The esthetic is often interpreted as having
> some relation to purpose; yet the Greek word means only what is per-
> ceptible to sense. Even imagination (*imago, imitor*), which originally re-
> ferred only to likeness and might thus mean likeness in purpose or value,
> quickly came to mean the seen likeness of a visible object. A philosophy
> is a world view (*vue*), that is, something seen. Contemplation comes
> from *contemplor* (to gaze at). Consideration is from *considero* (to
> look at closely); an interesting hint at man's early stargazing, for *sidus*
> (star) is concealed in the word. Even the ultraphilosophical German
> word, *Vernunft*, derives from *vernehmen*, which originally meant to see.[6]

---

[6] Gerard, "The biological basis of imagination," *loc. cit.*

The messages set up in the retina of the eye come from many kinds of receptor endings, sensitive to light intensity, color, pattern, and change. From the start, experience is filtered and distorted, and certain attributes of the "true" photographic image formed on the retina are emphasized.

For example, the receptors connect with neighboring ones so that each, when active, tends to quiet nearby ones. The discharge from each is raised by light on it, lowered by light on close ones. All units in an evenly bright area fire faster than do those in an evenly dull area, but those near the boundary between areas must, and do, behave in a special way. Units on the dull side of the margin, being near highly active units, are more inhibited than are other units in the uniform dull field; and those on the bright side of the margin, being near weakly active units, are less inhibited than their fellows elsewhere in the bright field. As a result, the edge between light and dark is underscored —this *outline* of area patterns is the main information sent to the brain.

In exactly the same way, receptors that have kept in low illumination discharge with extra frequency (like a high pitch) for a fraction of a second after receiving stronger light, before settling down to a maintained rate; and, conversely, when light is decreased, the pitch of their discharge falls momentarily far below the level at which it will settle. But note that it is normally just at the edge between bright and dull patches that such intensity changes are imposed on reactors, as the incessant small movements of the eyeball make the image of the visual field shimmer on the retina. Again, the eye is built to catch movement and to emphasize edges. Indeed, if such jiggling of the image on the retina is prevented, all pattern vision disappears and strange stuporous or hallucinatory states supervene.[7]

The new-born child faces a new and unstructured rain of stimulii—William James' blooming, buzzing confusion—and requires many weeks before sufficient regularity and repetition begin to give him some pattern. It takes so long before the eyes will fixate an object. And inevitably it *is* an object that first does give structure to experience, a material entity that remains reasonably constant or repetitive over time, that throws a real image on the retina— one that is demarcated from other parts of the visual field by good edges and that moves in the field as a whole. Objects are the first gestalts separated from their grounds; they are the nouns of our thought, the integers of our arithmetic, the primitive units of our universe. Only on the basis of such regularity in experience can measurement exist.

The objects with appropriate size and duration to be seen, those with space and time dimensions comparable to man's own, are the first entities of our experience and the ones first to receive attention—naïve or scientific. This is the first and greatest step—a qualitative one—in mind ordering nature. And it is, likewise, the first and greatest step in nature ordering mind; for the recurring patterns of messages, imposed on the brain by the sense-organs responding repetitiously to the real objects of the world, carve enduring neuron connections that channel future messages. This is the solution of the problem of Hume and Berkeley.

[7] R. W. Ditchburn, "Physical methods applied to the study of visual perception," *Bull.* *Inst. Physics,* 1959: 121-125.

Given an array of material entities, the next step is to group them. Here enters the second or taxonomic stage of experience and of science.

> Each discipline begins in a descriptive or classificatory manner. The subjects or entities of interest to it, the nouns of its language, are identified, described, tabulated, and ordered. This is the taxonomic stage, whether dealing with pure compounds in chemistry, minerals in geology, species in botany, structures in anatomy, or specific functions in physiology. Next is the static or structural stage, during which relations, as quantitative as possible, are established between these entities, and verbs of state are introduced. Pythagoras' law, Ohm's law, Boyle's law, Bell's law, Starling's law are fruits of such activity. Then comes the dynamic stage, and the verbs of change, when variations in time, space, and other conditions are introduced, and the shift in relations is examined. Integers preceded infinitesimals; electrostatics, electrodynamics; molecular structure, reaction rates; and the architecture of bodies, their action. Finally, with the holistic stage, the language is completed, the units in their variable relations are returned to the whole, the gestalt is recognized, the planet or the organism returns to the center of focus.
>
> But this is too simple, for these stages apply not to each science but to each level within it. The natural entities examined by science are not ultimate indivisible units but are built of units which are themselves entities built of lesser units, often in a long regression. Man first grapples nature at a level dictated by the dimensions of his unaided senses, then pushes his way up or down through the layers—the astronomer to supergalaxies, the physicist to subnucleons—as instrumental aids enrich his senses, and insight orders data. At the present rate of advance, at least in biology, scientists are moving at a level per generation. Before this century, the organism had been dissected, structurally and functionally, to the organ level; during the first half of the 1900's the analysis swept on to the tissue, then the cell; and during the second half, it is already pushing on to the organelle, particle, and molecule.
>
> Organ systems do not go out of bounds, however, when organelles come in. Each level advances through its own stages, development only being accelerated by the light reflected from other levels. Homeostasis is a holistic concept at the level of the organism. It gained in richness and precision from Claude Bernard to Cannon as the contributory organ systems were laid bare, as the actions of the liver and parathyroid and depressor nerve were recognized. It continues to gain as thiamine and cytochrome and cortisone enter the picture, and will so continue as ever more intimate mechanisms of membrane permeability, and enzyme action, and micellar architecture and gene reduplication are revealed. Similarly, behavior of the whole organism was studied for long at the descriptive level, while the nervous system was probed to nuclei and neurones and synapses, to action spikes and ion movements. Today, as these elements are recombined, the properties of neurone nets and potential fields and metabolic rhythms give more than promise of an understanding of behavior dynamics.[8]

Tabby and Mehitabel become generically "cats," Fido and Rover, "dogs," and Tom and Mary acquire the family name, Miller. This conceptual grouping of entities, putting stars into constellations, is at first sharp and total. Items are either in or out of a given set, species are cleanly separated, and

---

[8] Gerard, "The organization of science," *Ann. Rev. Physiol.,* 1952, *14:* 1-12.

nature does "come as clean as you think it." In biology, taxonomists identified and ordered species and gathered them into the larger taxa, flowering in
the early 18th century in Linnaeus' binomial plan. His triumph, of course, was
in choosing wisely the criteria on which sets were formed—not the obvious
ones of size or of habitat or of fur or feathers but such subtle ones as reproductive devices. So did Lavoisier open the way from useless entities, the compounds, to useful ones, the elements, by discarding color and hardness and
solubility as his ordering criteria, in favor of reactions with his newly understood oxygen and hydrogen. Similar problems of choosing the right units and
criteria we shall see repeated, for functional rather than morphologic entities
and in matters of nosology in physical and then in mental disease. Number
and measurement may well enter at this stage, as in the count of paired ap-
pendages or of days of symptom appearance; but such data are still only
qualitative indices, with no power as quantities.

Nature, however, does not come clean, and sharp types gradually blurred
into distributed populations—the straight-walled butte of a species weathered
into the hill of a continuous population. Mulattos connect Caucasians and
Negroes; intersexes, men and women; jack-asses, horses and donkeys; and
crosses are known between genera and even families. The qualitative differences of Aristotle have again been reduced to the quantitative variations of
Plato. Different numbers and assortments of genes in the population pools,
dealt out probabilistically to the individuals, account for the spread and the
groupings of the taxa of biology.

In the other direction, dissection rather than collection, the entities of initial interest were examined for their component or subordinate units.

> That this same principle held for the cell, was clearly stated in 1859 by
> Virchow, "Omnes cellula e cellula"; and the fuller significance of the cell in
> the normal and pathological life of the organism was thus recognized. Almost
> thirty years more elapsed before it became clear that nuclei and chromosomes
> were similarly self-perpetuating units, and another twenty before this was
> established for the genes, molecules that precisely reduplicate themselves.
>
> So we find ourselves at the molecular level. This is the domain of bio-
> chemistry, another daughter of the twentieth century although in gestation
> for most of the nineteenth, since Wöhler synthesized the first "organic" com-
> pound, urea (1828, or Henneld a year earlier); but the continuing story of
> the recognition of the molecules formed by living things, of proteins, sugars,
> fats, sterols, nucleic acids, of hormones, vitamins, enzymes, of food compo-
> nents, waste substances, structural materials of the body, and the drama of
> their analysis, synthesis, even "improvement," perhaps now belongs more to
> the chemists than to the biologists. What is here crucial is that architecture
> has been traced, at least in outline, from the elaborate multicellular organism
> through its organs and cells to the pure chemical molecules and their own
> atomic pattern. There are no gaps to fill; the sequence is complete.
>
> Biology and chemistry thus merge at the molecular level as do chemistry
> and physics at the atomic level. Structural chemistry explores the arrange-
> ment of atoms in molecules; and anatomy, or the more sophisticated term in-
> troduced by Goethe, morphology, goes on from there, with the newborn cyto-
> chemistry aspiring to locate all molecules within a cell. Physical chemistry
> explores the actions and interactions of atoms and molecules; and physiology,

including its related disciplines of pathology and pharmacology, even ecology and sociology, likewise goes on from there.[9]

This morphological stage follows the taxonomic one, probably because the separate individuals are thrust into attention more immediately than are the parts of one individual and because observation requires less in the way of tools—cells required microscopes and microsomes, ultra-microscopes to study or even to see them; but in both cases the problem is one of describing and ordering discontinuities or inhomogeneities. Taxonomy and morphology are thus sorts of ordinal scales, the more elementary identification of entities giving the nominal one. Only later, as functional entities are recognized and the continuous variables of behavior or action gain attention, do we see the need for interval and ratio scales and for differential equations becoming important.

Perhaps a science really comes of age when the easily perceived structural entities are supplemented, and largely superseded, in attention by the functional ones, and later by the developmental ones. This is the dynamic or physiological stage. If morphology, or "being," describes the time-constant aspects of a system, its enduring architecture, then physiology, or "behaving," describes the reversible changes in time, the adaptive or homeostatic adjustments to environmental pressure; and "becoming," development or evolution or history or learning, describes the irreversible secular changes that accumulate over time. Only when the useful attributes of behaving or becoming are identified, and the interesting variables applied to them—by appropriate observation or experiment—do the dynamics of change become worthy of measurement.

In physics, mass and velocity and force and their dynamic interactions are the entities, non-material, that give the equations of mechanics. After chemistry identified elements, it next found the structures of the molecules—an especially prolonged stage for the complex ones of the organic world—and then turned to such entities as valence, polarity, reaction rates, and the like. The discovery of radioactivity gave the real start to problems of the becoming of matter, and today biochemistry and geochemistry are in full cry on the problems of molecular synthesis, current or past. Biology, having described muscles and nerves and glands, concerned itself with contraction and conduction and secretion; having recognized species and genera and phyla, it attended to their evolution and embryology. To the physiologist, the nerve impulse is far more immanent and important than is the nerve fiber, though he studies only the nerve fiber for changes in its electrical or other state or looks for behavioral changes in other structures when this propagating state reaches them. The sociologist, similarly, studies the role performance in a social system rather than the person playing the role; and the anthropologist examines the shards or tools or even members of a society as clues to its culture, its rules and values and communication.

Finding the proper functional entities has not been easy. Phlogiston in chemistry, entelechies in biology, spirits (humoral and supernatural) in dis-

---

[9] Gerard, "From spirits to mechanism: two centuries of biology," in *Facing the Future's* *Risks,* ed. L. Bryson (New York: Harper and Bros., 1953), pp. 111-144.

ease, long retarded effective science. Psychology is perhaps still awaiting its Lavoisier or Mendeleev. As earlier mentioned, only material systems are open to manipulation and observation; the problems are to apply useful conditions to, and to find useful indicators of, the change brought about in the system. It is a quite sophisticated maneuver to expose an eye to edges, and one even more removed from naïve experiment to record the neural discharges from retinal receptors. Selection is of the essence in such research; the scientist is confronted always with a vast excess of "information." He must choose, digitalize, normalize, code, and manipulate to get meaningful relationships from the welter of possibilities. To do just such with raw input are his receptors and nervous system built. Man's instruments, to extend his motor control first, his senses next, and today his integrative manipulation of information and resultant decision making, are mere refinements of his natural machinery.

A two-way table spreads itself, with axes of the several imposed or independent and of the observed or dependent variables. These axes are unlimited in extent, the number of variables in each steadily increases, and the size of the matrix multiplies. It is mainly in following the relations of each pair of variables over their range of continuous variation that differential equations have found such exuberant application. It is mainly in filling in the cells that scientists are occupied during the periods of stable growth between the episodes of crisis and breakthrough in science.

Each science, then, starts with the recognition of material entities, perceptually of proper dimensions for man, moves to larger groupings of them into superordinate entities (epiorganisms in the life area—the species or ecosystems of most organisms, the nation-races or societies of man), to their component structures (organs and cells and molecules), to their functional entities, and finally to those of development. Here, again, if the levels from atom to society were ordered on a vertical axis and the attributes of being, behaving and becoming on a horizontal one, a table or matrix of cells would be generated. Each science starts at the middle left, the cell of individual and being, and spreads as semi-circular waves—up through groups and societies, down through organs and cells, and to the right through behaving and becoming.

> The pure morphologist, then, is concerned with the structure of particular objects and attempts to make his description ever more complete. Here is the gross anatomist and naturalist of the past as well as the old organic chemist describing a substance or the visiting anthropologist describing a village. (The electron microscopist or cytochemist or ethologist of the present, as well as the modern macro-molecule chemist or the factor analyst seeking primary abilities or the sociometrist noting contacts or quantifying opinion, is often busy with the specific case but is usually concerned really with the class.) He observes what is; and he seeks ever more powerful tools to identify a system and fix it at an instant of time, to reveal its finer detail, to discriminate its more subtle differences, and to do this more precisely on more limited samples. His concern is primarily with the individual instance, like the clinician's with his patient, the humanistic historian's with his character or period, the artist's with his poem or painting or other unique creation of man. When a class property becomes the focus of interest, comparative studies replace those of the individual, and descriptive morphology gives way to comparative mor-

phology or systematics or physiology or genetics or some other discipline concerned with relation or function or development. As the class or property replaces the individual—as the actuarial approach replaces the clinical approach—there is greater distance between the operator and his material, the material becomes more objectified . . . and analysis is added to description.[10]

It perhaps needs explicit note that such a cycle of development is valid for sub-areas of a science as well as for the whole. As biology moved from the individual level to subordinate ones, there were repeated for organs, cells, particulates, and molecules, the stages of identifying entities, classifying them, describing their structure, manipulating their behavior, and analyzing their formation.

It is impressive that the sciences developed from the qualitative stages of pattern to the quantitative ones of change, whereas mathematics mainly developed its power tools for dealing with magnitude before those for handling relations. True, the integers—the primitive elements of arithmetic—and geometry existed early; but algebra, analytic geometry, trigonometry, and the ubiquitous calculus, have long been at hand. Boolean algebra, probability theory, set theory, topology, stochastic theory, game theory, graph theory, information theory are more recent, some still in their earliest stages. These are the tools for dealing with patterns, for which Weaver cried only a decade ago, to handle the problems of "organized complexity" that permeate the life and social sciences.

> The same theme, with variations, carries over from material tools to intellectual ones. Biological theory has been, on the whole, nonquantitative; but only in part is this because of the complexity and fuzziness of the presenting phenomena. It has needed as well, and is getting, new mathematical methods to solve the problems. Mathematical biologists are contributing powerfully in reaction chain theory, in population genetics, in the analysis of information and communication, even in statistical theory proper. And statisticians are advising biologists on, "The Design of Experiments." Following Weaver's provocative analysis, mathematics early produced tools, as the calculus, to solve the "problems of simplicity" of classical physics and chemistry, epitomized in the two-variable problem. More recently, by statistical techniques of the probability kind, it has created tools to handle large groups of random events, as in thermodynamics, the "problems of disorganized complexity."
>
> Many problems of biology (and sociology) are, however, matters of "organized complexity"—inherent in the nature of organism—and for these new methods are needed. Some are along orthodox lines of deductive mathematics, other smack strongly of Bacon's inductive proposals. A virtue of the high speed electronic calculators is that, lacking formal solutions, trial and error answers can be obtained by allowing many variables to range freely over possible values. . . . All are devices for obtaining empirical relations where insight and deduction have not found a path through the maze of multiple interdependent variables.[11] [In current terms, computers can aid in finding the proper units and models for structuring the universe.]

It is noteworthy that, in several of these areas, numbers are of minimal im-

---

[10] Gerard, "Units and concepts of biology," *Beh. Sci.,* 1958, *3:* 197-206.

[11] Gerard, "The organization of science," *loc. cit.*

portance. From Aristotle's logic on, such aspects of formalized reasoning contributed greatly to sharpening concepts, selecting between alternate ones, guiding experimental design, and in general advancing scientific model-building and testing. They made largely all-or-none predictions, of inclusion or exclusion of possibilities, without involving instruments or measurements or even quantities. It is perhaps not quantification as such that is so fruitful and powerful in the scientific process, but clarification. When ideas, models, are put through the rigor of precise formulation, and the consequences of certain postulates are unequivocally exposed, the basic gains have been made. Heisenberg's indeterminacy principle yields a value for the irreducible uncertainty of measurement; Gödel's theorem proves only that in any logical system there exist indeterminate propositions; both have had a like impact on scientific thought. Who was it that said he had worked out a theory, explained it to his students, programmed a computer for it—and then understood it himself! (A wise teacher recently used this principle with the parent of a grade student learning mathematics by the newer methods. The parent, in distress, asked, "How can I help Johnny when I don't understand his work?" The teacher replied, "Let him explain it to you until you do understand.")

The basic creative act of the imagination is alike in art and science.

> Look at the past; what pessimists have men been! When regularity and predictability were established for the simpler material phenomena on earth, when geo-metry was developed and the action of levers understood, celestial events were still considered beyond man's understanding and daring. For a millennium, the angels still moved the heavenly bodies on their ways. Not until Newton demonstrated the universality of application of his equation for gravity, indeed not until Bunsen, a scant century ago, showed by spectroscopic analysis of sunlight that the same elements compose the sun as the earth was this tidemark finally flooded over.
>
> Or, consider the problem of the living. Almost to our day, if not actually into it, the animate was shrouded with the mysterious and the impenetrable. Vital spirits, presiding entelechies, a whole corps of benevolent gremlins made the parts of the body go through their chores and the whole execute the beautiful acts of living. Why, even in my own student days, secretion was an expression of the vital activity of glands; now it is analyzed in terms of oxidative energy, ionic interchange, differential permeability to polar molecules, and the like. A little over a century ago, the substances of the living were forever beyond the province of the chemist, a vital force alone could make "organic" compounds. Then Wöhler made one in the test tube, and the chemical hordes, given hope and courage, poured after with hundreds more. Yet organic compounds *are* different in many important respects from inorganic ones, and it is only in the immediate present that the underlying laws of molecular organization are reducing these differences from the qualitative to the quantitative. (This is an especially convincing instance to support the view that, at all levels, the qualitative jump will in time become a quantitative difference and that "prediction upwards" is not impossible but only enormously difficult.)[12]
>
> It has been a recurring source of excitement to me, when I have dabbled in medical history, to see how some great and tremendously courageous figure has stood against his times. Courage is perhaps the major touchstone of great-

[12] Gerard, "The scope of science," *loc. cit.*

ness in advancing knowledge. It takes enormous courage to disagree with pre-vailing convictions and to stick with the heresy, intellectual or otherwise. Yet these vigorous men, who were willing, even though feeling foolhardy, to assert something for which the time was not quite ripe, nevertheless undershot the mark. They were still not quite courageous or imaginative enough to say what would later become the commonplace. Only in 1874 did Wernicke say "Geisteskrankheiten sind Gehirnkrankheiten"; and another fifteen years passed before Oppenheim saw psychic changes as due to brain damage at the molec-ular level.[13]

To produce the new pattern—of thought in a theory, of form in a work of art, even of understanding during the learning process—the mind must run free. But to select from these varied productions the worthy ones is a very different matter in the several areas of human activity. In art, the criteria for judging beauty are not yet clarified, if indeed they are not entirely suigeneric; in sci-ence the criteria of validity are clear and collective. Hence the collective and cumulative and universal aspects of this most impressive creation of man. And hence the tremendous commitment of scientists to the rigorous testing by rea-son and measure, most clearly seen in quantification.

A recent study of physiological science in the United States[14] included a study of publications over a half century. Among the points examined, those of relevance to this conference included: the kind of experimental variable applied, the indicator observed, the level of the system examined, and the utilization of statistics and of mathematical, physical and chemical resources in either the experimental performance or the theoretical analysis. Inciden-tally, half of the nearly 6000 professional physiologists indicated, on a ques-tionnaire, that they were dissatisfied with their training in these fields.

All research reports in three major journals were examined for every fifth year from 1907 to 1947, and the data considered for five decades. No clear time trend appeared in the variable applied; at each period nearly 40 per cent of the papers involved an "endogenous" variable—age, season, sex, species, and the like—rather than an imposed one. Of the latter, a drug was by far the most commonly used tool, applied in over 20 per cent. Physical variables, such as electric stimuli, were used in 16 per cent of the researches in the 1900 decade, fell to 3 per cent in the following one, and then rose slowly, to 8 per cent in the forties. Metabolic responses were most used as measures at all periods. Experiments always were mostly directed to the whole organism, rather than to subordinate levels, as organ or cell or particulate; but a con-siderable shift toward the latter occurred with time.

The greatest precision was seen in papers in the areas of bioelectricity, bio-chemistry and metabolism, and cell structure. Over all, statistical treatment was widely applicable and widely used, especially in experimental design, over the entire time period; but the excellence of use improved greatly. In the first decade, use of this resource was judged "good" or "excellent" for only 17 per cent of the papers; in the last one, for 60 per cent. Mathematics, on the con-

<hr />

[13] Gerard, "Physiology from physicians—the nervous system," in *Disease and Advance-ment of Basic Science,* ed. H. K. Beecher (Boston: Harvard University Press, 1960), pp. 234-251.

[14] Gerard, *Mirror to Physiology: a Self-Survey of Physiological Science* (Wash., D.C.: American Physiological Society, 1958).

trary, was judged applicable in method but rarely; applicability rose sharply over the half century, however, from 2 per cent to 21 per cent, and effective use, from 0 per cent to 4 per cent. Physics was applicable at first to 27 per cent, at the end to 90 per cent, of the research procedures; and was used well in 2 per cent at first, 22 per cent later. In analysis all these tools were less applicable and much less used, especially in the early years. For the first and the last decades, the figures are: statistics, 98 per cent applicable, 0 to 7 per cent well used; mathematics, 2 to 30 per cent applicable, 1 to 5 per cent well used; physics, 46 to 92 per cent applicable, 0 to 33 per cent well used. A paragraph from the chapter summary states:

> Over the half-century, statistics were judged applicable in nearly all cases, mathematics only rarely at first. There has been an encouraging increase over time in the skill with which statistics have been used in designing and analyzing experiments, although analysis lags, and in the use of mathematics in theoretical interpretation. Chemistry, despite the separation of biochemistry, has had a large and improving role in physiological experimentation; and the use of physics has increased considerably, in techniques more than in conceptualization. Indeed, the indications are clear that biophysics is ready to follow the course of biochemistry as a separate entity. Despite these gains, the use of the basic tools of mathematics and the physical sciences is meager and reflects the feeling of physiologists, half of whom regard their training in physics, chemistry and biochemistry as inadequate.

Early in biology, credited by some as first, Harvey applied the full weight of quantitative argument to his problem—the circulation of the blood. A simple and unanswerable demonstration was to strip or milk a superficial vein centralward, using two fingers like pump valves to insure one way movement of the blood in the vein segment. Since this maneuver could be continued indefinitely, until far more blood had been passed centrally than existed in the body, blood must reach the periphery of the vein by other channels. The related qualitative argument was from the presence of valves in these same veins; that they did indeed hold back from peripheral movement was shown by milking in that direction, which left the vein collapsed until an incoming branch was opened.

A comparable proof that a fluid moves peripherally in nerves to make muscles contract was offered by Monro in 1732.[15]

> After opening the thorax of a living dog catch hold of and press one or both the phrenic nerves with the fingers, the diaphragm immediately ceases to contract. Cease to compress the nerves, and the muscle acts again. A second time lay hold of the nerve or nerves some way above the diaphragm, its motion stops. Keep firm the hold of the nerves, and, with the fingers of the other hand strip it down from the fingers which make the compression toward the diaphragm, and it again contracts. On repetition of this part of the experiment 3 or 4 times, it is always attended with the same results; but it then contracts no more, strip as you will, etc., etc., ... Let anyone try if he can imagine any other reasonable account of these appearances than ... pressure by the fingers stopped the course of the fluids in the nerve; that so much of this fluid

[15] A. B. Luckhardt, *Am. J. Pharmaceut. Educ.*, 1945, *9*: 299-345.

as remained in the nerve betwixt the fingers and the diaphragm was forced into that muscle by stripping; and when it was all pressed away, the fingers were removed and a fresh flow by that means was received from the spinal marrow or from that part of the nerve which had not yet been so stripped.

Monro was as wrong as Harvey was right, yet his experiment and conclusion seem as solid as the valid ones. It is not accident that the circulation came early into respectable modeling and measuring; it is indeed a hydraulic pump and tube and valve system, and once it had been recognized as such the well-developed concepts and equations of mechanics could be simply utilized. Not so the nervous system, which is only today emerging from the descriptive, even the mysterious. Galvani and Volta did not establish current electricity until the end of Monro's century, and another half century elapsed before the role of electric currents in the propagation of the nerve impulse began to appear. Monro could not ask the right questions about the right entities, in his area of research, a century after Harvey could do so in his.

"Multiple interdependent variables," "organized complexity," in such terms reside the essence of organism and of modern biology. What a chasm in concepts separates this from the biology of two centuries ago! In 1752 the vapors of Galen were still filling the body, although by then they were circulating in it; and they were still clouding the mind, although by then they were thinning and about to lift. Vesalius, two centuries earlier, had put human anatomy on a sound observational basis, and Bacon and Galileo had unfettered induction and experiment a few decades after him. Harvey's "De Motu Cordis et Sanguinis," the open sesame to valid physiological thinking, had been in the hands of scholars for 124 years. Malpighi, born the year De Motu was published, had founded microscopic anatomy, and van Leeuwenhoek's superb microscopic observations had been pouring out for nearly a century. Newton, who had rationalized the great coordinates of physical experience and had quantified the heavens, was dead but 26 years; and Voltaire, whose coruscating brilliance flashed the mechanistic consequences of these discoveries into all avenues of thought, had still 26 years to live.

In 1752, Lavoisier was but nine years old—Priestley only nineteen and oxygen undiscovered—and the birth of quantitative chemistry (and of democracy) lay decades ahead. Linneus was forty five; his great work on the classification of plants and animals was seventeen years old, but the binomial system was not due for another year. Haller, the same age as his Swedish rival, was just completing his study of irritability and was busy collecting all known biological writings and facts for his "Bibliotheca." Hales, then 73, had measured blood pressure and published his "Statical Essays" 14 years before. Hunter was 24 and his comparative anatomical studies were launched; but his protege, Jenner, was only three and vaccination was yet to be conceived and tested. Galvani was 15, and the discovery of electric currents not due for decades. Vic d'Azyr, who would clearly formulate the body functions, was four years old; and Gall, concerned most of his life with brain and mental performances, was not to be born for six years—although Swedenborg, then 64, had already theoretically placed the intelligence in the cerebral cortex, where Willis had placed memory a century earlier.[16]

The nature of the nerve impulse has been reasonably well understood for

---

[16] Gerard, "From spirits to mechanism: two centuries of biology," *loc. cit.*

close to a century at this time, and the properties of the junctions between nerve cells—the synapses which do or do not transmit the excitation from one neuron to others—have been decently at hand for half that time. But the machinery for the integrative action of the nervous system, for coordinated complex selective responses and decisions, is just today beginning to come clear in our modeling. Boolean algebra, topology, stochastics, and information theory—not to mention computer simulation—all have contributed heavily to this growing understanding. And this was inevitable, for they are the mathematics of relations, and the nervous system deals in such coin. Circulation, movement, metabolism, most of the physiologic topics of interest, are concerned largely with the manipulation of energy and substance, and they dominated physiology until the mid-century. The nervous system, and its receptors, deal with organization, pattern, information and its contained "form." The amount of energy and substance turnover involved in propagating the excited state, which carries the information, is very low; not the energy of air waves, but their pattern is important for communication by speech. Patterns in genes and chromosomes are similarly just entering strongly into our pictures of the becoming of individuals and species. Living systems differ most sharply from non-living systems in that they are highly organized—hence organisms; behavioral science, even biology, is only today at its dawning.

The quantitative study of integrated populations of nerve cells, and of the handling of information by individuals, is paralleled by studies of integrated populations of other units—i.e., systems at various levels. The rate of processing bits of information falls by a fairly constant factor for each superposed layer, from neuron to social institution.[17] The simple reproductive ratios of Mendel have expanded into Wright's rich equations expressing evolutionary pressures in a population. The instructions in a gene array begin to be understood, and their translation into chemical syntheses and morphogenesis is under vigorous study—all at a level of meaningful quantitation. Indeed, the insight of Malthus—that some sort of selection must operate to check a geometrically increasing population—was quantitative in full richness. And the further equations of Volterra and his followers have encompassed the balance of predator-prey populations.

Organization at the cellular level, and the cell as a locus of disease, as promulgated by Virchow, became the object of quantification, followed by that at the sub-cellular level, as soon as the possibility of such quantification was conceived and the tools for measurement were devised. Size and number of cells were noted with light microscopes, of cell particulates with electron microscopes. But real quantification awaited refined techniques—cytochemical, staining and adsorption, X-ray diffraction, radiograms, shadow casting, and the like—which are fully bridging the gap from molecule to cell.

Measuring the intangible is also far from new in biology. Lavoisier's bell jar experiments, with mouse or candle, were directed to measuring the portion of air that was dephlogisticated—Black's oxygen. Beaumont measured indefatigably the amounts of gastric juice formed by the stomach of Alexis St.

17 J. G. Miller, "Information input overload   1960, *116:* 695-704. and psychopathology," *Am. J. Psychiatry,*

Martin, but he was concerned only with the influence of various conditions on the rate of secretion. Pavlov's later conditioned reflex studies were entirely comparable. The tension-duration curves of muscle contraction were similar functional measures, as were the unsuccessful efforts to demonstrate a volume change of an active muscle. An especially brilliant experiment of a century ago, by Kühne, determined the action spectrum of chlorophyll with almost modern precision. A spectrum of sunlight was projected along a filament of the green alga, Spirogyra, and the oxygen released by the resulting photosynthesis served to nourish aerobic bacteria in the same fluid. The radius of the bacterial cloud surrounding the filament, at the incidence of each wave length, presented a visible curve which was the desired action spectrum.

Quantification of the intangible is today rapidly expanding into the realm of the mental, with or without physical indicators; two examples will suffice. The level of anxiety or apprehension was judged in some thirty patients in a mental hospital by six independent judges, each rank-ordering the entire group. Although the raters included psychiatrists and psychologists, ward and laboratory personnel, the concordance gave a P value better than 0.01 (Holmberg, 1960).[18] Further, the subjective order was borne out by an objective test, the cardiac acceleration produced by a certain drug, again with a $P < 0.01$. A second study, on rats, related the frequency with which an animal would press a bar, for avoidance of electric shocks, to the content of a specific enzyme in the animal's brain.[19] This research supplied clear quantitative evidence for the causal role of an amine in this behavior and for the action of a psychoactive drug by altering this substance.

Such quantification is now bringing mental illness along the course earlier taken by physical illness. As pointed out above, disease is a functional entity, to be studied by examination of physical entities.

> If we are concerned with the doctor contributing as a clinician to the advancement of scientific knowledge, then we must direct our attention to what he did in his role as a clinician; namely, while observing and handling sick human beings. The keynote of clinical study and observation is, therefore, disease. The doctor faces this set of natural phenomena exactly as the naturalist in biology faces another group of natural phenomena—the existence of plants and animals, or groups of them, their distributions or other attributes. His role was first to discover that certain things are so, that certain uniform patterns of reality exist; and, more than that, to make some preliminary structuring of the fuzzy world he was beginning to recognize. He identifies entities, has hunches and guesses and asks questions about it all, and forms some kind of conceptualization as to what it all means. This, I take it, is the essential role of the clinician *qua* clinician.
>
> Now, the scientist has the job of trying to answer these questions. Here are phenomena that have been recognized. Here are some guesses about them. Are they right? How can I go about testing them? How can I give further meaning to them? His job is that of the actuarian, as has sometimes been said, to grind out the figures and determine whether or not the guess checks. This

[18] G. Holmberg, "Autonomic and psychic effects of yohimbine hydrochloride," *J. of Pharmacology,* In Press.

[19] M. H. Aprison and C. D. Ferster, "Neurochemical Correlates of Behavior II," *J. of Neurochemistry,* In Press.

is an extreme picture, of course, because any good scientist soon begins to find his own new discoveries and to make guesses about them, and so to function in the double role.

What bothers me is that the physician, also, functions usually in the double role. A man is a total being. He may observe sick people as a clinician; but he may well stop functioning as an observer or guesser at the bedside and, as a scientist, take his problem into the laboratory or back to the clinic to use other humans as experimental subjects, mostly legitimately enough. He is then functioning as an investigator, not as a clinician. So the problem faces us of trying to dissociate the things that these men of history have done in each role. This, I assure you, is not an easy job.

There remain still other problems. When a physician applies to man scientific findings, the methods and apparatus and techniques, developed in connection with the laboratory, he is not functioning as a clinician. Yet, if he is using them to improve his ability to observe, discriminate, diagnose, discover new symptoms and signs, then he is functioning as a clinician. Conversely, many procedures now centered in the laboratory were originated in the clinic and by clinicians.

We return to the clinician, because disease is a functional entity.... The physician, in his role as a clinician treating patients, is interested in the particular individual and is trying to make him well. But in his role as a student of disease, the physician is interested in a functional entity of which the patient is simply the carrier. He needs many patients to understand this functional entity, and the person becomes a case or a statistic or an experiment.

This is why nosology is so crucial to the advance of medicine and of biological understanding. In clinical science, the nosological entities are the units of concern. The architecture at the presenting level of disease involves signs and symptoms and syndromes. At lower levels pathology and chemistry dominate; at higher levels come heredity, demography, patho-geography, and the like. In the "behaving" column are pathogenesis, course, and treatment. And under history come etiology, prognosis, population-genetics, and the like.[20]

Nosology is concerned with recognizing and characterizing true disease entities—whether by the qualitative and pathognomonic Koplic spots on the gums of a measles patient or by the quantitative fever curve of each type of malaria or by any pattern of signs and symptoms that consistently run together (form a syndrome), is immaterial. Only when the different types of fever or diarrhoea or cough were related to their various appropriate diseases did knowledge advance as to the nature of the disturbance and was progress made in the therapy. Pneumonia and tuberculosis, typhus and typhoid, the several types of influenza or of dysentery or of arthritis or encephalitis—each is a separate disease and demands distinctive handling. The great mental illness, schizophrenia, is probably an omnibus category and demands nosological dissection before more than accidental progress will be possible in following its pathogeneses or therapies.[21] And in the mental realm is being reenacted the war between the perceptive clinician, who first sees patterns in the muddled disease picture, and the rigorous actuarian, who quantitatively checks

[20] Gerard, "Physiology from physicians—the nervous system," *loc. cit.*

[21] Gerard, "The schizophrenia and psychopharmacology project," *loc. cit.*

these qualitative hunches for validity.[22] This point has been made in Shryock's paper and the discussion of it.

It is reassuring to find a recurrent texture in the fabric of knowledge. From the simple problems of molar physics, through the more difficult ones of molecular chemistry and the complex organizational ones of biology, to the intangible ones of mind and behavior, and including normal and disturbed functioning, the same historical sequence has been followed. Qualitative identification is followed by quantitative measurement of single variables, clusters, and full-blown architectures; superordinate and subordinate systems are subjected to study; functional and developmental entities push aside structural ones from the focus of research attention. The recurrent texture is no accident; it is that of the brain itself, formed by the impact of a real world on the malleable neurone groups that have flowered from the evolutionary process.

[22] P. E. Meehl, *Clinical Versus Statistical Prediction, a Theoretical Analysis and a Review of the Evidence.* (Minneapolis: Univ. of Minnesota Press, 1954). See also J. Cole and R. W. Gerard, eds. *Psychopharmacology: Problems in Evaluation.* Publ. # 583, NAS-NRC (Washington, D.C., 1959).

NOTES ON CONTRIBUTORS

HARRY WOOLF received his Ph.D. from Cornell University. The editor of *Isis* since 1958, he has taught physics at Boston University, history at Brandeis University, and the history of science at the University of Washington from 1955 to 1961. He is now professor of the history of science at The Johns Hopkins University. Author of *The Transits of Venus* (Princeton, 1959) and a Fellow of the American Association for the Advancement of Science, he is presently in India as a consultant to the University Grants Commission there on the development of teaching and research programs in the history of science in the Indian universities.

* * *

SAMUEL S. WILKS was born in Little Elm, Texas and attended North Texas State College and the University of Texas. He received his Ph.D. from the State University of Iowa and did post-doctoral work at Columbia, the University of London and Cambridge University. With a specialty in mathematical statistics and its applications, he is the author of four books and numerous research papers. He is a past president of the American Statistical Association and the Institute of Mathematical Statistics and former editor of the *Annals of Mathematical Statistics*. Since 1944, he has been professor of mathematical statistics at Princeton University.

* * *

ALISTAIR C. CROMBIE has been senior lecturer in the history of science at the University of Oxford since 1953. He is a graduate in natural science of the University of Melbourne and of Cambridge, where he took his doctorate and taught and carried out research in biology. He has also taught at the University of London, the University of Washington, and Princeton University. He is the author of numerous articles and reviews and of two books: *Augustine to Galileo. The History of Science A.D. 400-1650* and *Robert Grosseteste and the Origins of Experimental Science 1100-1700*. He

was the original editor of the *British Journal for the Philosophy of Science*.

* * *

THOMAS S. KUHN received both his undergraduate and graduate training at Harvard University, where he received the Ph.D. degree in theoretical physics. He has been a Junior Fellow of the Society of Fellows and assistant professor of general education and the history of science at Harvard, a Guggenheim Fellow, and Fellow of the Center for Advanced Study in the Behavorial Sciences at Palo Alto. In 1956, he moved to the University of California, Berkeley, to set up an experimental program of teaching and research in the history of science and he is now associate professor of the history of science at that institution. He is the author of *The Copernican Revolution* and of numerous articles, the latest being in the early history of thermodynamics.

* * *

HENRY GUERLAC received his A.B. at Cornell in chemistry and his Ph.D. in history at Harvard. He has taught at Harvard and the University of Wisconsin, and since 1946 has been professor of the history of science at Cornell. During World War II, he served as historian of the allied radar program. He is a past president of the History of Science Society and currently president of the Académie Internationale d'Histoire des Sciences. He has published numerous articles on the history of chemistry and various aspects of the history of science in France. His *Lavoisier—The Crucial Year* is shortly to be published by Cornell University Press.

* * *

RICHARD H. SHRYOCK, Librarian of the American Philosophical Society, was born in Philadelphia and received his Ph.D. in history at the University of Pennsylvania. His interest is in medical history, in combination with the more general field of American history. He is William H. Welch Professor Emeritus of the history of medicine at the Johns Hopkins University School of Medicine, and has been professor of history at Duke University and the University of Pennsylvania, as well as president of the American Association of the History of Medicine, the History of Science Society, and the American Association of University Professors. He has also served on the Social Science Research Council and the American Council of Learned Societies. Among his published works are: *The Development of Modern Medicine; American Medical Research: Past and Present; Medicine and Society in America: 1680-1860;* and *The University of Pennsylvania Faculty: A Study in American Higher Education.*

* * *

EDWIN G. BORING received his Ph.D. from Cornell University. Formerly director of the Harvard Psychological Laboratory and professor at Harvard, he is now Edgar Pierce Professor of Psychology Emeritus at Harvard and editor of *Contemporary Psychology.* He is past president of the American Psychological Association and a member of the Society of Experimental Psychologists, the American Philosophical Society and the National Academy of Sciences. Among his publications are *A History of Psychology* and *Sensation and Perception in the History of Experimental Psychology.* He has also written numerous papers on psychological factors that operate in the history of science and on the psychology of history.

* * *

JOSEPH J. SPENGLER is James B. Duke Professor of Economics at Duke University. In the past he has taught at Ohio State University (where he received his A.B., A.M., and Ph.D. degrees), the University of Arizona, the University of North Carolina, the University of Chicago, the University of Pittsburgh, the University of Malaya, and Kyota University. His main teaching and research interests are the history of economic thought, demography, and economic development. Among his most recent publications are: *Tradition, Values and Socio-Economic Development* (with R. B. Braibanti) ; *Theories of Economic Growth* (with B. F. Hoselitz, ed.) ; *Essays in Economic Thought* (with William R. Allen, ed.) ; *Demographic Analysis and Population Theory and Policy* (with Otis Dudley Duncan, ed.).

* * *

PAUL F. LAZARSFELD, a native of Vienna, received his Ph.D. there in mathematics. He came to this country in 1933 as a Rockefeller Fellow and has remained here. Since 1939, he has been at Columbia and is now chairman of the department of sociology. Among his publications are *The People's Choice, The Academic Mind, The Historian in Public Opinion Polls, Public Opinion Research and the Classical Tradition, Mathematical Thinking in the Social Sciences,* and *The Language of Social Research* (editor and contributor to last two). He is past president of the American Association of Public Opinion Research and president-elect of the American Sociological Association.

* * *

R. W. GERARD, who was born in Illinois, is a graduate of the University of Chicago and of Rush Medical College. He holds B.S., Ph.D., M.D., and D.Sc. degrees. He has done teaching and research at South Dakota University, Chicago Medical College, the University of Chicago, the University of Illinois, the Center of Behavioral Sciences of the Ford Foundation, and has since 1955 been director of the Mental Health Research Institute and professor of neurophysiology at the University of Michigan. He has been editor of several publications in his field and the author of a number of books and articles. His specialties include neurophysiology, neural metabolism, neural mechanisms of behavior, psychopharmacology, and experimental psychiatry.